UNDERSTANDING PHYSICAL CHEMISTRY: *Part One*

UNDERSTANDING PHYSICAL CHEMISTRY

a set of simple yet difficult examination questions and their methods of solution

PART ONE

Properties of matter, thermodynamics, chemical equilibrium

Arthur W. Adamson
University of Southern California

W. A. BENJAMIN, INC.
New York   Amsterdam   1964

UNDERSTANDING PHYSICAL CHEMISTRY: PART ONE

*A set of simple yet difficult examination
questions and their methods of solution*

Library of Congress Catalog Card Number 64-22292
Manufactured in the United States of America

The manuscript was put into production on
February 27, 1964, and this volume was
published on September 15, 1964

W. A. BENJAMIN, INC.
New York 10016

To the class of the sinking ship

Preface

General introduction

This collection of problems and worked-out answers is offered as something different from and, I hope, more helpful than the usual study aid for introductory physical chemistry. Students who follow the procedure recommended (see below) should find that this book can function as something like a "teaching machine" in leading them in a positive way into a better understanding of physical chemistry. The process will not be effortless but, given the effort, students at any level of capability should find that their ability to do physical chemistry has been quite materially improved.

Instructors should find this a source book of reasonably stiff examination questions. The chapters on wave mechanics and group theory can be used as source material for lectures on these subjects. They provide an approach to chemical bonding which has considerable depth, yet can be handled by first-year physical-chemistry students.

As a preamble to explaining the philosophy of this book, I would like to comment briefly on the role of problems and of problem solving in the teaching of physical chemistry. It is an American tradition, and basically a correct one, I believe, that the best test of a person's understanding of a scientific subject is his ability to use it. In physical chemistry, then, examinations in this country typically tend to stress numerical problems rather than the more philosophical essay type of question.

There is a second aspect to the use of numerical problems which also is important. Such problems may be just as easy or just as hard, just as straightforward or just as subtle, as essay-type questions. The virtue of the numerical problem is therefore not in any instrinsic difference in the level of understanding required to answer it, as compared to essay questions. Its value is simply that, being numerical, it is concrete, and the student is thus required to so sharpen his thinking as to be able to decide exactly what the question means and exactly how he will answer it. The numerical problem is thus a pedagogical device to ensure clear and unambiguous answers and to expose sloppy thinking.

There are several distinct types of numerical problems. In the lecture course in physical chemistry as taught at the University of Southern California, homework assignments include a group of straightforward "substitution" exercises, partly assigned ahead of the lectures as to topic and, frankly, designed to direct the average student's attention to the forthcoming material. A second part of the homework will consist of relatively long and difficult problems; certain calculations are intrinsically lengthy, yet need to be appreciated at least once. In addition, on a homework assignment, students can be expected to have to wrestle a bit with more advanced subject matter.

Neither of the above two types of problems is used in our examinations, however. I am interested in how well the student understands the material, there is little value in this respect in questions asking for a recitation of memorized equations or derivations, or in mere substitution problems. The second type of homework problem is not of much use in an examination situation, either. There is no time for lengthy calculations, nor for pondering some aspect not emphasized in lecture—unless, of course, one is able to assign weekend take-home examinations.

What has evolved instead, in the case of the quizzes used here, is a type of problem that requires the use only of those definitions, derivations, and equations so central that the student can reasonably be expected to know them if he has done even the first group of homework problems. In the examination, however, a situation is described that calls for a change or adaptation of the equation or derivation. The change is simple and straightforward, but it nonetheless must be determined from an analysis of the problem. These are the "simple yet difficult" problems referred to in the subtitle to this book.

Consider the ideal gas law—a simpler equation is hard to imagine. Yet, until they refresh their thinking, even graduate students have trouble working the problems in Chapter 1 within the time limits. (Dare I admit this may also be true of professors?) It is not that the problems are instrinsically difficult—when you see the answers, they seem ridiculously easy and often need barely a touch of the slide rule. It is just that one has to think rather carefully to see just how the gas law must be manipulated to fit the particular situation.

Such problems are *not* "trick" problems. Each is designed to test whether the student has so well grasped a particular aspect of a principle that he can recognize its implicit presence in the question, and do so quickly.

The following analogy may help to present what I have in mind. Let us suppose that a person who has never before seen an elephant is allowed to view one, posed, a slight distance away. The various features of the animal are explained carefully, and the person feels that he knows the beast. Yet the same elephant charging toward him, screaming and with raised trunk, or running away or bathing itself or feeding or viewed from the backside or the underside or from a perch behind the ears can look very different indeed. Only after many experiences of seeing the elephant in a variety of circumstances and actions will the person finally begin to know what an elephant is like, how he will act in a given situation, what his limitations are, and how to recognize him no matter how well he is hidden in the jungle.

Physical-chemical relationships can be much like this elephant. Typically, a particular one has been derived and explained in a clear, logical, and straightforward manner and illustrated with a numerical example. It seems entirely limpid and reasonable. The student feels that he understands it perfectly and, later, cannot explain how he could possibly have had so much trouble with it on the quiz.

As with the elephant, a concept or an equation if viewed from a new reference point can suddenly look very strange. Thus the ideal gas law may seem very elementary indeed, until the student is asked to apply it to a situation involving a gas distributed between two interconnected flasks which are not at the same temperature. The freezing-point-depression effect, whereby dissolved solute B in solvent A lowers the freezing point of the latter, is given by a plain enough equation whose use is easy. It is another matter to recognize that the same equation treats the solubility of solid A in solvent B, i.e., to see that this is merely a restatement of a freezing-point depression from a different point of view, and with an interchange of the labels "solvent" and "solute."

In each chapter, then, a group of centrally important equations and concepts is presented, by means of problems, in a diversity of guises. The problems are worked out in detail so that the solutions are as much a part of this study aid as are the problems themselves. Through working the problems and studying the answers, the student should gain a better perspective and a better understanding of physical chemistry. He should develop some ability to see what principles are relevent to a situation and the confidence to fashion or to modify equations as appropriate.

As the last sentence suggests, I hope that the pedagogical approach embodied in this collection of problems is one that inculcates analytical and inductive ability. Such ability is essential to the good physical chemist and I feel that its nurture is one of the major responsibilities of the course in physical chemistry. With respect to this point, it seems to me that the teacher of a modern physical chemistry course faces a dilemma. He must acquaint the student with the more important developments in the application of wave mechanics to chemistry. The mathematical underpinning of wave mechanical calculations is generally too complicated to take up in detail, yet if only the final results are given, the material becomes merely descriptive and not conducive to any real understanding. There is the further danger of instilling an unscientific attitude of accepting equations on the basis of authority rather than understanding. A partial resolution of this dilemma is attempted in Chapters 20 and 21 by selecting and concentrating on a group of topics in wave mechanics and chemical bonding, so chosen that it is possible to ask the student to develop a certain amount of insight into them.

In conclusion, I would greatly appreciate receiving your comments, corrections, criticisms and, perhaps above all, contributions of good problems.

To the student: a suggested procedure

First, a few points of information are in order. The problems come from actual quizzes (or, if so indicated, final examinations) and the time given for their working is that which was actually allowed. You can construct a typical quiz by selecting two or three problems whose time allowance totals thirty minutes.

Beginning with Chapter 4, you will find problems requiring the use of partial derivatives and partial differential relationships. It will help, if you are shaky on this subject, to proceed to the appendix at the end of Part I. A short outline of the principal relations is given, along with a special collection of problems which you should find very enlightening.

The concepts involved and the equations needed are given at the beginning of each chapter, along with some informal comments

about their use. Read these introductory sections carefully before
starting on the problems. The problems are closed book unless
otherwise indicated. In most instances it does not really matter
as they are harder to do open book than closed book! (With open
book, you waste too much time looking up equations you should
know anyway.) As you start working a chapter you may want to
use the list of equations as a kind of crib sheet but, honestly, if
you need this you are not going to be able to do the problems
within the time limits.

Most of the time allowance is for thinking; the actual calculations are usually quite short. Try to train yourself not to rush into
arithmetic before you know where you want to go. In grading these
quizzes, we allowed 80 per cent credit for correctly setting up the
solution and 20 per cent for correct arithmetic, which is another
reason for saving the slide-rule work for the last. Keep in mind,
too, that the numerical data are often carefully chosen so as to
facilitate the calculation through cancellations or through opening
up shortcuts or quick approximations. Approximations, however,
should not impair the usual criterion of slide-rule accuracy. Thus
numbers given to only one significant figure are to be understood
as being accurate to 1 per cent.

If you have trouble at first, as you tackle these problems, give
yourself about three times the indicated time, then study the answer carefully. Try to see what you missed or where you went
wrong in your analysis. Try to generalize your conclusions so as
to have something you can then keep in mind when going on to the
next problem. Your goal is to complete the problem within the
time limit and to have it substantially correct.

After completing a chapter, review all the problems in it.
Make an outline of the various ways in which the subjects were
approached and assign each problem to a spot in your outline. The
idea is to develop a close association in your mind between each
relationship or principle and the ways in which it may be used. If
you get discouraged, it may help your morale to ask a graduate
student to work one of the problems within the time limit!

Best wishes and good luck!

To the instructor: some further comments

Although this collection of problems is presented primarily as
a new kind of study aid for students, I believe it also constitutes a
good source of examination questions. The problems are largely
original, although some are modifications of homework problems

from various sources. The collection is large enough so that there is not much chance that a student having this book will remember a particular solution. If you want to make small changes in the numerical data given, it might be wise to check the solution, since in some cases the particular numbers used were carefully chosen to facilitate calculation.

The sequence of topics is approximately that followed in the lecture course at the University of Southern California. To an appreciable extent, then, the problems become more sophisticated as one proceeds through the collection. There is also an increasing use of actual experimental data and of situations that approximate experimental ones.

The last chapter, on group theory as applied to molecular symmetry and chemical bonding, is definitely experimental, as this topic has not yet found its way into first-year physical-chemistry books. It is not particularly difficult, however, and by introducing the subject at this level students are permitted to gain a real grasp of how wave mechanics is actually used in qualitative applications to chemical bonding. The introduction to this chapter is detailed enough to serve as a text for the material, although some recommended references are listed.

Chapter 20, on wave mechanics, is likewise somewhat experimental in that the problems are restricted to a few topics, but then go into them in some detail. Thus a quite complete listing of hydrogenlike wave functions is given and the student is expected to become really familiar with their radial and angular properties. This concentration on a few topics does imply a sacrifice of material at a more descriptive level, but I do not think it is possible otherwise to provide sufficient depth of presentation to allow the student to gain a feeling of understanding and of appreciation of wave mechanics.

The paperback edition of this book is issued in two volumes (Parts One and Two) for mechanical and monetary convenience to the reader. While the division is necessarily somewhat arbitrary, the two parts do roughly correspond to the first- and second-semester portions of the physical chemistry course as taught here.

For the convenience of the reader, in the paperback editions, Part One contains the table of contents for Part Two on the back cover and Part Two contains the contents for Part One on the back cover. Both parts have the full index.

Arthur W. Adamson

Los Angeles
July 16, 1964

Contents

Preface   **vii**

Part One: PROPERTIES OF MATTER, THERMODYNAMICS, CHEMICAL EQUILIBRIUM

1 *The ideal gas law*   1

2 *Nonideal gases; condensation*   12

3 *Kinetic molecular theory of gases*   28

4 *Some physical properties of molecules*   37

5 *First law of thermodynamics*   54

6 *Heat capacity of gases and thermochemistry*   **73**

7 *Second law of thermodynamics*   90

8 *Liquids and their simple phase equilibria*   111

9 *Solutions*   **133**

10 *Colligative properties*   **165**

11 *Heterogeneous and homogeneous gas equilibrium*   188

12 *Heterogeneous equilibrium; phase diagrams*   207

Appendix to Part One: *Partial derivatives*   **253.1**

Index   **xv**

1 *The ideal gas law*

Comments

The ideal gas law is simplicity itself, algebraically speaking.
Remember, though, that it relates pressure, volume, weight, molecular weight, and temperature. These are a lot of variables!

In the problems that follow, various ancillary conditions are
apt to be inherent in the situation that is described. Pressure may
be constant, or may be some function of volume or of temperature;
it may depend on the height in a gravitation field. Likewise, the
other variables may be interrelated by the circumstances of the
problem.

Look for such implicit restrictions, and combine them with
the ideal gas law. Try to get a feeling for how gases behave in
various simple situations.

Equations and concepts

The principal equations and concepts used in the problems that follow are assembled below. This will be done at the beginning of each chapter. Primarily these listings serve as a quick guide to the contents. Use them, if you wish, as a kind of "crib sheet."

Ideal Gas Law: $PV = nRT$, or $PV = wRT/M$, or $PM = \rho RT$
[The second two are merely alternative forms in which the number of moles $\underline{n}$ has been replaced by (weight)/(molecular weight) and in which $\underline{w}/V$ has been replaced by density ρ.]

Dalton's Law of Partial Pressures: $P_{total} = \Sigma P_i$; $P_i = N_i P_{total}$
(P_i denotes the partial pressure of the ith species; N_i is its mole fraction.) Also $P_i V = n_i RT$.

Gas Constant: You will find it convenient to keep in mind the various units in which R, the gas constant, is commonly expressed. Thus $R = 0.082$ liter-atm/mole-deg = 82 cc-atm/mole-deg = 8.31×10^7 ergs/mole-deg = 1.98 cal/mole-deg.

STP Conditions: 0°C or 273° K and 1 atm pressure.

Barometric Equation: Differential form: $d \ln P = \dfrac{Mg}{RT} dh$
Integrated form: $RT \ln P_2/P_1 = -Mgh$ (assuming $P = P_1$ at $h = 0$); g is the gravitational constant.

Problems

1. (11 min) A flask filled with pure helium (atomic weight 4) at 1 atm and 25° C contains 0.80 g of the gas. What weight of argon (atomic weight 40) would have to be added to the bulb so that the combined weight of the two gases (at 25° C) would equal that of an equal volume of air (at 1 atm and 25° C)? (The average molecular weight of air is 29.) Give also the average molecular weight of the He-Ar mixture.

2. (7.5 min) Air is approximately 80% nitrogen and 20% oxygen (on a mole basis). If 4.0 g of hydrogen is added to a 22.4-liter flask maintained at 0° C and initially filled with air at 1 atm pressure, what will be the molecular weight (i.e., the average molecular weight) of the hydrogen-air mixture?

3. (9 min) An iron pipe 2 m long and closed at one end is lowered vertically into water until the closed end is flush with the water surface (see Fig. 1-1). Calculate the height h of the water level in the pipe. Miscellaneous data: 25°C, diam. of pipe is 3 in., density of water is 1.00 g/cc, barometric pressure is 1.00 atm. Also, 1 atm = 10^6 dynes/cm^2 = 10 m hydrostatic head of water (neglect the effect of water vapor pressure).

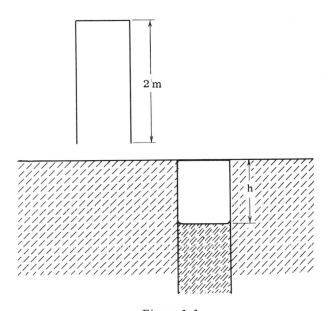

Figure 1-1

4. (11 min) Hydrogen gas will dissociate into atoms at a high enough temperature, i.e., $H_2 = 2H$. Assuming ideal gas behavior for H_2 and H, what should be the density of hydrogen at 2000° C if it is 33% dissociated into atoms? The pressure is 1 atm.

5. (9 min) The two flasks shown in Fig. 1-2 are filled with nitrogen gas and, when both are immersed in boiling water, the gas pressure inside the system is 0.5 atm. One of the flasks is then immersed in an ice-water mixture, keeping the other in the boiling water. Calculate the new pressure for the system.

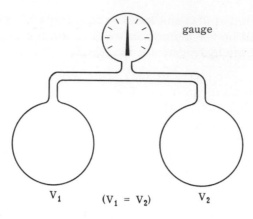

Figure 1-2

6. (12 min) An 11-liter flask contains 20 g of neon and an unknown weight of hydrogen. The gas density is found to be 0.002 g/cc at 0° C. Calculate the average molecular weight and the number of grams of hydrogen present, and also the pressure. The atomic weight of neon is 20 g/mole.

7. (9 min) A pioneer aeronaut is planning the design of a hot-air balloon. What volume of air at 100° C should be used if the balloon is to have a gross lifting power of 200 kg (defined as the mass of displaced air minus the mass of hot air)? The ambient temperature and pressure are 25° C and 1 atm, and the average molecular weight of air is 29 g/mole, whereas that of the hot air is 32 g/mole (due to the presence of some CO_2).

8. (11 min) A Dumas bulb is filled with chlorine gas at the ambient pressure and is found to contain 7.1 g of chlorine when the temperature is T° K. The bulb is then placed in a second thermostat bath whose temperature is 30° C hotter than the first one. The stopcock on the bulb is opened so that the chlorine-gas pressure returns to the original value. The bulb is now found to contain 6.4 g of chlorine. Calculate the value of the original temperature. If the volume of the bulb was 2.24 liters, what was the ambient pressure? The atomic weight of chlorine is 35.5.

9. (11 min) A balloon is filled with 1000 moles of helium at 1 atm and 25°C. The buoyancy of the balloon may be defined as the mass of the helium subtracted from that of the displaced air. What is the buoyancy of the balloon when first filled if the outside pressure and temperature are also 1 atm and 25° C?

The balloon is now placed in a large tank, which is pumped out until the pressure outside the balloon corresponds to an altitude of 10 miles. Assuming that the temperature of the helium in the balloon is the same as the outside temperature, which is now 0°C, and that the fabric of the balloon is sufficiently elastic so that the helium pressure is also the same as that outside, will the buoyancy now be more than, the same as, or less than it was before? The average molecular weight of air is 29 g/mole.

10. (16 min) Two flasks of equal volume (see Fig. 1-3) are connected by a narrow tube (of negligible volume): Initially both flasks are at 27°C and contain 0.70 moles of hydrogen gas, the pressure being 0.50 atm. One of the flasks is then immersed in a hot oil bath at 127°C, while the other is kept at 27°C. Calculate the final pressure of, and the moles of hydrogen in, each flask.

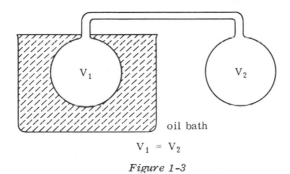

oil bath

$V_1 = V_2$

Figure 1-3

11. (7 min) Two separate bulbs contain ideal gases A and B, respectively. The density of gas A is twice that of gas B, and the molecular weight of gas A is half that of gas B; the two gases are at the same temperature. Calculate the ratio of the pressure of gas A to that of gas B.

12. (12 min) A 2-liter Dumas bulb contains n moles of nitrogen at 0.5 atm pressure and at T°K. On addition of 0.01 moles of oxygen, it is necessary to cool the bulb to a temperature of 10°C in order to maintain the same pressure. Calculate n and T.

13. (13 min) It is desired to prepare a gas mixture containing 5 mole % of butane and 95% of argon (a mixture of this type is used

in filling Geiger-Müller counter tubes). A gas cylinder is evacuated and gaseous butane is let in until the butane pressure is 1
atm. The tank or cylinder is then weighed, and compressed argon
gas forced in until a certain weight w (in grams), has been added.
The volume of the cylinder is 40 liters, and the operation is carried out at 25°C. Calculate the weight of argon that gives a mixture of the desired composition, and the total pressure of the final
mixture. The atomic weight of argon is 40 g/mole.

14. (12 min) Calculate the number of moles of air in a column
1 cm^2 in area and rising from sea level to an altitude of 1.5×10^6
cm (about 10 miles), allowing for the barometric decrease in
pressure. Assume air to be a uniform gas of molecular weight
29, and a uniform temperature of 0°C. Note that the atmospheric
pressure is equal to the total weight of gas in a column of unit
area and of infinite height. Conversion factors: R = 0.082 liter-
atm/mole-deg = 8.31×10^7 ergs/mole-deg = 1.98 cal/mole-deg;
1 atm = 760 mm Hg = 1×10^6 dynes/cm^2.

15. (6 min) Curve 1 in the graph of Fig. 1-4 represents a plot of
the variation of pressure with altitude according to the simple barometric equation which assumes T and g to be constant.

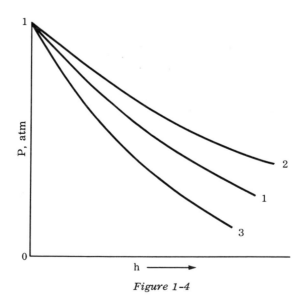

Figure 1-4

If, instead of assuming T to be constant in the derivation, one had assumed it to decrease with altitude (e.g., T = a − bh), would the resulting calculated curve lie above or below curve 1, i.e., would it resemble curve 2 or curve 3? Similarly, if instead of assuming **g** to be constant, one assumed it to decrease with altitude (e.g., g = a − bh), would the resulting curve more nearly resemble 2 or 3?

16. (15 min) The gravitational constant **g** decreases by 1.0 cm/sec^2/km of altitude. Assuming a constant temperature of 25°C, derive a modified barometric equation that recognizes this variation in **g**. Calculate the pressure of nitrogen at 300 km altitude, taking sea-level pressure to be 1 atm and using this modified equation.

17. (15 min) When 2 g of gaseous substance A is introduced into an initially evacuated flask kept at 25°C, the pressure is found to be 1 atm. Three grams of gaseous substance B is then added to the 2 g of A, and the pressure is now found to be 1.5 atm. Assuming ideal gas behavior, calculate the ratio of molecular weights, i.e., M_A/M_B.

Answers

1. $Wt_{air} = \dfrac{M_{air}}{M_{He}} Wt_{He}$ since the comparison is for the same V, P, and T. $Wt_{air} = (29 \times 0.80)/4 = 5.8$ g. One therefore needs to add 5.0 g of argon to the 0.8 of helium. M_{av} = total weight/total moles, so

$$M_{av} = \frac{5.8}{\dfrac{0.8}{4} + \dfrac{5.0}{40}} = \underline{17.9 \text{ g/mole}}$$

2. Since we have 22.4 liters of air at STP, we have 1 mole of air.

$$M_{av} = \frac{\Sigma n_i M_i}{\Sigma n_i} \quad (\text{i.e., = total weight/total moles})$$

$$M_{av} = \frac{0.80 \times 28 + 0.20 \times 32 + 4}{1 + 2} = 32.8/3 = \underline{11 \text{ g/mole}}$$

3. Since temperature is constant,

$$P_{fin} = P_{init}\left(\frac{\text{initial volume}}{\text{final volume}}\right)$$

$$= P_{init}\left(\frac{2 \times \text{area of pipe}}{h \times \text{area of pipe}}\right) = 2P_{init}/h$$

but P_{fin} = h + 10 (in meters). Thus

$$h + 10 = 2 \times 10/h \text{ or } h^2 + 10h = 20 \text{ and } h = \underline{1.7 \text{ m}}$$

4. It is convenient to think in terms of 1 mole of H_2 before dissociation, as a basis for the calculation. Then

after dissociation: 0.67 mole H_2 left
0.66 mole of H (from the dissociation
total moles: 1.33   of the 0.33 mole of H_2)

For a mixture of gases, the density ρ is given by $\rho = PM_{av}/RT$. In this case, M_{av} = total weight/total moles = 2 g/1.33 = 1.5 g/mole. Then

$$\rho = \frac{1 \times 1.5}{0.082 \times 2273} = \underline{8.07 \times 10^{-3} \text{ g/liter}}$$

5. Here, the number of moles of gas remains constant, and we can write

$$n = n_1 + n_2 = \frac{P}{R}\left(\frac{V_1}{373} + \frac{V_2}{373}\right)$$

$$= \frac{0.5 \text{ V}}{R}\left(\frac{2}{373}\right) \quad \text{(initially)} \quad (V = V_1 = V_2)$$

Also

$$n = n_1' + n_2' = \frac{P'V}{R}\left(\frac{1}{273} + \frac{1}{373}\right)$$

Equating the two expressions for n, cancelling out V/R, and rearranging:

$$P' = 0.5(2/373)\left(\frac{273 \times 373}{273 + 363}\right) = (0.5 \times 546)/646 = \underline{0.423 \text{ atm}}$$

6. Since the density is 2 g/liter, the 11 liters contain 22 g; hence 2 g of hydrogen in addition to the 20 of neon. This is 1 mole of each or 2 moles total. Then M_{av} = 22/2 = 11 g/mole;

$$P = nRT/V = (2 \times 0.082 \times 273)/11 = 4.07 \text{ atm}$$

7. Since the mass of gas at a given P, V, T is given by PVM/RT, we have $w_{air} - w_{hot\ air} = 2 \times 10^5$ g $= \dfrac{1 \times V}{0.082} (29/298 - 32/373)$.

From this, V = 1.4×10^6 liters.

8. The original 7.1 g corresponds to 0.1 moles, and the final 6.4 g to 10% less, hence 0.09 moles.

We are comparing two cases that involve the same volume and pressure, hence in this instance, $n_1 T_1 = n_2 T_2$ or 0.1 T_1 = 0.09 $(T_1 + 30)$. Or, T_1 = 270°K.

If the volume is 22.4 liters, then P = $(0.1 \times 0.082 \times 270)/2.24$ = 0.99 atm.

9. The weight of air occupying the same volume and at the same P and T as the helium will be 29/4 times the weight of helium. The weight of helium is 4000 g. The buoyancy is then $(29/4 - 1) \times 4000 = 25,000$ g.

In the second part, the buoyancy will be unchanged. Note that the above calculation is independent of the actual pressure and temperature.

10. Using the equation n = PV/RT, the initial condition is that 0.7 = P $\times$ 2V/R $\times$ 300 where V is the volume of one bulb, so V/R = 0.7 $\times$ 300. With one bulb heated, the same 0.7 mole is now equal to $n_1 + n_2$; i.e.,

$$0.7 = \frac{PV}{R} (1/300 + 1/400)$$

On inserting the value of V/R;

$$0.7 = P \times 0.7 \times 300 (1/300 + 1/400)$$

from which P = 0.57 atm. Also, n_1 = 0.57 V/300 R = 0.4 mole, hence n_2 = 0.3 mole.

11. Use the gas law in the form P = ρRT/M; then

$$P_A/P_B = \frac{\rho_A/\rho_B}{M_A/M_B} + 2/\tfrac{1}{2} = 4$$

12. The condition after the addition of the oxygen is given as
$(n + 0.01) = PV/RT = (1/2)(2)/0.082 \times 283 = 0.0432$. Hence

$$\underline{n = 0.0332}$$

Then

$$T = PV/nR = (1/2)(2)/0.0332 \times 0.082 = \underline{367°K}$$

13. The moles of butane present are given by $n = PV/RT$: $n_{bu} =$
$(1 \times 40)/0.082 \times 298 = 1.64$. One then wants 95 parts of argon to
5 of butane or 19 to 1, so

$$n_{Ar} = 19 \times 1.64 = 31.1 \text{ moles Ar} \quad \text{or} \quad 31.1 \times 40$$

$$\text{or} \quad \underline{1240 \text{ g Ar}}$$

The final pressure is proportional to the change in number of
moles, so $P_f = 1 \text{ atm} \times 20/1 = \underline{20 \text{ atm.}}$

14. The pressure at this altitude is given by the barometric equation as:

$$\log (P_2/1 \text{ atm}) = -\frac{Mg}{2.3RT} h = -\frac{29 \times 980 \times 1.5 \times 10^6}{8.31 \times 10^7 \times 273 \times 2.3}$$

$$= -0.817$$

Hence $P_2 = 0.152$ atm.

Since the weight of a complete column of air extending down to
sea level is 10^6 dynes/cm^2, the weight of a column extending down
only to the given altitude will be 0.152×10^6 dynes/cm^2, and therefore the weight of the column between sea level and this altitude is
0.848×10^6 dynes/cm^2.

Therefore:

$$0.848 \times 10^6 = nMg \quad \text{or} \quad n = 0.848 \times 10^6/29 \times 980$$

$$= \underline{29.8 \text{ moles}}$$

15. The basic differential equation is:

$$d \ln P = -\frac{Mg}{RT} dh$$

Hence, if T decreases with increasing h, the rate of change of ln P will increase, i.e., pressure will drop more rapidly: Curve 3.

Correspondingly, if g decreases with increasing h, the rate of change in ln P will decrease, and pressure will drop less rapidly: Curve 2.

16. The problem states that $g = 980 - 10^{-5}h$, if h is in centimeters. Inserting this into the basic differential equation gives

$$d \ln P = -\frac{M}{RT}(980 - 10^{-5}h)\ dh$$

or,

$$2.3 \log(P/0.8) = -\frac{M}{RT}(980h - 5 \times 10^{-6}h^2)$$

$$= -\frac{28}{8.31 \times 10^7 \times 298}$$

$$(980 \times 3 \times 10^7 - 4.5 \times 10^9)$$

Hence

$$\log(P/0.8) = -12.1 \quad \text{or} \quad P = 6.4 \times 10^{-13}\ \text{atm}$$

17. Since V and T are constant, P is proportional to the number of moles n. Evidently 3 g of B corresponds to half as many moles as does 2 g of A, or 6 g of B has the same number of moles as does 2 of A, and therefore $M_A/M_B = \frac{2}{6} = \frac{1}{3}$.

2 *Nonideal gases; condensation*

Comments

We now take a look at gases as they really are—imperfect, capable of condensation, and showing critical phenomena. The equations capable of representing such behavior can become algebraically quite complex; they must, after all, be based on much more sophisticated models than that for the ideal gas. In a sense the subject has become open-ended in that we could go almost indefinitely into higher and higher degrees of refinement.

Rather than do this, however, we limit ourselves to a few common nonideal gas equations of state, mainly the van der Waals equation. As in Chapter I, the attempt is made to pose problems that require some situational analysis to see what to do. In addition, you will find questions probing how good your qualitative or intuitive understanding of nonideal gas and condensation behavior is.

Equations and concepts

van der Waals Equation: $(P + a/V^2)(V - b) = RT$, where V is the molar volume.

Virial Equation: $PV/RT = 1 + B/V + C/V^2 + \cdots$, where B and C depend on temperature (but not on V).

Critical Temperature, Pressure, and Volume: In the case of a van der Waals gas,

$$V_c = 3b, \qquad P_c = a/27b^2 \text{ and } T_c = 8a/27bR$$

Principle of Corresponding States: Plots of compressibility factor, PV/RT, vs. P/P_c are the same for all real gases at the same value of T/T_c. Reduced equation of state for a van der Waals gas: $(\alpha + 3/\beta^2)(3\beta - 1) = 8\gamma$, where α, β, and γ are the reduced pressure, volume, and temperature, respectively.

General Characteristics of P-V-T Behavior: You should know the general shape of plots of the compressibility factor vs. reduced pressure, and of the van der Waals equation. In particular you should have some feeling for the physical interpretation of iso-thermal plots of the van der Waals equation. Thus for a tempera-ture below the critical temperature, the plot will go through a max-imum and a minimum, but the physical interpretation is that con-densation occurs. The vapor pressure at which this happens is de-termined by a virtual work principle (see your text). Also, the minimum may occur at a negative pressure value and can then be interpreted as giving a positive tensile strength for the liquid.[*]

Miscellaneous definitions include that of the Boyle temperature as that temperature such that the derivative $d(PV)/dP$ becomes zero as P approaches zero. A useful rule to remember is that the normal boiling point is usually about two-thirds of the critical temperature (expressed in degrees absolute).

Problems

1. (11 min) Two separate bulbs contain gases A and B, respec-tively. The pressures and volumes are such that the PV product is the same for both gases. However, gas A is an ideal gas, and

---

[*]See, for example; S. W. Benson and E. Gerjuoy, *J. Chem. Phys.*, **17**, 914 (1949).

gas B is nonideal and is at a pressure and temperature less than
the critical values. Explain, preferably with the aid of an appropriate graph, whether the temperature of gas B should be the
same as, more than, or less than that of gas A.

2. (10 min) (Open Book) Doubling the temperature at constant
pressure will (more than, less than) double the volume of a gas
if the gas is (ideal, nonideal and below T_C, nonideal and above
its Boyle temperature, nonideal and at low pressure).

3. (13 min) A nonideal gas of molecular weight 150 obeys the van
der Waals equation; its critical pressure and temperature are 100
atm and 100°C, respectively.

   (a) The compressibility factor PV/RT will be greater than
unity at (500 atm and 80°C, 500 atm and 120°C, 50 atm and 60°C,
50 atm and 120°C, none of these).

   (b) Calculate the value of the compressibility factor at the
critical point.

4. (10 min) A certain substance obeys the van der Waals equation, and its constants a and b are known. Name six types of
properties or coefficients that may be calculated for this substance, using the above information.

5. (11 min) The curve for a reduced temperature of 0.8 is repro-
duced in Fig. 2-1 in terms of compressibility factor vs. reduced
pressure. The curve stops abruptly at point X, since condensation to liquid is supposed to occur at this point.

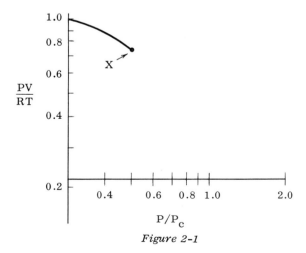

Figure 2-1

(a) Sketch the continuation of the line up to a reduced pressure of 1.5; i.e., show how the compressibility factor should vary as one goes through and then past the condensation region.

(b) Assuming the point X represents C_2H_4 at $-46°C$ and 17 atm, show how to calculate (or estimate) P_c, T_c, V_c, and the normal boiling point of ethylene.

6. (10 min) Make a semiquantitative plot of T vs. V for water at 1 atm pressure. The range of V values should be from about 17 cc/mole to about 40 liters/mole.

7. (12 min) Given the P vs V plot of Fig. 2-2 for a certain gas at 25°C, calculated according to the van der Waals equation using the appropriate a and b values, estimate numerical values for the following: (a) The tensile strength of the liquid, (b) the vapor pressure of the liquid, (c) the molar volume of the liquid, and (d) the critical volume V_c.

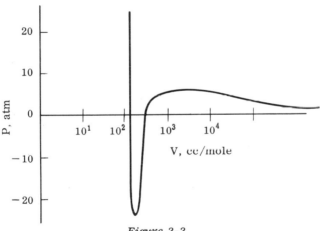

Figure 2-2

8. (6 min) Given the following data for a certain nonideal gas at 25°C:

ρ/P, g/liter-atm:	10	11	10	(ρ = density)
P, atm:	1	10	20	

The critical pressure of this gas must then be (greater than 10 atm, greater than 20 atm, between 1 and 20 atm, between 1 and 10 atm, less than 20 atm, can't tell).

9. (5 min) The critical temperature and pressure are 32°C and 48 atm for ethane. Sketch the plot of the compressibility factor,

PV/RT, vs. P for the case of t = 40°C. Extend the plot up to
100 atm pressure.

10. (12 min) Figure 2-3 shows several isotherms calculated from
the van der Waals equation for a representative gas (the dotted
lines locate the actual vapor pressures for the various isotherms).
Locate on the graph the conditions of P and T such that (a) the
b term is negligible compared to V, (b) the a/V^2 term is negligible compared to P, (c) P is negligible compared to a/V^2, and
(d) V is negligible compared to b. (Answer "none" if no conditions exist under which the statement would be true.) (e) On the
volume axis mark the approximate value of b.

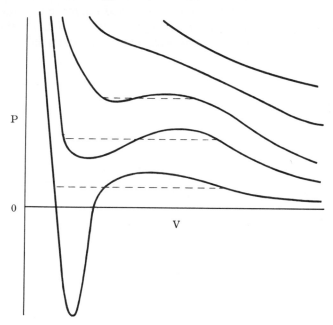

Figure 2-3

11. (13 min) A gas obeys the van der Waals equation, with P_c =
30 atm and T_c = 200°C. The compressibility factor PV/RT will
be more than one (at P = 50 atm, T = 250°C; at P = 1 atm,
T = 100°C; P = 500 atm, T = 500°C; none of these). The gas
will approach ideality at (low T, low density, low values of the
compressibility factor, none of these). Calculate the van der
Waals constant b for this gas.

12. (12 min) The critical temperature and pressure for NO gas are 177°K and 64 atm, respectively, and for CCl_4 they are 550°K and 45 atm, respectively. Which gas (a) has the smaller value of the van der Waals constant b, (b) the smaller value of the van der Waals constant a, (c) has the larger critical volume, and (d) is most nearly ideal in behavior at 300°K and 10 atm?

13. (5 min) The compressibility plot for a certain gas is shown in Fig. 2-4 for 100°C. It follows that the critical temperature of the gas is (greater than 100°C, less than 100°C, can't tell) and that the critical pressure of the gas is (greater than 10 atm, less than 10 atm, can't tell).

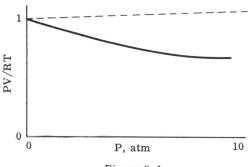

Figure 2-4

14. (3 min) A nonideal gas is below its critical temperature. On compression, the plot of volume vs. pressure (volume as ordinate) will lie (above, below) the corresponding curve for an ideal gas.

15. (13 min) The molecular weight of a vapor is determined by measuring the vapor density at a known P and T. Even though no chemical association or dissociation occurs, the molecular weight will be in error (in general) if it is calculated by means of the ideal gas law, since the vapor is nonideal. The critical temperature and pressure of this particular substance are 100°C and 1.0 atm, respectively.

(a) The molecular weight as calculated from the ideal gas law would be low if the vapor density were measured at (the critical point, at a sufficiently low temperature, at a sufficiently high pressure, none of these).

(b) If the vapor density were measured at 0°C, (the ideal-gas-law molecular weight would be low, would be high, the measurement is impossible since the vapor would necessarily have condensed to a liquid, none of these).

(c) Explain briefly how, from measurements of vapor density, T, and P only, you would obtain an accurate molecular weight.

16. (3 min) A certain nonideal gas is at its critical temperature and at a pressure 10% greater than its critical pressure. Doubling the pressure of the gas at constant temperature should (more than, less than) halve its volume.

17. (10 min) Gases A, B, C, and D obey the van der Waals equation, with a and b values as given (liter-atm system of units):

	A	B	C	D
a	6	6	20	0.05
b	0.025	0.15	0.10	0.02

Which gas has the highest critical temperature, the largest molecules, the most nearly ideal behavior at STP? (Not necessarily the same gas!)

18. (13 min) A certain gas obeys the van der Waals equation. Its T_C is 100°C and its P_C is 90 atm. Underline the most appropriate choice to complete each statement below.

(a) The gas will approach ideality at (high pressures, low values of the PV product, low temperatures, none of these).

(b) The gas definitely will show a positive deviation from ideality (i.e., PV > RT) (at low temperatures, low PV products, around 100°C provided the pressure is high enough, at any pressure below P_C, none of these).

(c) The gas must at least partially condense to a liquid if cooled below T_C (true, false).

19. (6 min) The experimental value of RT/V is 1.10 for 1 mole of a certain nonideal gas. The gas is at 1 atm and its temperature is below the critical temperature. If the pressure is now halved, at constant temperature, it is to be expected that the new volume will be (more than twice, less than twice) the original volume.

20. (5 min) Select the appropriate statement. The density of a nonideal gas (increases with decreasing pressure, at constant temperature; is proportional to the molecular weight of the gas; increases with increasing PV product; none of these).

21. (7 min) Given that a certain gas obeys the van der Waals equation, underline the most appropriate choice to complete each statement below.

(a) The gas approaches ideality at (high pressures, low values of the PV product, low temperatures, none of these).

(b) The equation for n moles of the gas is $PV = nRT$, $(P + a/V^2)(V - b) - nRT$, $(P + a/n^2V^2)(nV - b) = nRT$, $(P + an^2/V^2) \times (V/n - b) = RT$, none of these.

22. (4.5 min) The barometric formula (see page 2) is employed to calculate the air pressure on the top of Mt. Whitney (14,500 ft), taking 76 cm Hg as sea-level pressure. State briefly the reasons why this calculation would be inaccurate.

23. (10 min) As illustrated in many texts for the CO_2 system, it takes a three-dimensional plot of P vs. V vs. T to show the complete behavior of a substance. For convenience one ordinarily deals with sections of the solid model so that a two-dimensional representation is possible. One thus has isotherms (P vs. V or V vs. P, with T constant), isobars (T vs. V or V vs. T, with P constant), and isochors (T vs. P or P vs. T, with V constant). The three diagrams of Fig. 2-5 give an isotherm, an isochor, and an isobar for water. State which diagram is which, and label each abscissa and ordinate.

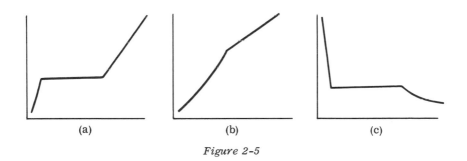

(a)   (b)   (c)

Figure 2-5

24. (10 min) The values of P_C and T_C for N_2 are 126°K for T_C and 34 atm for P_C, whereas for C_2H_6 they are 48 atm and 305°K, respectively. (a) Which gas has the smaller van der Waals constant b? (b) Which has the smaller a value? (c) Which has the larger V_C value? (d) Which should show the most nearly ideal behavior at 25°C and 10 atm pressure?

25. (9 min) The van der Waals constants for gases A, B, and C are:

Gas	a, liters^2-atm/mole	b, liters/mole
A	4.0	0.027
B	12.0	0.030
C	6.0	0.032

Which gas has (a) the highest critical temperature, (b) the largest molecular volume, and (c) most ideal general behavior around STP.

26. (15 min) Some P-V plots are shown for a gas that obeys the van der Waals equation. Calculate the constants a and b for this gas. Since your calculation is necessarily approximate, it is necessary to show very clearly just how you have obtained numbers for the graph of Fig. 2-6 and how you have used them. Give the units of a and b also.

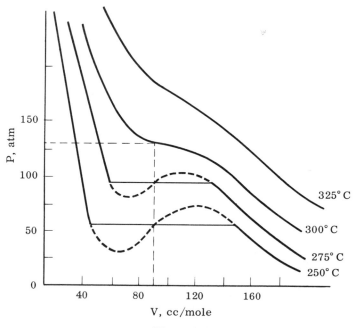

Figure 2-6

Answers

1. According to the principle of corresponding states, the compressibility factor PV/RT is the same for all gases at a given P/P_C and T/T_C. In this case, P and T for gas B are less than P_C and T_C, so that, as shown in Fig. 2-7, the value of PV/RT should be less than unity. Since PV is the same for both gases, it follows that T must be <u>greater</u> for gas B than for gas A.

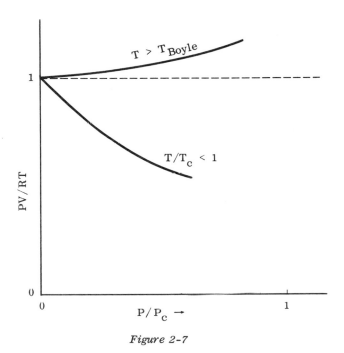

Figure 2-7

2. If the gas is to be either more than or less than double its volume, it cannot be ideal. Referring to the diagram above, if the gas is nonideal and below T_C, doubling the temperature will increase PV/RT, hence V will more than double. If it is above its Boyle temperature, the doubling of T will decrease PV/RT and V will less than double. The third choice is contradictory, as gases approach ideality at low pressure.

3. For the compressibility factor to be greater than unity, we want a high pressure and temperature, hence <u>500 atm and 120°C</u>.

For a van der Waals gas, $V_c = 3b$, $T_c = 8a/27Rb$, and $P_c = a/27b^2$, hence $P_c V_c / R T_c = \frac{3}{8}$.

4. (a) P, V, or T, if the other two are known. (b) Its critical point. (c) The vapor pressure of the liquid. (d) The heat of vaporization. (e) The ideal tensile strength of the liquid. (f) Coefficient of compressibility. (g) Coefficient of thermal expansion. (h) Surface tension.

5. At point X of Fig. 2-8 condensation begins, and V decreases with no change in pressure to the value for the liquid; there is therefore a vertical drop in PV/RT to some much lower value. When condensation is complete, V ceases to change much, so PV/RT now rises in approximate proportion to P.

If T is −46°C or 227°K when T/T_c is 0.8, when $T_c = \underline{283°K}$. Further, point $\underline{X}$ occurs at 17 atm and at P/P_c of about 0.5, hence P_c = ca. 34 $\underline{atm}$. For a van der Waals gas, $P_c V_c / R T_c$ is $\frac{3}{8}$, hence

$$V_c = \frac{0.082 \times 283 \times 3}{34 \times 8} = \underline{0.26 \text{ liter/mole}}$$

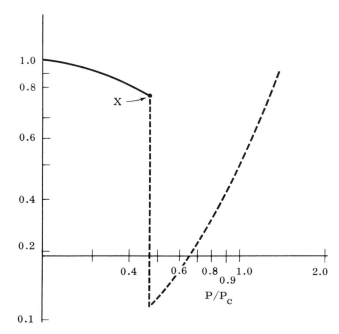

Figure 2-8

6. In Fig. 2-9, the main points are: (a) the molar volume of liquid water is 18 cc/mole, and for water at this volume to exert 1 atm pressure it must be at its boiling point; reduction in temperature leads to a slight decrease in liquid volume. (b) Any attempt to increase T simply results in vaporization and increase in V until the water is all vaporized, at which point one has 1 mole of vapor at 1 atm and 100°C, or a V value of about 30 liters. (c) The temperature may now increase, with V rising proportionally.

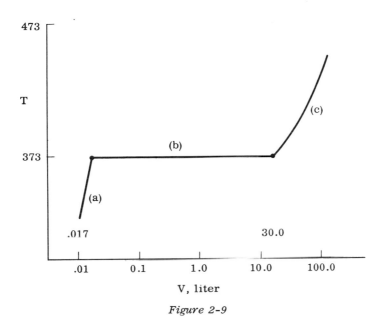

Figure 2-9

7. The tensile strength is given by the most negative pressure attainable, i.e., ca. 20 atm. The vapor pressure is estimated by locating a horizontal line in Fig. 2-10, so that the net area between it and the curve is zero, and would be ca. 5 atm. The molar volume of the liquid is the liquid volume at its vapor pressure, or about 110 cc/mole, and the critical volume will be about three times larger, or about 330 cc/mole.

8. Since density is w/V, then ρ/P = w/PV. Therefore, at a given temperature ρ/P varies inversely as the compressibility

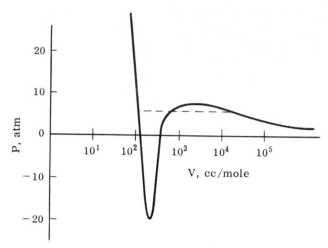

Figure 2-10

factor, so that the maximum in ρ/P means a minimum in PV/RT. In plots of PV/RT vs. P/P_C, such a minimum occurs only for $T < T_C$ and $P > P_C$ and we know that the minimum lies between 1 and 20 atm. P_C could be greater or less than 1 or 10 atm, but must be <u>less than 20 atm.</u>

9. At 40°C, $T/T_C = 1.03$. PV/RT will then vary with pressure as indicated in Fig. 2-11.

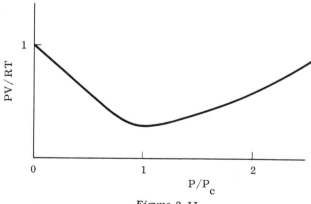

Figure 2-11

10. (a) The right-hand region, i.e., where V is large. (b) the right-hand and upper region where V and/or P are large. (c) The lower-left region where P and V are small, especially the region of negative pressure. (d) None. (e) Approximately the value of V where the lowest temperature isotherm cuts the P = 0 line.

11. PV/RT should be greater than one at the highest P and T choice, 500 atm and 500°C as both, the first especially, are far above the critical values. Ideality will be approached at low density. Since for a van der Waals gas $P_C V_C /RT_C = \frac{3}{8}$, and $b = V_C/3$, then b = 0.082 × 473/8 × 30 = 0.163 liter/mole.

12. For a van der Waals gas, $V_C = 3b$, $P_C = a/27b^2$, and $T_C = 8a/27bR$. Therefore b and hence V_C are proportional to T_C/P_C, and NO should have the smaller b value (this can be argued qualitatively on the grounds that NO should be the smaller molecule); similarly CCl_4 should have the largest b and hence the largest V_C value. The constant a is proportional to $P_C V_C^2$ or to T_C^2 /P_C, and will therefore be smallest for NO (again, this can be argued qualitatively on the basis that the much lower critical temperature for NO means smaller intermolecular attractive forces and hence a smaller a value). NO gas should be the more ideal since 300°K is above its critical temperature, but below that of CCl_4.

13. The critical pressure could be less than 10 atm, in which case T_C < 100°C; it could be greater than 10 atm, with T_C either greater or less than 100°C. Hence the answer in both cases is can't tell.

14. It will lie below (except at extremely high pressures).

15. (a) Molecular weight = w(RT/PV), hence is inversely proportional to the compressibility factor; the calculated value will be low under conditions such that the compressibility factor is greater than unity, i.e., at a sufficiently high pressure.

(b) At 0°C one is below the critical temperature (and presumably at about 1 atm pressure) so PV/RT is less than one and the calculated molecular weight would be high.

(c) To obtain an accurate molecular weight it would be necessary to measure density at several pressures and extrapolate ρ/P vs. P to zero pressure; this limiting value is now exactly equal to M/RT.

16. Under the conditions stated, the compressibility factor will be slightly past its minimum value, hence will increase when pressure is doubled. The volume will therefore be less than halved.

17. Since T_c is proportional to a/b, <u>gas A</u> has the highest T_c. Since b gives a measure of molecular volume, <u>gas C</u>. That gas having the lowest critical temperature and pressure will be most nearly ideal at STP. <u>Gas D</u> has the lowest a/b, and hence T_c, and also the lowest a/b^2 and hence P_c.

18. (a) The gas will approach ideality at low pressures; <u>none of these</u>.
    (b) PV/RT would exceed unity at a high enough pressure.
    (c) <u>False</u> (depends on the pressure).

19. The value of PV/RT is evidently 1/1.10 = 0.9. The compressibility factor will increase as pressure is reduced, hence the new volume will be <u>more than</u> twice the original.

20. Strictly speaking, <u>none of these</u>. It will be approximately proportional to molecular weight, keeping P and T constant, but not exactly proportional as different gases will differently depart from ideality.

21. (a) <u>None of these</u>. (b) $(P + an^2/V^2)(V/n - b) = RT$ (replacing V/n by molar volume returns the equation to the usual form).

22. The usual integrated form of the barometric equation, based on the ideal gas law, makes several assumptions that are not strictly true. These are: constant gravity, constant temperature. In addition, air is a mixture of gases and is partially fractionated with elevation, so that the average molecular weight is changing. Then, of course, air is a real gas and not perfectly ideal in behavior. Finally, of course, wind velocity and meteorological conditions can cause the pressure to vary unpredictably.

23. (c) is the easiest and is clearly an isotherm involving the region of condensation, with P the ordinate and V the abscissa. On reflection, (b) must be a plot of P as ordinate vs. T as abscissa, hence an isochor. The first portion shows the increase in liquid vapor pressure and the subsequent linear portion, simply Charles' law for the vapor after all the liquid has evaporated. (a) Must then be an isobar, and evidently T is ordinate and V, the abscissa.

24. See Problem 10. b and thus V_c are proportional to T_c/P_c and therefore are largest for C_2H_6 (this could be argued qualitatively just on the grounds of which molecule should be largest).

a is proportional to T_C^2/P_C, and hence is largest for C_2H_6. Again this could be deduced qualitatively just by noting how much higher T_C is for ethane. Since 25°C is above T_C for nitrogen but close to T_C for ethane, the nitrogen will clearly be the more ideal at this temperature. Answers are then: (a) N_2; (b) N_2; (c) C_2H_6; (d) N_2.

25. T_C is proportional to a/b, hence gas B has the largest T_C. (Since the b values are not very different, this conclusion could have been reached just on the qualitative argument that the larger a value for gas B means greater intermolecular attractive forces, hence a larger T_C needed to overcome them.) b and V_C are proportional, hence gas C has the largest V_C. Since the b values are so similar, ideality around STP will largely be determined by the a values. Gas A, having the smallest a value, should be the most ideal in behavior.

26. The 300°C isotherm appears to be very close to the critical one, and we can estimate P_C, V_C from the point of inflection. Then P_C = 125 atm, V_C = 90 cc/mole, and T_C = 300°C or 573°K. The constant b is then $V_C/3$ or 30 cc/mole, and since $P_C = a/27b^2$, we find a = 125 × 27 × 30² = 3 × 10⁶ cc² atm/mole².

3 Kinetic molecular theory of gases

Comments

The kinetic molecular theory of gases, in all its glory, can be a rather complicated affair. We restrain ourselves here to the very simplest aspects. For example, if one neglects the volume that molecules occupy and assumes them to be in random motion with an average velocity c, the first equation below is easily obtained, as is the second, in combination with the ideal gas law.

The form of the formula for wall collision frequency can also be obtained without a very elaborate derivation. By means of it you can deal with the effusion of gases and Graham's law. The point here is that, if we have a small hole in a thin wall, it is safe to assume that the rate at which molecules pass through is simply the rate at which they would collide with the same area of wall.

We shouldn't completely ignore, however, the fact that molecules actually do have a distribution of velocities and that the matter can be treated in a fairly straightforward way with the use of the Boltzman principle. From the velocity distribution equation, and a more refined approach, it turns out that c in the equation $PV = \frac{1}{3}Mc^2$ is actually the root-mean-square velocity and that c in the wall-collision-frequency formula is the ordinary average velocity. You should know how these average velocities are related to each other.

As in Chapter 1, the problems are concerned mainly with how well you can analyze a situation and how fluently you can deal with added restrictions that modify these simple equations. Later in the discussion of chemical kinetics (Chapter 16) a few further aspects of kinetic molecular theory will be made use of.

Equations and concepts

Simple Kinetic Theory Equations: $PV = \frac{1}{3}Mc^2$, $c = (3RT/M)^{1/2}$. Here, c is the root-mean-square velocity; note that R should be in units of ergs/mole-deg if c is to be in cm/sec.

$Z = \frac{1}{6}P(3/MRT)^{1/2}$ where Z is moles of collisions per cm^2 per sec. A more accurate equation is $Z = \frac{1}{4}Cc$ where C denotes moles/cc, and c is the mean velocity. Note that in the first equation P should be in dynes/cm^2 and R in ergs/mole-deg.

Effusion: For two gases at the same pressure and temperature, the ratio of rates of leakage through a small hole will be equal to the ratio of wall collision frequencies. Thus $v_2/v_1 = Z_2/Z_1 = (M_1/M_2)^{1/2}$. This is known as Graham's law. If the velocity of effusion is expressed as weight rather than moles per unit time, then $w_2/w_1 = M_2Z_2/M_1Z_1 = (M_2/M_1)^{1/2}$.

Velocity Distribution Equations: Probability of having velocity between c and c + dc:

$$dN/N_0 = \left(\frac{M}{2\pi RT}\right)^{3/2} 4\pi\, e^{-Mc^2/2RT}\, c^2\, dc$$

Mean velocity: $\bar{c} = (8RT/\pi M)^{1/2}$. Root-mean-square velocity, $(\overline{c^2})^{1/2} = (3RT/M)^{1/2}$. Most probable velocity: $c_p = (2RT/M)^{1/2}$.

Viscosity: Frictional force is given by fv, where f is the friction coefficient and v is the velocity. For a sphere, f is given by Stokes' law as $f = 6\pi\eta r$.

Problems

1. (7 min) Arrange in order of increasing value: most probable velocity of molecules of a gas, root-mean-square velocity, average velocity. Would you expect the difference between these three to increase, decrease, or remain the same with increasing temperature?

2. (12 min) Graham's law is sometimes given in terms of the rate of change dV/dt in the volume of a gas kept at constant P and T, owing to its escaping through a pinhole of area A. Derive the equation for dV/dt, i.e., dV/dt as a function of P, T, mol. wt. M, A, etc.

If M and T are such that the root-mean-square velocity is 4×10^5 cm/sec, calculate dV/dt per cm². (Assume ideal gas behavior.) [You may, if you wish, make use of the equation $Z \times$ (moles/cm²-sec) $= \frac{1}{6}P(3/MRT)^{1/2}$.]

3. (9 min) In which case, H_2 (at 1 atm and 50°K) or O_2 (at 2 atm and 200°K) would there be the greatest number of grams of gas hitting a unit area in unit time? (The wall-collision-frequency formula in Problem 2 is available for use here.)

4. (11 min) From the kinetic theory point of view, the pressure exerted by a gas is an average resulting from many individual collisions of molecules with the wall. It is also possible to talk of the local pressure at the point of impact of a single molecule. To

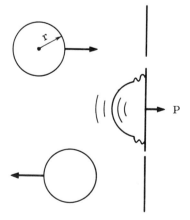

Figure 3-1

do this, one imagines that a molecule of radius r approaches the wall head on, flattens somewhat on impact, then rebounds elastically (see Fig. 3-1). The collision thus takes place over a time interval of about 2r/c sec, where c is the average velocity, and the local pressure is exerted over an area approximating the cross-section of the molecule. It is thus possible to obtain an expression in which the local pressure is given as a function of m (molecular mass), c, and r. Derive this function.

5. (9 min) Two separate bulbs are filled with neon and argon gas, respectively. If conditions are such that the Ar is at twice the absolute temperature and half the density of the Ne, what is the ratio of wall collision frequencies? Atomic weight Ne = 20, Ar = 40.

6. (16 min) (a) The velocity of H_2 molecules is 2×10^5 cm/sec at t°C. Calculate the number of grams of hydrogen per second hitting 1 cm² of wall if the pressure of the gas is such that the molar volume is 1 liter.

(b) Under a new set of conditions, the hydrogen pressure is twice that in (a), but the molar volume is still 1 liter. Calculate the ratio of the new collision frequency to that in (a).

7. (5 min) For argon and krypton the vapor densities at the respective normal boiling points are the same. This means that, at their respective normal boiling points, the molecular velocity in the argon vapor is (greater than, less than, the same as, can't tell) the molecular velocity in the krypton vapor.

8. (6 min) Given the collision frequency formula $Z = \frac{1}{6}P(3/MRT)^{1/2}$, what will be the ratio of final to initial Z for a given gas if its temperature is doubled at constant volume?

9. (15 min) The total volume of a vacuum line system is 22.4 liters. On pumping out the air in the system, it is found that a pinhole leak is letting air in at a rate such that the pressure in the vacuum line is increasing by 0.002 atm/sec. Air may be considered to be an ideal gas of average molecular weight 29; the temperature is 0°C (it is a cold day). Assuming that every air molecule that hits the pinhole enters the vacuum line, calculate what the area (in cm²) of the pinhole must be. Atmospheric pressure is 1 atm. (Gas constant R: 0.082 liter-atm/mole-°K; 82 cc-atm/mole-°K; 1.98 cal/mole-° K; 8.3×10^7 ergs/mole-°K. One atmosphere pressure is equivalent to 10^6 dynes/cm². The density of mercury is 13.6 g/cc. Acceleration due to gravity is 980 cm/sec^2.)

10. (13 min) A container is filled with an ideal gas at a certain pressure and temperature. (a) The container is cooled to one-half the original absolute temperature. (b) The amount of gas is halved, keeping the original temperature. (c) The gas is replaced by the same weight of another ideal gas, keeping the original temperature. This second gas has twice the molecular weight of the first one.

For each case, give the numerical value of the ratio of wall collision frequency Z before the change to that after the change. For which of the three cases will the average molecular velocity be the largest?

11. (10 min) Give the ratio c_1/c_2 of molecular velocities and Z_1/Z_2 of wall collision frequencies for the following changes in conditions of an ideal gas: (a) T is doubled at constant P. (b) P is doubled at constant T.

12. (11 min) A flask contains a mixture of H_2 and O_2 at 0°C and 1 atm total pressure (no sparks or catalyst present!). The mixture contains 36% by weight of H_2. Calculate the ratio Z_{H_2}/Z_{O_2} where Z denotes the wall collision frequency in moles/cm^2-sec.

13. (8.5 min) (Open Book, final examination question) Gas A has twice the molecular weight of gas B. Assuming ideal behavior, if the densities and temperatures of the two gases are the same, then the grams of molecules of gas A hitting area per unit time will be _____ times the corresponding number of grams of gas B.

14. (6 min) Given the wall collision frequency formula $Z = \frac{1}{6} P(3/MRT)^{1/2}$, what will be the ratio of final to initial Z values for a given gas if P is doubled at constant gas density?

15. (15 min) A 2-liter flask contains 15 g of an ideal gas at 3 atm pressure. Calculate how long it should take for 2% of the gas to escape through a pinhole 10^{-4} cm^2 in area.

16. (7.5 min) An object falling through air reaches a terminal or limiting steady velocity. Explain why this is so in terms of quantitative reasoning. The reasoning is to be specific and clear, but no detailed derivations are required.

Answers

1. Order of increasing value is: most probable, average, root-mean-square. These are all proportional to $T^{1/2}$, so their ratio remains constant, but the difference between them will increase with increasing temperature.

2. Since Z is $-dn/dt$ where n is the number of moles of gas remaining, one can write $Z = \dfrac{P}{RT} \, dV/dt$. Using the formula given for Z and rearranging, $dV/dt = -\frac{1}{6}A(3RT/M)^{1/2}$ or $dV/dt = -\frac{1}{6}Ac$ where c is the root-mean-square velocity.

From the value of c that is given, $dV/dt = -6.67 \times 104$ cc/sec-cm^2.

3. Since we want grams of gas hitting rather than moles, the value of Z must be multiplied by M, i.e, $ZM = \frac{1}{6}P(3M/RT)^{1/2}$. The ratio of ZM for the two gases is then:

$$ ZM_{H_2} / ZM_{O_2} = (1/2)[(2 \times 200)(32 \times 50)]^{1/2} = \underline{1/4} $$

4. The force of the impact will be $F = d(mc)/dt$ or $F = \dfrac{2mc}{2r/v} = mc^2/r$. Pressure $= F/\text{area}$, so $P = (mc^2/r)/\pi r^2 = \underline{mc^2/\pi r^3}$ (of the order of 1000 atm for a small molecule at STP).

5. The formula $Z = \frac{1}{6} P(3/MRT)^{1/2}$ is convenient to use here. First, from the ideal gas law $MP = \rho RT$ (ρ is density), so that

$$ \frac{M_{Ar} P_{Ar}}{M_{Ne} P_{Ne}} = \frac{\rho_{Ar} T_{Ar}}{\rho_{Ne} T_{Ne}} \quad \text{or} \quad 2P_{Ar} / P_{Ne} = (1/2)(2) $$

and $P_{Ar} = P_{Ne}/2$. Then

$$ Z_{Ar} / Z_{Ne} = (1/2)[(1/2)(1/2)]^{1/2} = \underline{1/4} $$

6. (a) Starting with the same formula as above, the grams of hydrogen hitting unit area per second is $Z_g = ZM = \frac{1}{6} P(3M/RT)^{1/2}$. If the molar volume is 1 liter, then, by the ideal gas law $P = CRT$, where C is 10^{-3} moles/cc, so that

$$ Z_g = \frac{1}{6}CM(3RT/M)^{1/2} = cCM/6 = 2 \times 10^5 \times 10^{-3} \times \frac{2}{6} $$

$$ = \underline{66.7 \text{ g/cm}^2\text{-sec}} $$

(b) For the molar volume still to be 1 liter after doubling the pressure, the temperature must have doubled; hence the new Z_g will be $(2)^{1/2}$ times the original value.

7. The root-mean-square velocity is $c = (3RT/M)^{1/2}$, but from the ideal gas law, $RT/M = P/\rho$, then $c = (3P/\rho)^{1/2}$. Since the densities are the same and, by definition of normal boiling point, the vapor pressures are both 1 atm, it follows the velocities are the same.

8. Substituting $P = RT/V$, $Z = \frac{1}{6}(1/V)(3RT/M)^{1/2}$; hence the ratio of final to initial Z is $(2)^{1/2} = 1.41$.

9. Since the volume and temperature of the vacuum line are constant, $dn/dt = (V/RT)dP/dt = dP/dt$ (P in atm, since $22.4 = V = 0.082 \times 273$). From the wall-collision-frequency formula, $Z = \frac{1}{6} P(3/MRT)^{1/2}$ moles/cm²-sec. Hence

$$Z = \frac{1}{6}(1 \times 10^6)[(3/29 \times 8.3 \times 10^7 \times 273]^{1/2}$$

$$= 0.355 \text{ moles/cm}^2\text{-sec}$$

But $dn/dt = 0.002 = Z$ (area), hence area $= 0.0056 \text{ cm}^2$. (Perhaps the main source of trouble in this problem is with units.)

10. In each case it is necessary to make a change of variable in the wall-collision-frequency formula $Z = \frac{1}{6} P(3/MRT)^{1/2}$ so as to show explicitly the variable being held constant.

(a) Volume is constant, so replace P by nRT/V and $Z = \frac{1}{6}(n/V)(3RT/M)^{1/2}$. The ratio of old to new Z is now seen to be $(2)^{1/2}$ or 1.41.

(b) Halving the amount at constant temperature (and volume) must halve the pressure. The ratio of old to new Z is then 2.

(c) The substitution halves the number of moles (and hence the pressure) while doubling the molecular weight, hence the ratio is $(2)(2)^{1/2} = 2.8$.

The average molecular velocity is proportional to $(3RT/M)^{1/2}$. Hence in (a) it is reduced by $(2)^{1/2}$, in (b) it is unchanged, and in (c) it is reduced by $(2)^{1/2}$. Therefore of the three cases, c is largest for case (b).

11. Since velocity is proportional to $(T)^{1/2}$, c_1/c_2 is $1/(2)^{1/2} = 0.71$, and 1, respectively. Since Z is proportional to $P/(T)^{1/2}$, the value of Z_1/Z_2 is $(2)^{1/2}$ or 1.41 for case (a) and is $\frac{1}{2}$ for case (b).

12. If the weight ratio is $36/64$, the mole ratio is $(36/2)/(64/32)$ or $9/1$; thus also the ratio of partial pressures. Therefore,

$$Z_{H_2}/Z_{O_2} = \tfrac{9}{1}(32/2)^{1/2} = \underline{36}$$

13. First, $\rho = PM/RT$ or $\rho T = PM/R$. Thus, if ρ and T are the same for the two gases, the product PM must be the same. The ratio of weights of the two gases that hit unit area per unit time will be

$$w_A/w_B = M_A Z_A/M_B Z_B = \frac{M_A P_A}{M_B P_B}\left(\frac{M_B}{M_A}\right)^{1/2}$$

But $M_A P_A = M_B P_B$ and $M_B/M_A = 1/2$, so the desired ratio $w_A/w_B - (1/2)^{1/2} - \underline{0.71}$.

14. Since $M/RT = \rho/P$, if P is doubled with ρ constant, then M/T is halved and T is doubled. Then $Z_2/Z_1 = (P_2/P_1)(T_1/T_2)^{1/2} = (2)(1/2)^{1/2} = \underline{1.41}$.

15. The problem here is to re-express the wall-collision-frequency equation so as to involve only those quantities that are given. We have $Z = \tfrac{1}{6}P(3/MRT)^{1/2}$. First, convert to dw/dt or grams hitting unit area per second by multiplying by M:

$$dw/dt = \tfrac{1}{6}P(3M/RT)^{1/2}$$

Next, from the ideal gas law $PV = wRT/M$ it follows that $M/RT = w/PV$ so that

$$dw/dt = \tfrac{1}{6}P(3w/PV)^{1/2} = \tfrac{1}{6}(3wP/V)^{1/2} = \tfrac{1}{6}$$

$$\times\left(\frac{3\times15\times3\times10^6}{2000}\right)^{1/2} = 43.2 \text{ g/cm}^2\text{-sec}$$

For the pinhole in question, dw/dt is then 0.00432 g/sec. The time for 2% or 0.3 g of gas to escape is then $0.3/0.00432 = \underline{69 \text{ sec}}$.

16. The object is subject to two forces. The first is a constant one, namely, that due to gravity: $F_1 = mg$. The second force arises from the friction against the air; for a sphere the friction coefficient would be $f = 6\pi\eta r$ where η is the viscosity of the air and r the radius of the object. In a viscous medium, velocity is proportional to force: $v = F_2/f$ or the frictional force F_2 is given by $F_2 = vf$. As the falling object accelerates due to F_1, a velocity must eventually be reached such that $F_2 = F_1$. At this point no further change in speed occurs (until impact!).

4 Some physical
properties of molecules

Comments

We concentrate, in this section, on three useful and widely
used physical properties that reflect molecular structure: absorption of light, index of refraction, and dielectric constant. As with
an iceberg, there is a lot more to these topics than the simple
equations below indicate. Light absorption lifts a molecule to a
higher energy state—electronic, vibrational, or rotational, or
some combination of these—so that an absorption spectrum tells
us something about the electronic and geometric organization of a
molecule. Roughly speaking, electronic transitions require light
of an energy corresponding to the visible or ultraviolet region of
the spectrum; a change in vibrational state requires energy corresponding to light in the deep red or infrared region; and radia-
tion in the microwave region suffices to bring about changes in
the rotational state of a molecule.

Index of refraction depends on the polarizability, or ease of

electrical distortion, and is largely an atomic property, only
moderately dependent on the presence of chemical bonding.
Polarizabilities or molar refractions are therefore nearly additive properties. Dielectric constants reflect both polarizability
and the presence of dipoles. Knowledge of the dipole moment of a
molecule can be very useful, as it may settle questions about
molecular geometry as well as indicate how polar the bonds are.

The main concern in this section is to acquaint you with the
Beer-Lambert law of light absorption in a variety of situations,
with the additivity principle that has more applications than just
to molar refraction, and with the workings of the interrelations
between index of refraction, dielectric constant, dipole moment,
and molecular structure. As you gain appreciation of how these
properties behave in various circumstances, hopefully, the theo-
retical background of them will become more real and more inter-
esting.

Equations and concepts

Beer-Lambert Law: $I/I_0 = e^{-k\ell C}$ where ℓ = path length and C
denotes concentration. Alternative form: $D = \epsilon \ell C$ where D is the
optical density (absorbancy) defined as $D = \log I_0/I$, ϵ is the extinction coefficient (or absorbancy index), and ℓ and C are in units
of centimeters and moles/liter, respectively.

for a mixture of absorbing species: $D = \Sigma D_i = \ell \Sigma \epsilon_i C_i$

Molar Refraction: $M_r = \dfrac{M}{\rho} \dfrac{n^2 - 1}{n^2 + 2}$ where M/ρ is the volume in
which 1 mole is present, and n is the index of refraction. To a
fair degree of approximation, the molar refraction of a molecule
can be expressed as the sum of molar refractions for the atoms
in the molecule.

Molar Polarization: $P = \dfrac{M}{\rho} \dfrac{D-1}{D+2}$ where M/ρ again denotes the
volume in which 1 mole is present and D is the dielectric con-
stant. Also, $P = \frac{4}{3}\pi N\alpha + \frac{4}{3}\pi N(\mu^2/3kT)$, where α is the polarizability and the term $\frac{4}{3}\pi N\alpha$ may be approximated, if so desired, by
M_r, and μ is the dipole moment. Dipole moment is defined as
$\mu = ed$, where e is the value in electrostatic units (esu) of equal

and opposite charges, which are separated by distance d. A customary unit is the debye: 1 debye = 10^{-18} esu-cm. The net dipole moment of a molecule is the vector sum of the contributions from each bond.

Problems

1. (10 min) Cell A is 1 cm deep and, when filled with a certain solution, the per cent transmission for light of a given wavelength is 70%. Cell B is 2 cm deep and, when filled with another certain solution, transmits 60% of light of this same wavelength. The per cent transmission for light passing through both cells (of this wavelength) will then be: 10%, 24%, 70%, 60%, none of these within 1%.

2. (9 min) The light absorption is measured vertically through a cuvette (of square cross-section) containing a 1-cm depth of a 0.02-M aqueous solution of a chromic salt (see Fig. 4-la). At 350 mμ the optical density is found to be 0.5. If pure water is added so that the solution is diluted to the point where the depth is 3 cm, as in Fig. 4-1b, the optical density becomes 0.6. Neglecting any absorption by the cuvette itself, calculate the optical density of 1 cm thickness of pure water and the extinction coefficient at this wave length for the chromic ion.

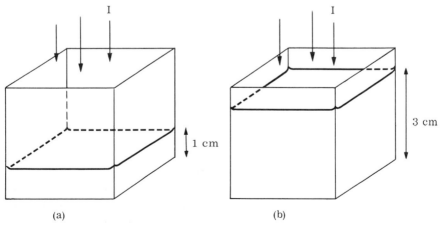

I   I

1 cm   3 cm

(a)   (b)

Figure 4-1

3. (12 min) Given the following molor refractions: CH_3I, 19.5; CH_3Br, 14.5; HBr, 9.9; and CH_4, 6.8; calculate the value for CH_2BrI.

4. (6 min) The molar polarization of $NH_3(g)$ obeys the equation $P = A + B/T$ where A and B have the values 5.6 and 12,000 in cc/mole, respectively. Calculate the dielectric constant of $NH_3(g)$ at STP.

5. (6 min) The extinction coefficient for $Coen_2 Br_2^+$ is 40 at 650 $m\mu$. Calculate the per cent transmission for a 5-cm cell filled with 0.01 m solution. Neglect solvent absorption.

6. (10 min) The index of refraction of a gaseous normal paraffin (i.e., of formula C_nH_{2n+2}) is found to be 1.00139 when the gas is at STP. Given that the atomic refractions are 1.1 and 2.42 (cc/mole) for H and C, respectively, determine the formula for the hydrocarbon, i.e., the value of n in the formula.

7. (10 min) A 0.003-M solution of $Co(NH_3)_6^{3+}$ transmits 75% of incident light of 500 $m\mu$ if the path length is 1 cm. Calculate the extinction coefficient and the per cent absorption for a 0.001-M solution (other factors remaining constant).

8. (10 min) If Δ is defined as the decimal part of the index of refraction ($\Delta = n - 1$), show that for an ideal gas Δ should be proportional to pressure at constant temperature, at low pressures.

9. (8 min) (Open book) The total optical density D of a 0.05-M solution of $Cr(H_2O)_6(ClO_4)_3$ is 0.60 at 310 $m\mu$, and is 1.10 for a 0.10-M solution. Assuming Beer's law to hold, the optical density of the solvent is most nearly (0, 0.1, 0.2, 0.4, 0.6, 1.1), and the molar extinction coefficient of the salt is most nearly (0, 1, 2, 3, 10, 12, 20). The cell depth is 1 cm.

10. (12 min) Ninety per cent of incident light of wavelength 570 $m\mu$ is absorbed by a solution that is 1 M in $Cr(H_2O)_6^{3+}$ (species A) and 1.5 M in SCN^-, using a 1-cm cell. On standing, a reaction takes place whereby all of A is converted into $Cr(H_2O)_5SCN^{2+}$ (species B). The extinction coefficient for B is three times that for A at this wavelength.

    (a) Calculate the optical density D for the original solution.

    (b) Assuming that A and B are the only absorbing species involved, calculate D and the per cent transmission for the solution after standing.

    (c) The answer to (b) is obtained assuming no absorption by

solvent. If it is recognized that the optical density of the solvent at 370 mμ is actually 0.1, then show what the value of D should be for the final solution.

11. (12 min) A pure liquid hydrocarbon is known to belong to the series C_nH_{2n+2}, but its actual molecular weight is not known. Its density is 0.66 and its index of refraction is 1.38. In addition, one knows that the atomic refraction is 1.10 for H and 2.42 for C. Determine from the above information the value of n in the formula C_nH_{2n+2} and then the molecular weight of the compound.

12. (11 min) A 0.03-M solution of $Co(C_2O_4)_3^{3-}$ has an optical density of 2.0 at 660 mμ, using a 1-cm cell. Calculate (a) the value of the extinction coefficient ϵ, (b) the value of I/I_0, and (c) the per cent absorption for a 0.015-M solution in the same cell. Neglect solvent absorption.

13. (7 min) Arrange in order of decreasing dipole moment (group together compounds having the same value): Cl_2, SO_2, CO_2, H_2O, O-dinitrobenzene, HI, CH_4.

14. (4 min) A 2-cm cell filled with a 0.005-M solution of bromine transmits 1% of light of 436 mμ. Calculate the extinction coefficient ϵ for bromine at this wavelength.

15. (7 min) Sugden's parachor **P** is another type of molar volume that is handled in the same way as is the molar refraction. Calculate **P** for C_2H_6 given that **P** = 110, 73, and 71 for CH_3Cl, CH_4, and HCl, respectively.

16. (7 min) The index of refraction for liquid water at 25°C is 1.33; calculate n for water vapor at a pressure and temperature such that the density is 1 g/liter. No other information is needed, except that the density of liquid water is 1 g/cc.

17. (15 min) The optical density of 2×10^{-4} M K_2PtCl_6 is 0.50 at 264 mμ, using a 1-cm cell.
    (a) To what per cent transmission does this correspond?
    (b) What is the extinction coefficient ϵ for K_2PtCl_6 at 264 mμ?
    (c) For what concentration of K_2PtCl_6 would the per cent absorption be 90% (1-cm cell, 264 mμ)?
    (d) If the same 1-cm cell when filled with water gives an optical density of 0.15 with light of 264 mμ, what is the correct value of ϵ for $KTPtCl_6$?

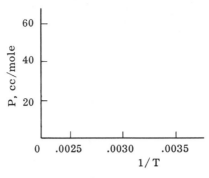

Figure 4-2

18. (12 min) Given the data of Table 4-1 as an aid, for each substance plot the molar polarization **P** against $1/T$ on Fig. 4-2. The plots need be semiquantitative only, but close attention should be paid to the <u>relative</u> positions and slopes of the lines.

Table 4-1

Substance	M_r, cc/mole	μ, debyes
(a) benzene	26	0
(b) CH_4^*	6.8	
(c) C_6H_5Cl	31	1.7
(d) O-dinitrobenzene*		

*You are expected to make your own estimates of missing information.

19. (4 min) A 0.001-M solution of $PtBr_6^{2-}$ absorbs 99% of the incident light of wavelength 400 mμ, using a 1-cm cell. For what length cell would 90% of the incident light be absorbed, other aspects remaining the same?

20. (9 min) Calculate the index of refraction of chlorine gas at STP. The molar refraction for chlorine is 11.2 cc/mole.

21. (9 min) List in order of increasing dipole moment (Put those

of equal dipole moment in a common category): H_2, o-dinitrobenzene, He, Br_2, H_2O, CCl_4, HI, HCl.

22. (9 min) Given the following molar refractions: $CH_3CH_2CH_2CH_3$,
20.6; CH_3CH_2OH, 12.9; and CH_3OH, 8.3; calculate that for
$CH_3CH_2CH_2CH_2OH$.

23. (12 min) The extinction coefficient for cis-$Coen_2Cl_2^+Cl^-$ is 50
at 387 mμ (in aqueous solution). The per cent transmission for a
1-cm cell was determined for a certain solution, and it was concluded that the concentration was 0.006 M.
   (a) Calculate the per cent transmission that was measured.
   (b) It was then discovered that an impurity was present, which
contributed an optical density of 0.15 to the solution. What was
the correct concentration of the complex?

24. (5 min) A 2-cm cell filled with a certain gas at STP absorbs
60% of incident light of wavelength 580 mμ. Give the per cent
transmission for a 2-cm cell with the gas at 2 atm (same wavelength and T).

25. (15 min) Given that

$$\mathbf{P} \ (cc/mole) = \frac{M}{\rho} \frac{D-1}{D+2} = \frac{4\pi N}{3} [\alpha + \mu^2/3kT]$$

(D = dielectric constant, α = polarizability, μ = dipole moment) and
that for $CH_3Cl(g)$ **P** is 90 cc/mole at $1/T = 0.004$, and 50 cc/mole
extrapolated to $1/T = 0$, (a) calculate α and μ for CH_3Cl and
(b) calculate the dielectric constant for $CH_3Cl(g)$ at 500°K and 20
atm pressure.

26. (15 min) The extinction coefficients for ferrocyanide and ferricyanide ions are 250 and 1000, respectively, at 320 mμ (in $M^{-1} \times$
cm^{-1}). (a) What length of cell, when filled with 1×10^{-3} M ferricyanide solution, would absorb 99% of incident light of 320 mμ?
(b) How many moles per liter of ferricyanide must be added to a
10^{-3}-M solution of ferrocyanide so that the resulting solution will
absorb 90% of the incident light of 320 mμ when placed in a 1-cm
cell?

27. (6 min) Given that the molar refractions for CH_4 and C_2H_6
are 6.8 and 11.4, respectively, calculate the atomic refractions
for C and H.

28. (18 min) A 0.01-M solution of $KCr(C_2O_4)_2(H_2O)_2$ in a 1-cm cell absorbs half as much light of wavelength 250 mμ as does a 0.001-M solution of Br_2 in a 2-cm cell. Calculate ϵ for the oxalate complex if ϵ for Br_2 is 150.

29. (10 min) The molar refraction M_r is 1.643 for oxygen in an ether group, and is 6.818 for methane and 13.279 for dimethyl ether (CH_3-O-CH_3). Calculate the value for diethyl ether.

30. (10 min) The extinction coefficient for Fe^{3+} is 250 $M^{-1}cm^{-1}$ at 290 mμ. Calculate the per cent of light absorbed by a 2-cm cell filled with 2×10^{-3}-M solution of ferric nitrate. Calculate also the per cent of light transmitted if the concentration is doubled. Neglect absorption by solvent.

31. (10 min) Given the plot of Fig. 4-3 of molar polarization vs. 1/T, list the four substances in order of increasing dipole moment and also in order of increasing polarizability α.

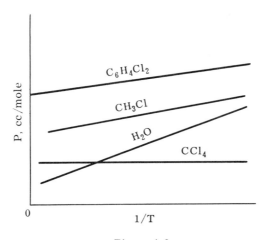

Figure 4-3

32. (10 min) The concentration of ferrous iron in an unknown is to be determined by measuring the absorption of light (of 540 mμ) by the solution (with added dioxime to give the proper colored complex). It is found that a 3-cm-length cell absorbs 64% of the incident light when filled with the unknown solution. From previous work, it is known that a 0.003-M solution of ferrous iron, similarly treated, will absorb 40% of the incident light when placed in a 1-cm cell. Calculate the concentration of ferrous iron in the unknown solution.

33. (10 min) Given the following molar refractions: CH_4 = 6.82, C_2H_6 = 11.44, C_3H_8 = 16.06, $CH_3CH_2CH_2OH$ = 17.58, calculate the molar refraction of glycol, $HO-CH_2-CH_2-OH$, and the index of refraction (density is 1.115 g/cc).

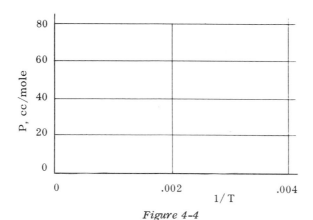

Figure 4-4

34. (12 min) Given the partially completed table of information (Table 4-2), make semiquantitative plots (see Fig. 4-4) of the expected variation of the molar polarization of each substance with 1/T. Pay special attention to having correct relative slopes and intercepts.

Table 4-2

Compound	Molar refraction, cc/mole	Dipole moment, debyes
Benzene	26	
O–Dichlorobenzene		
Water	3.8	1.8
Ethanol	12.8	1.7

35. (10 min) Assume for the purpose of this problem that the bond angle in H_2S is exactly $90°$ and that the $H-S$ bond length is 1.8 A. If the diple moment of each $H-S$ bond is 0.78 debyes, calculate (a) the dipole moment for the molecule as a whole and (b) the effective charge on each hydrogen atom. (One electronic charge equal 4.8×10^{-10} esu.)

36. (9 min) A spectrophotometer cell, when filled with liquid A transmits 50% of incident light of a certain wavelength (corresponding to an optical density of 0.3) and, when filled with liquid B transmits, only 25% of light of this wavelength. What would be the optical density at this wavelength if the cell were filled with a mixture of equal volumes of the two liquids? Show your work.

Answers

1. The answer is just the product of the fractions transmitted or 42%.

2. Since the cross-section is constant, that part of the absorption resulting from the chromic ion is unchanged by the increase in depth of solution, hence the difference $0.6 - 0.5$ is due to the extra 2 cm of water. The optical density for 1 cm water is then 0.05. That caused by chromic ion is then $0.5 - 0.05$ or 0.45, and its extinction coefficient is: $\epsilon = 0.45/1 \times 0.02 = \underline{22.5.}$

3. Molar refractions are treated as additive, and there are several ways of combining the data to get the desired answer; here is one.

$$M_r(CH_2) \quad = M_r(CH_3Br) - M_r(HBr) = 14.5 - 9.9 = 4.6$$

$$M_r(H) \quad = [M_r(CH_4) - M_r(CH_2)]/2 = (6.8 - 4.6)/2$$

$$= 1.1$$

$$M_r(I) \quad = M_r(CH_3I) - M_r(CH_2) - M_r(H) = 13.8$$

$$M_r(CH_2BrI) = M_r(CH_3Br) - M_r(H) + M_r(I) = \underline{27.2}$$

4. P at $273°K$ is then $P = (5.6 + 12,000)/273 = 49.4$ cc/mole, and this divided by 22,400 cc/mole molar volume at STP gives 0.00221 for $(D - 1)/(D + 2)$. Since D the dielectric constant will be nearly unity, as a good approximation, $D = 1 + 3 \times 0.00221 = \underline{1.00663.}$

5. Using the relationship $D = \epsilon C \ell$, $D = 40 \times 5 \times 0.01 = 2$. Hence $-\log I_0/I = 2$ and $I/I_0 = 0.01$, so 1% transmission.

6. Since the molar volume at STP is 22,400 cc/mole,

$$M_r = 22,400 \frac{(1.00139)^2 - 1}{(1.00139)^2 + 2}$$

As a good approximation, $(1.00139)^2 = 1.00278$, so $M_r = 22.4 \times 2.78/3 = 20.7$. Then $20.7 = 2.42n + 1.1(2n + 2) = 4.62n + 2.2$, whence $n = 4$.

7. $D = \log I_0/I = \log 1/0.75 = 0.126$, hence $\epsilon = 0.126/0.003 = \underline{42.}$ For the 0.001-M solution, D will then be 0.042, and $I_0/I = 1.10$, which corresponds to 91% transmission or 9% absorption. This last answer can be obtained by the short cut of noting that, if the concentration is reduced by a factor of three, then I/I_0 goes to its cube root: $(I/I_0)^{1/3} = (0.75)^{1/3} = 0.91$.

8. The molar volume of an ideal gas is RT/P, hence $M_r = (RT/P) \times (n^2 - 1)/(n^2 + 2)$. At low pressure n will be close to unity, so $n^2 = \text{ca. } 1 + 2\Delta$ and $n^2 + 2 = \text{ca. } 3$. The equation then becomes: $\Delta - (3M_r/2RT)P = \text{const.} \times P$.

9. The situation is that the observed optical density is the sum of that resulting from the dissolved salt and that caused by solvent water, i.e., $D = D_{salt} + D_W$. For the first case, $0.60 = D_{.05 \, salt} + D_W$, whereas in the second, the optical density due to the salt should be doubled, so $1.10 = 2D_{.05 \, salt} + D_W$. Subtracting the two equations gives $D_{.05 \, salt} = 0.50$ and $D_W = \underline{0.1}$. Hence $\epsilon_{salt} = 0.5/.05 = \underline{10.}$

10. (a) $D = \log I_0/I = \log 1/0.1 = \underline{1.}$

(b) The extinction coefficient of the absorbing species is tripled and so is D, i.e., $\underline{D = 3.}$

(c) D, owing to the salt, will now be $1 - 0.1 = 0.9$, and this is tripled in the final solution. The final total D is then $2.7 + 0.1 = \underline{2.8.}$

11. We proceed as follows:

$$M_r = \frac{M}{0.66} \frac{n^2 - 1}{n^2 + 2} = \frac{M}{0.66} \frac{0.902}{3.9} = 0.35 M$$

Also $M_r = 2.42n + 1.1(2n + 2) = 4.62n + 2.2$, and $M = 12n + 2n + 2 = 14n + 2$. Therefore $4.62n + 2.2 = 0.35(14n + 2) = 4.90 M + 0.7$ or $n = \text{ca. } 5$ and $M = \underline{72.}$

12. (a) $\epsilon = D/C = 2.0/0.03 = \underline{66.7.}$ (b) $\log I_0/I = 2$, so $I/I_0 = \underline{0.01.}$ (c) D for a 0.015-M solution will be 1, hence $I/I_0 = 0.1$, so $\underline{90\%}$ absorption.

13. Molecules with a center of symmetry will have zero net dipole moment. This applies to Cl_2 and CO_2, similarly to CH_4 as a regular tetrahedron. If a net moment is expected, it should be larger the more polar the bonds, and the less similar moments should oppose each other. The sequence is then: o-dinitrobenzene, H_2O, SO_2, HI, (Cl_2, CO_2, CH_4).

14. $\epsilon = D/2C$; $D = \log I_0/(0.01 \times I_0) = 2$. Hence $\epsilon = 2/(0.005 \times 2) = \underline{200.}$

15. Treating **P** as an additive quantity, $\mathbf{P}_{CH_2} = \mathbf{P}_{CH_3Cl} - \mathbf{P}_{HCl} = 110 - 71 = 39$. Then $\mathbf{P}_{C_2H_6} = \mathbf{P}_{CH_4} + \mathbf{P}_{CH_2} = 73 + 39 = \underline{112.}$

16. From the data for liquid water: $\mathbf{M_r} = 18 \dfrac{1.33^2 - 1}{1.33^2 + 2} = 3.67.$ Then $3.67 = \dfrac{18}{0.001} \dfrac{n^2 - 1}{n^2 + 2}$. Since n for the vapor will be close to unity, a good approximation will be $n^2 - 1 = 3 \times 3.67 \times 10^{-3}/18 = 6.12 \times 10^{-4}$. Again, since n is close to unity, if $n = 1 + \Delta$, then $n^2 - 1 = 2\Delta$. Hence $\Delta = 3.06 \times 10^{-4}$ and $n = \underline{1.000306.}$

17. (a) $\log I_0/I = D = 0.5$, hence $I/I_0 = 0.316$, so $\underline{31.6\%}$ transmission.

(b) $\epsilon = D/C\ell$, so $\epsilon = 0.50/(2 \times 10^{-4}) = \underline{2500.}$

(c) 90% absorption or 10% transmission corresponds to $D = 1$, hence $C = 1/\epsilon = \underline{4 \times 10^{-4} \text{ M.}}$

(d) The net optical density resulting from the salt is now $0.5 - 0.15$ or 0.35, hence $\epsilon = 0.35/(2 \times 10^{-4}) = \underline{1750.}$

18. First approximate the missing items in the table. The dipole moment of CH_4 should be zero on grounds of symmetry, and both $\mathbf{M_r}$ and μ should be the largest for o-dinitrobenzene as it is a large molecule with two polar groups acting somewhat in parallel.

The relationship involved is $\mathbf{P} = \mathbf{M_r} + \frac{4}{3} \pi N \mu^2/3kT$; the plots of Fig. 4-5 should then consist of straight lines, of intercepts $\mathbf{M_r}$, and slopes given by $4\pi N \mu^2/9k$. An order of magnitude calculation gives: $(12/9)(36 \times 10^{46})(10^{-36})/8 \times 10^7$ or about 6000. For a μ of one, **P** should increase by 6 cc/mole for each increment of 0.001 in 1/T. With this in mind, one can now sketch qualitative answers as indicated in the graph.

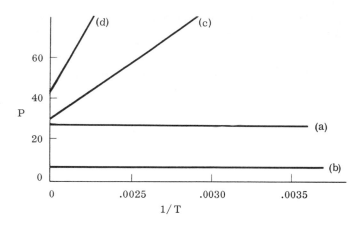

Figure 4-5

19. 99% absorption corresponds to $I_0/I = 100$ and hence $D = 2$, whereas 90% absorption corresponds to $D = 1$. Therefore the cell length must be <u>halved.</u>

20. Since the molar volume of a gas at STP is 22,400 cc/mole,

$11.2 = 22,400 \dfrac{n^2 - 1}{n^2 + 2}$. Since n is close to unity, it follows that

$n^2 - 1 = (3 \times 11.2)/22,400 = 0.0015$. Hence $n = \underline{1.00075}$ $[(1.0075)^2 = 1.0015]$.

21. Molecules with a center of symmetry have zero dipole moment (H_2, He, Br_2), as does a regular tetrahedron (CCl_4). Otherwise, the dipole moment increases the more polar the bond and, if more than one like bond, the less they tend to cancel. <u>Answer:</u> (H_2, He, Br_2, CCl_4), HI, HCl, H_2O, <u>o</u>-dinitrobenzene.

22. Since molar refractions are treated as additive: $\mathbf{M_r}(CH_2) = \mathbf{M_r}(CH_3CH_2OH) - \mathbf{M_r}(CH_3OH) = 12.9 - 8.3 = 4.6$. Hence

$$\mathbf{M_r}(CH_3CH_2CH_2CH_2OH) = \mathbf{M_r}(CH_3CH_2OH) + 2\mathbf{M_r}(CH_2)$$

$$= 12.9 + 9.2 = \underline{22.1}$$

23. (a) Since $D = \epsilon C \ell$, the observed D was $D = 50 \times 0.006 = 0.3$. Since $D = \log I_0/I$, the observed I/I_0 must have been 0.5; i.e., 50% transmission.

(b) Allowing for the impurity, the net D was then $0.3 - 0.15$

or 0.15, hence the correct concentration was one-half 0.006 or 0.003 M.

24. Initially, $I/I_0 = 0.4 = \epsilon^{-kC\ell}$. Doubling the pressure doubles the concentration, hence squares I/I_0, which now has the value 0.16. Answer: 16%.

25. At $1/T = 0$, $P = 4\pi N/3\alpha$, hence $\alpha = (50 \times 3)/(4\pi \times 6 \times 10^{23}) = 1.98 \times 10^{-23}$ cc/molecule. (a) At $1/T = 0.004$, the second term in the equation is $90 - 50 = 40$ cc/mole, hence

$$40 = 4\pi N\mu^2/9kT$$

or

$$\mu^2 = (40 \times 9 \times 8.3 \times 10^7)/(4\pi \times 36 \times 10^{46} \times 0.004)$$

$$= 8.3 \times 10^8/16\pi \times 10^{43}$$

$$\mu^2 = 1.64 \times 10^{-36} \quad \text{and} \quad \mu = 1.28 \text{ debyes}$$

(b) At $500°K$, $1/T = 0.002$, hence $P = 50 + 40/2 = 70$. M/ρ, the molar volume will be $22,400\,(500/273)(1/20) = 2,050$ cc/mole. Then $\dfrac{D-1}{D+2} = 70/2050 = 0.0326$ and $D = 1.096$.

26. (a) 99% absorption means $I/I_0 = 0.01$, and $D = \log I_0/I = 2$. Since $D = \epsilon C\ell$, $\ell = 2/1000 \times 10^{-3} = 2$ cm.
(b) 90% absorption means a D of 1. Since D's are additive:

$$1 = \epsilon_{ferro}C_{ferro} + \epsilon_{ferri}C_{ferri} = 10^{-3} \times 250 + 1000\,C_{ferri}$$

Hence

$$1000\,C_{ferri} = 1 - 0.25 = 0.75 \quad \text{and} \quad C_{ferri} = 7.5 \times 10^{-4} \text{ M}$$

27. Molar refractions are taken to be additive, so $2M_r(H) = 2M_r(CH_4) - M_r(C_2H_6) = 13.6 - 11.4 = 2.2$, hence for H, $M_r = 1.1$. Then $M_r(C) = M_r(CH_4) - 4 \times 1.1 = 2.4$.

28. Let A denote the complex and B denote Br_2, then the statement is: $[(I_0 - I)/I_0]_A = \frac{1}{2}[(I_0 - I)/I_0]_B$ or $2(I/I_0)_A = 1 + (I/I_0)_B$. The Br_2 solution has an optical density, $D = 150 \times 0.001 \times 2 = 0.3$, hence $(I/I_0)_B = 0.5$. Therefore $(I/I_0)_A = 0.75$ and $D_A = 0.126$; therefore $\epsilon_A = 0.126/0.01 = \underline{12.6}$.

29. Using the additivity principle, we find $M_r(C_2H_6) = M_r$ (dimethyl ether) $- M_r(O) = 13.279 - 1.643 = 11.636$. Then $2M(H) = 2M_r(CH_4) - M_r(C_2H_6) = 2$ and $M_r(CH_2) = M_r(CH_4) - 2M_r(H) = 4.818$. Finally, M_r (dimethyl ether) $= M_r$ (dimethyl ether) $+ 2M_r(CH_2) = \underline{22.915}$.

30. $D = \epsilon C \ell = 250 \times 2 \times 10^{-3} \times 2 = 1$; hence $I/I_0 = 0.1$ or $\underline{90\%}$ absorbed. If C is doubled, $D = 2$, hence $I/I_0 = 0.01$ or $\underline{1\%}$ transmitted.

31. This is merely a matter of intercepts and slopes. The former are a measure of the polarizability α and the latter, of the dipole moment. The two sequences are

$$\text{dipole moment:} \quad CCl_4, \ C_6H_4Cl_2, \ CH_3Cl, \ H_2O$$

$$\alpha: \quad H_2O, \ CCl_4, \ CH_3Cl, \ C_6H_4Cl_2$$

32. The two equations are:

$$0.36 = \epsilon^{-k\ell C} = \epsilon^{-k3C}$$

$$0.60 = \epsilon^{-k\ell 0.003}$$

Since $0.36 = (0.60)^2$, then $(3kC) = 2(0.003k)$ or $C = \underline{0.002}$.

33. (a) Using the additivity principle,
$2M_r(H) = 2M_r(CH_4) - M_r(C_2H_6) = 13.64 - 11.44 = 2.2$ or $M_r(H) = 1.1$.
$M_r(CH_3{-}CH_2{-}CH_2{-}OH) - M_r(CH_3{-}CH_2{-}CH_3) = M_r(OH) - M_r(H) = 1.52$, hence $M_r(OH) = 2.62$. $M_r(CH_2) = M_r(CH_4) - 2M_r(H) = 6.82 - 2.2 = 4.62$. Then $M_r(\text{glycol}) = 2M_r(OH) + 2M_r(CH_2) = 5.24 + 9.24 = \underline{14.48}$.
(b) The molar volume of glycol $= M/\rho = 62/1.115 = 55$ cc/mole. Hence $14.48 = 55 \dfrac{n^2 - 1}{n^2 + 2}$ or $n^2 + 2 = 3.85\,(n^2 - 1)$ or $n^2 = 2.05$, $\underline{n = 1.43}$.

34. First, we can complete the table with rough guesses as to the missing values. M_r for o-dichlorobenzene should definitely be larger than that for benzene, say, about 35 cc/mole. The dipole moment of benzene should be zero, since the molecule has a center of symmetry, whereas that for o-dichlorobenzene should be quite

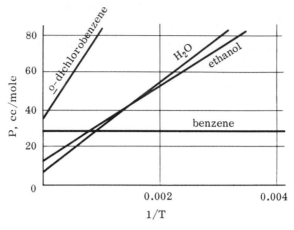

Figure 4-6

large, as there are two nearly parallel polar bonds—let us guess
a value of about 3. The plots in Fig. 4-6 of **P** vs 1/T should be
linear, with intercept M_r and slope proportional to μ^2. Very
roughly, the term in μ^2 contributes about 20 cc/mole to **P** at
25°C and $\mu = 1$. With these points in mind, the required straight-
line plots are those shown in the figure.

35. (a) The force triangle is evidently that shown in Fig. 4-7, so
that the net dipole moment is given by the hypotenuse of a right-
angle triangle. Thus $\mu = (2 \times 0.78^2)^{1/2} = \underline{1.10 \text{ debyes.}}$
     (b) Since $\mu = ed$, we have $0.78 \times 10^{-18} = 1.8 \times 10^{-8} \times Z \times$
4.8×10^{-10}, whence $\underline{Z = 0.09}$ units of electronic charge.

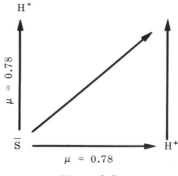

Figure 4-7

36. The optical density for pure liquid B is log 4 or 0.62. On mixing equal volumes, each liquid is diluted to half of its original concentration, so contributes only half of its original optical density. The total optical density of the mixture must then be D = 0.15 + 0.31 = <u>0.46</u>.

5 *First law*
of thermodynamics

Comments

We come now to the first law of thermodynamics—a most
serious topic indeed! It, and the other two laws (Chapter 7) form
the foundation of classical physical chemistry. Along with the first
law itself comes the idea of variables of state—quantities that depend only on the state of the system and not on how it got there.
Pressure, volume, temperature, and, now, energy and enthalpy,
are such quantities. Mathematically, this means making the ac-
quaintance with the total (or exact) differential and with partial
differentials and the relations between them.

In contrast to state variables are those quantities that do depend on path, such as q the heat absorbed and w the work done
by the system as the change occurs. One learns that there are
reversible paths where, at each stage along the change, the

system is essentially at equilibrium. For our purposes in this chapter, this means that temperature and pressure are uniform; later we shall add the additional meaning that the chemical potential of each substance is uniform throughout the system. These reversible paths come in a variety of common kinds, and you will need to become familiar with them. The concept of heat capacity as a function of type of path enters the picture, too.

Then there are irreversible paths or processes. These are much harder to deal with generally, because in a system of non-uniform pressure or temperature it is hard to calculate q and w. For example, in a reversible isothermal expansion, the pressure is everywhere uniform, and hence the pressure inside the system equals the external pressure, and the work done is $\int P_{ext} \, dV = \int P_{int} \, dV$. For an ideal gas, we know that $P_{int} = RT/V$ and if the temperature is constant, the integral becomes $RT \int dV/V = RT \ln V_2/V_1$. If, however, the isothermal expansion is irreversible, then P_{int} is not uniform, and therefore $P_{int} \neq P_{ext}$. The work is still $\int P_{ext} \, dV$, but now we can't replace P_{ext} by P_{int}, and so can't use the ideal gas law to relate pressure and volume.

There are a few special cases in which w can be obtained easily for an irreversible process, however. If, say, the gas expands isothermally into an evacuated flask, we know that no external work is done, so $w_{irrev} = 0$. Or suppose that the gas is confined in a piston and cylinder, with the piston held down by a catch. On releasing the catch, the piston flies up, and the work done is just the pressure resulting from the piston (i.e., the weight of the piston divided by its area) times the volume it sweeps out. So again, w_{irrev} can be calculated.

Many of the problems that follow begin with: "A mole of an ideal, monatomic gas ...." This repetition is not due to any lack of imagination; it's no trouble to take several moles of a nonideal, polyatomic gas and thereby add a lot of interest (and time) to the problem. After all, these were examination questions, and the quoted phrase tells you that you can use the ideal gas law, and that C_v and C_p are $3R/2$ and $5R/2$, respectively. You can then proceed with maximum efficiency to show how well you understand the workings of the first law. Good luck!

Equations and concepts

First Law of Thermodynamics: $dE = \delta q - \delta w$ (hereafter written dq and dw, although they are not exact differentials).

Definitions: Enthalpy H: $H = E + PV$. Work done by the system: $dw = P\,dV$ or $w = \int P\,dV$. Heat capacity C: $C = dq/dT$. C_p, C_v, etc., are so written to indicate that P, V, or some other variable is held constant during the temperature change. Joule-Thompson coefficient μ: $\mu = (\partial T/\partial P)_H$.

Special Relations for an Ideal Gas: For any change, reversible or not: $dE = C_v\,dT$ and $dH = C_p\,dT$. Also, $dE = dH + R\,dT$.

The relationships for the following <u>reversible</u> processes involving an ideal gas are useful.

Isothermal: $dE = 0$, $dH = 0$

$$w = RT\,\ln(V_2/V_1) = RT\,\ln(P_1/P_2)$$

$$q = \Delta E + w$$

Isobaric: $dE = C_v\,dT$, $dH = C_p\,dT$, $q = \Delta H = \int C_p\,dT$

$$w = P\Delta V = R\Delta T$$

Isochoric: $dE = C_v\,dT$, $dH = C_p\,dT$, $q = \Delta E = \int C_v\,dT$

$$w = 0$$

Adiabatic: $q = 0$ so $dE = -dw$ or $C_v\,dT = -P\,dV$

and $C_v\,\ln(T_2/T_1) = -R\,\ln(V_2/V_1)$

or $C_p\,\ln(T_2/T_1) = R\,\ln(P_2/P_1)$

Total and Partial Differentials: Total differential of $z = f(x,y)$: $dz = (\partial z/\partial x)_y\,dx + (\partial z/\partial y)_x\,dy = M\,dx + N\,dy$. Test that an equation $dz = M\,dx + N\,dy$ is a total differential: $(\partial M/\partial y)_x = (\partial N/\partial x)_y$.
Other relationships: $0 = (\partial z/\partial x)_y + (\partial x/\partial y)_x(\partial y/\partial x)_z$.

Also, if w is another function of x and y, then $(\partial z/\partial x)_w = (\partial z/\partial x)_y + (\partial z/\partial y)_x(\partial y/\partial x)_w$. (See Appendix.)

Problems

1. (6 min) Derive from the first law of thermodynamics and related definitions:

$$C_V = -(\partial E/\partial V)_T \, (\partial V/\partial T)_E$$

2. (10 min) A cyclic process involving 1 mole of an ideal monatomic gas has a w of 100 cal/cycle. Per cycle, q is then (zero, 100 cal, −100 cal, can't tell since the process is not stated to be reversible).

3. (12 min) An ideal gas undergoes a reversible isothermal expansion from an initial volume of V_1 to a final volume $10V_1$ and thereby does 10,000 cal of work. The initial pressure was 100 atm. (a) Calculate V_1. (b) If there were 2 moles of gas, what must its temperature have been?

4. (18 min) One mole of an ideal gas of C_V - 5.0 cal/mole-deg initially at STP is put through the following reversible cycle. A: State 1 to state 2, heated at constant volume to twice the initial temperature. B: State 2 to state 3, expanded adiabatically until it is back to the initial temperature. C: State 3 to state 1, compressed isothermally back to state 1. Calculate q, w, ΔE, and ΔH for steps A and B and for the cycle.

5. (18 min) The volume of 1 mole of an ideal monatomic gas initially at 2 atm and 25°C (and 12.2 liters volume) is doubled by (a) isothermal expansion, (b) adiabatic expansion, and (c) expansion along the path P = 0.1V + b, where P is in atm and V in liters/mole. All paths are reversible. Calculate the final P for each case. Sketch each path on a plot of P vs. V. Arrange the ΔE's in order of decreasing magnitude. Do likewise for the w's. Calculate q, w, and ΔE for one path.

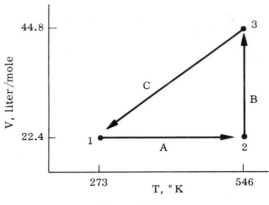

Figure 5-1

6. (18 min) One mole of an ideal monatomic gas is carried through the cycle of Fig. 5-1, consisting of steps A, B, and C, and involving states 1, 2, and 3. Fill in Tables 5-1 and 5-2 below. Assume reversible steps.

Table 5-1

State	P, atm	V, liter	T, °K
1	_____	22.4	273
2	_____	22.4	546
3	_____	44.8	546

Table 5-2

Step	Name of process	q, cal	w, cal	ΔE, cal
A	_____	____	____	____
B	_____	____	____	____
C	_____	____	____	____
cycle		____	____	____

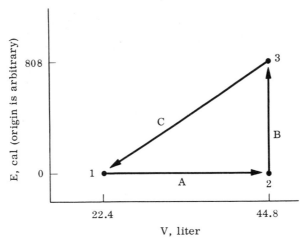

Figure 5-2

7. (21 min) One mole of an ideal monatomic gas initially at STP is taken through the reversible sequence of steps shown in Fig. 5-2. Fill in the information called for in Tables 5-3 and 5-4.

Table 5-3

State	P, atm	V, liter	T, °K
1	1	22.4	273
2	_____	44.8	_____
3	_____	44.8	_____

Table 5-4

Step	Type of process	q, cal	w, cal	ΔE, cal
A	_____	_____	_____	_____
B	_____	_____	_____	_____
C	_____	_____	_____	_____
	cycle	_____	_____	_____

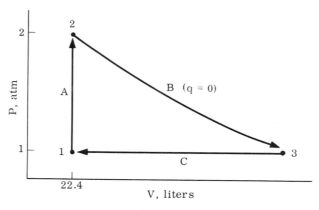

Figure 5-3

8. (18 min) One mole of an ideal monatomic gas is put through the three-step cycle shown on the graph of Fig. 5-3. Complete the information called for in Tables 5-5 and 5-6.

Table 5-5

State	P, atm	V, liter	T, °K
1	1	22.4	———
2	2	22.4	———
3	1	———	———

Table 5-6

Step	Type of process	q, cal	w, cal	ΔE, cal
A	———————	———	———	———
B	———————	———	———	———
C	cycle	———	———	———

9. (3 min) Derive the equation $(\partial H / \partial P)_T = -\mu C_p$, where μ is the Joule-Thompson coefficient.

10. (21 min) One mole of an ideal monatomic gas is taken through the three steps shown on the P vs T plot of Fig. 5-4.

(a) Sketch and similarly label the same three steps on a plot of P vs. V.

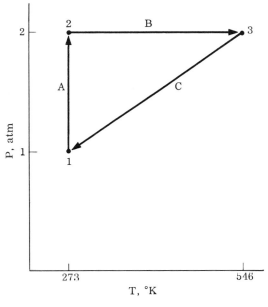

Figure 5-4

(b) Complete the following table:

	Step A	Step B	Step C	Cycle
ΔE	_____	_____	−810 cal	_____
q	_____	1356 cal	_____	_____
w	−373 cal	_____	_____	_____

(c) The above steps are all reversible. The numerical magnitude of w for the cycle is therefore a (maximum, minimum).

11. (5 min) One mole of an ideal monatomic gas is to be taken from P_1 = 1 atm and T_1 = 300°K to P_2 = 10 atm and T_2 = 600°K by some combination of isobaric, isothermal, adiabatic, and isochoric steps. (a) Give that path, involving only the above types of processes, which will require the least reversible work for the over-all change (you may use some or all of the types of steps). (b) Calculate this minimum work.

12. (15 min) One mole of an ideal monatomic gas initially at P_1 = 2 atm, T_1 = 273°K is taken to a pressure of P_2 = 4 atm by the reversible path defined by P/V = constant. Calculate V_1, V_2, and T_2. Calculate ΔE, ΔH, q, and w (in cal).

13. (24 min) One mole of an ideal monatomic gas is reversibly (1) expanded from 10 atm and 2 liters to 5 atm, isothermally, and (2) expanded from 10 atm and 2 liters to 5 atm, adiabatically. (a) Calculate q, w, ΔE, and ΔH (in cal) for processes (1) and (2). (b) Sketch, in a P vs. V diagram, the path taken by the gas in each process. (c) There is a third process (3) which would show as a straight line on the P vs. V diagram, and is such that process (2) plus process (3) gives the same final state as process (1). What is the nature of (3) (isothermal, isochoric, isobaric, etc.)?

14. (6 min) Referring to Problem 12, calculate the heat capacity of the gas along this path, i.e., the heat absorbed per degree rise in temperature under the restriction P/V = constant.

15. (19 min) The heat capacity ratio γ for a gas is determined in the following simple experiment: A carboy is filled with the gas to a pressure of 1.10 atm (laboratory pressure is 1.00 atm). The stopper to the carboy is then suddenly removed, so that the gas expands adiabatically; after a few seconds, the stopper is replaced and the gas is allowed to warm up to room temperature, and the pressure is now found to be 1.03 atm. Assuming the gas to be ideal, calculate C_p and C_v.

16. (24 min) One mole of an ideal monatomic gas is put through the indicated cycle (see Fig. 5-5). Step A: isochoric reduction in pressure; step B: isobaric increase in volume; step C: return to initial state by straight-line path (this is not isothermal). Assuming the steps to be reversible, calculate q, w, and ΔE for each step and for the entire cycle, in calories.

Summary: State 1: 4 atm, 11.2 liters, 546°K; state 2: 2 atm, 11.2 liters, 273°K; state 3: 2 atm, 22.4 liters, 546°K.

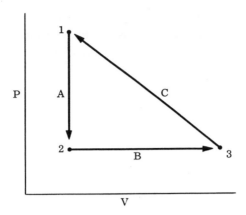

Figure 5-5

17. The equation $dE = (\partial E/\partial V)_T \, dV + (\partial E/\partial T)_V \, dT$ may be written $dE = C_V \, dT + (\partial E/\partial V)_T \, dV$ since $(\partial E/\partial T)_V = C_V$. One can also write $dE = dq + (\partial E/\partial V)_T \, dV$, since $C_V \, dT = dq$. By comparison with the first law statement $(dE = dq - P \, dV)$, it appears that $(\partial E/\partial V)_T = -P$. This conclusion is <u>not</u> correct; explain the error in the derivation.

18. (21 min) One mole of a perfect monatomic gas is put through a cycle consisting of the following three reversible steps: (A) isothermal compression from 2 atm and 10 liters to 20 atm and 1 liter; (B) isobaric expansion to return the gas to the original volume of 10 liters with T going from T_1 to T_2; (C) cooling at constant volume to bring the gas to the original pressure and temperature. The steps are shown schematically in Fig. 5-6.

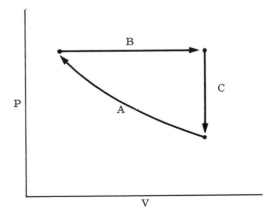

Figure 5-6

(a) Calculate T_1 and T_2.

(b) Calculate ΔE, q, and w, in calories, for each step and for the cycle.

19. (30 min) One mole of an ideal monatomic gas experiences the reversible steps shown in Fig. 5-7. Fill in the values called for by the blanks in Tables 5-7 and 5-8.

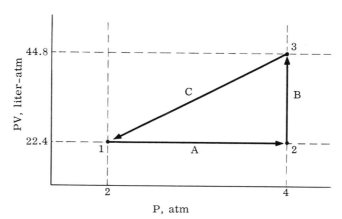

Figure 5-7

Table 5-7

State	P, atm	V, liters	T, °K
1	2	_____	_____
2	4	_____	_____
3	4	_____	_____

Table 5-8

Path	Type (isothermal, etc.)	q, cal	w, cal	ΔE, cal
A	_____	____	____	____
B	_____	____	____	____
C	_____	____	____	____
Cycle		____	____	____

If the above cycle were carried out irreversibly and in a manner such that the net work were zero, calculate or explain what can be said about the values of ΔE and q for the cycle.

20. (18 min) One mole of an ideal monatomic gas initially at 2 atm and 11.2 liters is taken to a final pressure of 4 atm along the reversible path defined by PT = constant. Calculate (a) the final volume and temperature, (b) ΔE and ΔH, and (c) the work done w.

Answers

1. This looks like one of the relations from a total differential expression, so try writing $C_V = (\partial E/\partial T)_V$. It is now seen that the desired equation follows from

$$dE = (\partial E/\partial V)_T dV + (\partial E/\partial T)_V dT$$

by dividing through by dT, keeping E constant:

$$0 = (\partial E/\partial V)_T (\partial V/\partial T)_E + (\partial E/\partial T)_V$$

2. This one is easy. For any cycle ΔE is zero and hence q = w = 100 cal.

3. (a) $w - nRT \ln V_2/V_1 = 2.3\ nRT$. But $P_1V_1 = nRT = w/2.3 = 10,000/2.3 = 4,340$ cal. Hence $V_1 = (4,340/100)(0.041$ liter-atm/cal) – 1.78 liters. (b) If n = 2, then $T = 4,340/2 \times 1.98 = 1100°K$.

4. In problems of this kind do the easiest things first:
(i) For the cycle, ΔH and ΔE are zero.
(ii) Step A is isochoric, hence w = 0; $\Delta E = C_V \Delta T = 5 \times 273 = 1365$ cal; $\Delta H = C_p \Delta T = 1911$ cal; $q = C_V \Delta T = 1365$ cal.
(iii) Step B is adiabatic, so q = 0; $\Delta E = C_V \Delta T = -1365$ cal; $\Delta H = -1911$ cal; $w = -\Delta E$.
(iv) Step C is isothermal, hence ΔE and ΔH are zero. q = w = $-RT \ln V_3/V_1$. Now $V_2 = V_1$ and, for step 2, $C_V \ln T_2/T_3 = -R \ln V_2/V_3 = R \ln V_3/V_1$. But $T_2/T_3 = 2$, so $R \ln V_3/V_1 = 2 \times 2.3 \log 2 = 1.38$. Therefore w for step C is $-1.38 \times 273 = -377$ cal.
(v) For the cycle, then, w = 0 + 1365 − 377 = −988 cal. q = w.

5. (a) If volume is doubled isothermally, then $P_{final} = 1$ atm.

(b) If volume is doubled adiabatically, then

$$\log T_2/T_1 = -(R/C_v)\log V_2/V_1 = (R/C_p)\log P_2/P_1$$

Hence

$$\log P_2/P_1 = -(C_p/C_v)\log 2 = -0.5; \ P_2/P_1 = 0.316;$$

$$P_2 = 0.73 \text{ atm}.$$

(c) If expansion is along the given path, $P_2 = 0.1 \times 24.4 + b$ but $b = P - 0.1V = 2 - 0.1 \times 12.2 = 0.78$ or $P_2 = 3.22$ atm. The paths are sketched in Fig. 5-9.

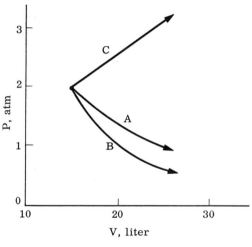

Figure 5-9

ΔE's: The ΔE's will be in the same relation as the ΔT's. ΔT_a is zero, ΔT_b may be obtained from the equation for an adiabatic expansion:

$$\log T_2/T_1 = -(R/C_v)\log V_2/V_1 = -0.3/1.5 = -0.2$$

so

$$T_2 = 0.632 \times 298 = 188°K, \ \Delta T_b = -110°$$

T_2 for step C is $3.22 \times 24.4/R = 958°K$, $\Delta T_c = 660$. Thus $\Delta T_b < \Delta T_a < \Delta T_c$ and likewise for the ΔE's. (The relative positions could have been guessed: ΔT_b must be negative as one had an adiabatic expansion; ΔT_a is zero; ΔT_c must be positive as the process called for an increase in both P and V.)

The relative order of the w's is given most quickly simply by noting the relative areas under the three paths in the P vs. V plot: $w_b < w_a < w_c$. Step A is probably the easiest by which to get q, w, and ΔE. $\Delta E = 0$, $q = w = RT \ln V_2/V_1 = 1.98 \times 298 \times 2.3 \log 2 = 408$ cal.

6. Table 5-1: for state 1, P is obviously 1 atm (22.4 liters is the STP volume); hence for state 2, P is 2 atm as T is doubled. For state 3, P must be back to 1 atm, as V is doubled.

Table 5-2: Processes A, B, and C must be isochoric, isothermal, and isobaric, respectively; you need only notice which quantity is constant during them.

ΔE: these values can be written down immediately as equal to $C_V \Delta T$ or $3 \Delta T$: A: $3 \times 273 = 819$ cal; B: $3 \times 0/2 = 0$ cal; C: -819 cal; cycle: 0 cal.

q: these values likewise can be written down immediately as $q = C \Delta T$. A: $q = 3 \times 273 = 819$ cal; B: $q = w$; C: $q = -5 \times 273 = -1365$ cal.

w: A: $w = 0$ (V constant); B: $w = RT \ln V_2/V_1 = 1.98 \times 546 \times 2.3 \log 2 = 748$ cal; C: $w = q - \Delta E = -1365 + 819 = -546$ cal.

Then for the cycle, $q = 819 + 748 - 1365 = 202$ cal and $w = q$.

7. Table 5-3: E and hence T must be constant for step A, so $T_2 = T_1 = 273$, and P_2 is therefore 0.5 atm. E increases by 808 cal in step B, so $\Delta T = 808/(3R/2) = 273$. T_3 is therefore 543° K, and P_3 is 1 atm.

Table 5-4: The steps are isothermal, isochoric, and isobaric, respectively.

Step A: $\Delta E = 0$, so $q = w = RT \ln V_2/V_1 = 1.98 \times 273 \times 2.3 \log 2 = 377$ cal.

Step B: $\Delta E = 808$ cal (from graph). Since $\Delta V = 0$, $w = 0$, and $q = \Delta E$.

Step C: The endpoints of step C are at the same pressure, but, technically, it should be shown that P is constant at all points on the path. This can be done by noting that, for the path, $dE = (C_V \times 273/22.4) dV$ and that $dE = C_V dT$, hence $dT = (273/22.4) dV$, true only if P is constant at 1 atm. The process is then isobaric, $q = C_p \Delta T = (5R/2) \Delta T = -1350$ cal; $\Delta E = -808$, hence $w = -1350 + 808 = -542$ cal. Cycle: $\Delta E = 0$, $w = 377 - 542 = -165$ cal, $q = w$.

8. Table 5-5: T_1 is evidently 273° K, and T_2 is 546°K. State 3 is determined by noting that step B is adiabatic, and since P_3/P_2 is given, the appropriate equation is $C_p \ln T_3/T_2 = R \ln P_3/P_2$ or $\log T_3/T_2 = (2/5) \log (1/2)$ or $T_3/T_2 = 0.758$ and $T_3 = 414°K$. V_3 is then $22.4 \times 414/273 = 34$ liters.

Table 5-6: The processes are isochoric, adiabatic, and iso-baric, respectively.

Step A: $w = 0$, $\Delta E = q = C_V \Delta T = (3R/2)273 = 808$ cal.

Step B: $q = 0$, $-w = \Delta E = C_V \Delta T = (3R/2)(-132) = -392$ cal.

Step C: $\Delta E = C_V \Delta T = -416$ cal; $q = C_p \Delta T = -695$ cal; $w = q - \Delta E = -279$ cal.

Cycle: $\Delta E = 0$, $w = q = 808 + 0 - 695 = 113$ cal.

9. The Joule-Thompson coefficient is defined as $\mu = (\partial T/\partial P)_H$. On inserting this in the equation, inspection of the arrangement of variables suggests that the equation might come from the total differential for H:

$$dH = (\partial H/\partial P)_T \, dP + (\partial H/\partial T)_P \, dT$$

If we divide through by dP at constant H, then $0 = (\partial H/\partial P)_T + (\partial H/\partial T)_P(\partial T/\partial P)_H$. On inserting the definition of μ, and remembering that $C_p = (\partial H/\partial T)_P$, the above rearranges to the desired equation.

10. The required P vs. V plot is shown in Fig. 5-8. To construct it, V_1 must be 22.4 liters and V_2 11.2 liters. Since T is doubled in B, V_3 is back to 22.4 liters.

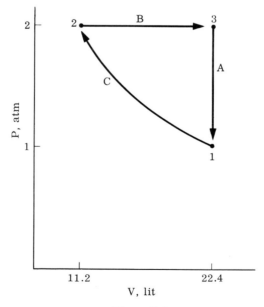

Figure 5-8

Step A: isothermal, so $\Delta E = 0$, $q = w = -373$ cal.

Step B: isobaric; $\Delta E = C_V \Delta T = (3R/2)273 = 808$ cal. $w = q - \Delta E = 1356 - 808 = 548$ cal.

Step C: isochoric; $w = 0$, so $q = \Delta E = -810$ cal.

Cycle: $\Delta E = 0$, $q = w = -373 + 1356 - 810 = 173$ cal.

Work is done by the cycle, so w is a maximum.

11. The situation is shown schematically Fig. 5-10. The idea is to get from state 1 to state 2 by a route having a minimum area. Since we have a hypothetical ideal gas, we cool at constant volume to 0°K, reducing P to zero, then compress isothermally to the final volume ($V_{int} = 24.5$ liters, $V_{final} = 4.9$ liters), and heat isochorically to 600°K. $w = 0$, $q = \Delta E = C_V \Delta T = (3R/2)300 = 890$ cal.

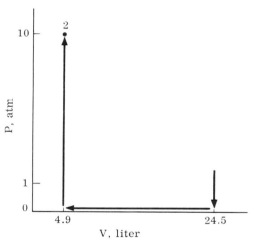

Figure 5-10

12. V_1 must be 11.2 liters; since P/V is constant, V_2 must be 22.4 liters. Combining $P/V =$ constant with $PV = RT$:

$T/V^2 =$ constant, so $T_2 = 4T_1 = 1092$°K. $\Delta E = C_V \Delta T = (3R/2)819 = 2420$ cal; $\Delta H = C_p \Delta T = 4040$ cal. To get w, we must evaluate $w = \int P \, dV$. From the initial conditions,

$$P/V = \text{constant} = 2/11.2 = 0.178$$

then:

$$w = 0.178 \int V \, dV = 0.089(V_2^2 - V_1^2) = 0.089 \times 375$$

$$= 33.3 \text{ liter-atm}$$

or

$$w = 813 \text{ cal;} \quad q = \Delta E + w = 3230 \text{ cal}$$

13. (a) The initial T_1 is 244°K. For step A, T_2 = 244°K; V_2 then is 4 liters. ΔE, ΔH = 0; q = w = RT ln V_2/V_1 = 1.98 × 244 × 2.3 log 2 = 334 cal. For process B, q = 0; T_2 is given by: C_p log T_2/T_1 = R log P_2/P_1 or log T_2/T_1 = 0.4 log 1/2 = −0.12; T_2 = 185°K. Hence −w = ΔE = (3R/2)59 or 175 cal. ΔH = (5R/2)59 = 298 cal.
   (b) See Fig. 5-11.
   (c) The adiabatic process gives a lower final temperature and therefore volume than the isothermal one. Step C is then an isobaric heating back to 244°K.

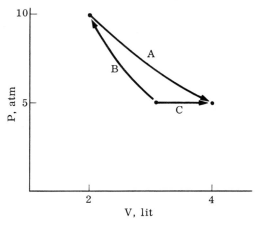

Figure 5-11

14. From the first law, dE = dq − dw, and for an ideal gas

$$C_V \, dT = dq - P \, dV$$

where P dV is governed by $P/V = b$ (a constant). We want $(dq/dT)_{path} = C_V + P(dV/dT)_{path}$. To get the last term, combine $P/V = b$ with $PV = RT$ and get: $V^2 = RT/b$. Then $2V\,dV = (R/b) \times dT$ and $dV/dT = R/2bV$. Then

$$(dq/dT)_{path} = C_V + P(R/2bV) = C_V + R/2$$

15. Combining the equations $C_V \log T_2/T_1 = -R \log V_2/V_1$ and $C_p \log T_2/T_1 = R \log P_2/P_1$ for an adiabatic process, one gets:

$$-(C_p/C_V) \log V_2/V_1 = \log P_2/P_1$$

We know P_2/P_1; it is $1.00/1.10$. The final volume is that of the carboy, V_1, plus the gas that escaped. We know, however, that gas remaining was $1.03/1.10$ of V_1; hence V_2 was $1.10V_1/1.03$.

Then $-(C_p/C_V) \log (1.10/1.03) = \log (1.00/1.10)$, from which $C_p/C_V = 1.38$. But $C_p = C_V + R$, whence $C_V = 5.2$, $C_p = 7.2$.

16. Step A: since the step is isochoric, $w = 0$. $q = \Delta E = C_V \Delta T = -(3R/2)273 = -808$ cal.

Step B: $\Delta E = C_V \Delta T = 808$ cal. $q = C_p \Delta T = (5R/2)273 = 1350$ cal; $w = q - \Delta E = 542$ cal.

Step C: $\Delta E = 0$, since there is no over-all change in temperature. T varies along the path, however, so w is not given by the isothermal-work formula. It can be obtained, however, as the area under the path $\int P\,dV$. From the geometry of the straight-line path, this area is $2 \times 11.2 + (1/2)2 \times 11.2$ or -33.6 liter-atm (negative as the direction is from left to right) or -820 cal. Then $q = w$. For the cycle: $\Delta E = 0$, $q = w = -278$ cal.

17. The difficulty is that the first law statement is applicable to any path; q and w are not defined; only their difference equals ΔE. The first equation says that dE is the sum of dq_V (i.e., absorption of heat on a constant volume heating) and a second term corresponding to a second step, one at constant temperature.

18. $T_1 = P_1V_1/R = 244°K$; $T_2 - 20 \times 10/0.082 = 2440°K$.
Step A: $\Delta E = 0$, $w = RT \ln V_2/V_1 = 1.98 \times 244 \times 2.3 \log 1/10 = -1110$ cal; $q = w$.

Step B: $\Delta E = C_V \Delta T = (3R/2)2200 = 6520$ cal; $q = C_p = (5R/2)2200 = 10,900$ cal; $w = q - \Delta E = 4380$ cal.

Step C: $w = 0$; $q = \Delta E = C_V \Delta T = -6520$ cal.

Cycle: $\Delta E = 0$; $q = w = -1110 + 4380 = 3270$ cal.

19. Table 5-7: State (1): $V_1 = 22.4/2 = 11.2$ liters. Hence $T_1 = 273°K$ ($PV = 22.4$). State (2): $V_2 = 22.4/4 = 5.6$ liters. Also $T_2 = 273°K$ (same PV value). State (3): $V_3 = 44.8/4 = 11.2$ liters; $T_3 = 2 \times 273 = 546°K$.

Table 5-8: The processes are evidently isothermal, isobaric, and isochoric, respectively.

For A: $\Delta E = 0$, $q = w = RT \ln V_2/V_1 = 1.98 \times 273 \times$
$$2.31 \log 1/2 = -373 \text{ cal.}$$

For B: $\Delta E = C_V \Delta T = (3R/2)273 = 808$ cal; $q = C_p \Delta T =$
$$(5R/2)273 = 1350 \text{ cal;} \quad w = q - \Delta E = 542 \text{ cal.}$$

For C: $w = 0$; $\Delta E = q = C_V \Delta T = -808$ cal.

Cycle: $\Delta E = 0$, $q = w = -372 + 542 = 169$ cal. For the irreversible cycle, ΔE is still zero; if $w = 0$, then $q = 0$.

20. By comparison with the molar volume at STP, the initial temperature is evidently 273°K. Then $PT = 2 \times 273 = 546$.

(a) The final temperature must then be $T = 546/4 = 136°K$, so the final volume must be $V = 0.082 \times 138/4 = 2.82$ liters.

(b) $\Delta E = C_V \Delta T = (3R/2)(136 - 273) = -402$ cal. $\Delta H = C_p \Delta T = (5R/2)(136 - 273) = -672$ cal.

(c) To get w, we must evaluate $\int P\, dV$. To begin, we must express P in terms of V. Thus $P = 546/T = 546 R/PV$, so $P^2 = 546 R/V$. The integral then becomes $w = (546R)^{1/2} \times \int dV/V^{1/2} = 2(546R)^{1/2} (V_2^{1/2} - V_1^{1/2}) = 2(P^2V)^{1/2} (V_2^{1/2} - V_1^{1/2}) = 2(P_2V_2 - P_1V_1) = 2(4 \times 2.82 - 2 \times 11.2) = -22.4$ liter-atm or -547 cal.

6   *Heat capacity of gases and thermochemistry*

Comments

The topics of this section should constitute a bit of a breather between the first and the second laws of thermodynamics. Be careful with your handling of signs, though!

Thermochemistry <u>is</u> straightforward; you add or subtract ΔH's or ΔE's as you do the equations to which they apply. Since we have no idea of what absolute energies are for things, we always deal with Δ quantities. Often, for convenience, these are heats of formation. They may, however, be heats of combustion, and note Problem 7 for another type.

The Δ quantities change with temperature according to the integral of ΔC_p or ΔC_v. In an adiabatic reaction, the products warm or cool as they are formed, but ΔH and ΔE are state functions, independent of path, so we choose a path of convenience. That is, we imagine that the reaction takes place isothermally, then use the heat produced or absorbed to see how much the products can be warmed or cooled.

The topic of heat capacity of gases is dealt with here entirely in terms of ideal gases. We allow a contribution of R/2 cal/deg-mole for each degree of translational and rotational freedom. There are always three degrees of translational freedom, but, depending on whether the molecule is linear, there will be two or three degrees of rotational freedom. Vibrational degrees of freedom count R cal/deg-mole each, and their number is easily obtained by subtracting the total of translational and rotational degrees of freedom from the 3n-grand-total degrees of freedom for a molecule, where n is the number of atoms. As a useful approximation to the actual situation, we suppose that only about 20 per cent of the vibrational contribution to heat capacity is developed at room temperature.

Equations and concepts

"Δ" Operator: The sum of values for the products minus the sum of values for the reactants. Thus ΔH, ΔE, ΔC_p, Δn, etc.

Hess's Law: ΔH's and ΔE's are added and subtracted as are the equations, and the value for a particular reaction is independent of the choice of reactions combined in order to obtain it. That is, ΔH and ΔE are independent of path.

Heats of Formation and Combustion: Heat of formation is the ΔH per mole required to form the species from the elements in their standard states. Heat of combustion is the heat of reaction of the compound with oxygen to give CO_2 and H_2O, usually $H_2O(\ell)$.

Change of ΔH and ΔE with Temperature: $\Delta H_2 = \Delta H_1 + \int_{T_1}^{T_2} \Delta C_p \, dT$

and $\Delta E_2 = \Delta E_1 + \int_{T_1}^{T_2} \Delta C_V \, dT$.

Miscellaneous Topics and Relations: Variation of heat capacity with temperature: usually expressed as a power series in T. Relation between ΔH and ΔE: $\Delta H = \Delta E + \Delta n_g RT$ where n_g is the mole number of gaseous species and Δn_g is the difference between moles of gaseous products and gaseous reactants.

Heat of solution. Maximum temperature of an explosion.

17   -- 24

Problems

1. (13 min) Given
heat of formation at 25°: $H_2O(g)$ — 57.8 kcal; $CH_4(g)$ — 17.9 kcal
heat of combustion at 25° C to CO_2 and $H_2O(g)$: $CH_4(g)$ — 192.0
kcal.
Calculate ΔH at 25°C for $C(s) + 2H_2O(g) = CO_2(g) + 2H_2(g)$. Calculate ΔE at 25°C for this same reaction.

2. (9 min) Estimate the value of C_p for each substance in the reaction of problem 1, i.e., $C(s) + 2H_2O(g) = CO_2(g) + 2H_2(g)$.

3. (21 min) Given the following information:
Reaction: $4C_2H_5Cl(g) + 13O_2(g) = 2Cl_2(g) + 8CO_2(g) + 10H_2O(g)$
$$\Delta H_{298°K} = -1229.6 \text{ kcal}$$
heat of combustion per mole of ethane $[C_2H_6(g)]$ to $CO_2(g)$ and
$H_2O(g) = -341$ kcal.

heat of formation per mole of $H_2O(g)$: -57.8 kcal
heat of formation per mole of $HCl(g)$: -21 kcal.
    (a) Calculate $\Delta H_{298°K}$ for the reaction $C_2H_6(g) + Cl_2(g) = C_2H_5Cl(g) + HCl(g)$.
    (b) Assuming ΔC_p for the first reaction to be -10 cal/deg, calculate $\Delta H_{398°K}$.
    (c) Calculate $\Delta E_{298°K}$ for the first reaction.

4. (9 min) Estimate C_p for each species in reaction 1 of Problem 3, to the nearest whole number of cal/deg-mole (at 25°C).

5. (30 min) Given the following information:
heats of formation at 298°K: $CO_2(g)$ — 94.0 kcal
                                  $C_2H_4O_2(l)$(acetic acid) -116.4 kcal
                                  $H_2O(g)$ — 57.8 kcal
heat of combusion of $CH_4(g)$ to give $CO_2(g)$ and $H_2O(g)$: -192.7 kcal
heat of vaporization of water: 9.4 kcal/mole at 100°C.
C_p values (in cal/deg-mole): $C_2H_4O(g)$(acetaldehyde): 12.5
                            $CO(g)$:   7.5 $CH_4(g)$:   9.0
                          $H_2O(g)$: 7.3 $H_2O(l)$: 18.0
    (a) Calculate the heat of formation of $H_2O(l)$ at 298°K.
    (b) Calculate $\Delta H_{298°K}$ for the reaction: $C_2H_4O_2(l) = CH_4(g) + CO_2(g)$.
    (c) Calculate the temperature at which ΔH for the reaction $C_2H_4O(g) = CH_4(g) + CO(g)$ should be zero. $\Delta H_{298°K}$ is -4.0 kcal.

6. (12 min) Locate the following (a-f) in the correct range of C_p values:

	C_p, cal/deg-mole
(a) $H_2(g)$ at $-150°C$	20-25
	15-20
(b) $N_2(g)$ at $25°C$	12-15
	10-12
(c) $He(g)$ at $1000°C$	8-10
	7
(d) $NaBr(s)$ at $25°C$	6
	5
(e) Pb at $25°C$	4
	3
(f) $C_2H_5OH(g)$ at $25°C$	2
	1

7. (9 min) The "heat of total cracking," H_{TC} for a hydrocarbon is defined, for the purpose of this question, as the $\Delta H_{298°K}$ for a reaction of the type:

$$C_n H_m (g) + (2n - m/2)H_2(g) = nCH_4(g)$$

Given that H_{TC} is -15.6 kcal for $C_2H_6(g)$ and -20.9 kcal for $C_3H_8(g)$, and that the heat of formation of $CH_4(g)$ at $25°C$ is -17.9 kcal, calculate $\Delta H_{298°K}$ for:

$$CH_4(g) + C_3H_8(g) = 2C_2H_6(g)$$

8. (21 min) Given the reaction below, whereby H_2 is burned in excess O_2, $H_2(g, 25°C) + 10O_2(g, 25°C) = H_2O(g, 25°C) +$ excess $O_2(g, 25°C)$ and also that the heat of formation of $H_2O(g, 25°C)$ is -58 kcal and that C_p is 6.5 cal/deg-mole for H_2 and for O_2 and 7.5 cal/deg-mole for $H_2O(g)$; (a) Calculate ΔE at $25°C$ for the reaction; (b) calculate $\Delta H_{498°K}$ for the reaction; and (c) calculate the maximum temperature in an adiabatic explosion of the mixture in a sealed bomb, if the reactants are initially at $25°C$.

9. (9 min) Estimate C_p (in cal/deg-mole) for each of the follow-ing, to about 1 cal/deg mole:

(a) argon gas at 1000°C

(b) Be(metal) at -100°C

(c) H_2(g) at 300°C

(d) C_2H_6(g) at 25°C

(e) Au(metal) at 500°C

(f) H_2S(g) at 25°C

10. (30 min) Given the following information:

heat of formation at 298°K: CO_2(g) -94 kcal

$\qquad\qquad\qquad\qquad\qquad\quad$ H_2O(g) -58 kcal

heats of reaction at 298°K:

$\quad$ H_2O(g) + C(s) = H_2(g) + CO(g)(water gas reaction) $\Delta H = 32$ kcal

$\quad$ H_2(g) = 2H(g) $\qquad$ $\Delta H = 103$ kcal

$\quad$ O_2(g) = 2O(g) $\qquad$ $\Delta H = 34$ kcal

heat capacities: Take C_p to be 7.00 cal/deg-mole for all gases
and 2.5 cal/deg-mole for C(s).

Calculate (a) the heat of combustion of graphite at 298°K, in kcal/g;
(b) the heat of combustion, at 298°K, of the H_2 and CO formed by
the complete reaction of water with 1 g of carbon; (c) ΔE for the
water gas reaction at 298°K; (d) ΔH at 600°K for the water gas
reaction; (e) the H—O bond energy.

11. (12 min) Estimate the following C_V values to the nearest
2 cal/deg-mole (all at 25°C): Ar(g), H_2(g), CO_2(g), N_2(g), Ag(s),
C(diamond), C_6H_6(g), H_2O(g), H_2O(l).

12. (18 min) The heat of formation of C_2H_5OH(l) is -66 kcal/mole,
while the heat of combustion to CO_2(g) and H_2O(l) of the isomeric
CH_3—O—CH_3(g) is -348 kcal/mole. The heat of formation of
H_2O(l) is -68 kcal/mole, and the heat of combustion of carbon to
CO_2(g) is -94 kcal/mole (all data for 25°C). (a) Calculate $\Delta H_{298°K}$
for the isomerization reaction

$\qquad$ C_2H_5OH(l) = CH_3—O—CH_3(g)

(b) Assuming the answer to part (a) to be -10 kcal, what would
$\Delta E_{298°K}$ be?

13. (12 min) The heat of formation of HBr(g) from H_2(g) and Br_2(g) at 25°C is -9 kcal/mole. Assuming that all diatomic gases have a constant C_p of 7 cal/deg-mole, (a) show what the heat of formation of HBr would be at 125°C. (b) If 1 mole of H_2 and 99 moles of Br_2 are exploded in an insulated bomb, then, neglecting the heat capacity of the bomb itself, calculate the final temperature if the initial temperature was 25°C.

14. (9 min) Substance X is an ideal gas containing n atoms per molecule. (a) C_p for X(g) and for N_2(g) is the same at 0°C (consider the contribution of vibrational degrees of freedom to the heat capacity to be negligible at 0°C). (b) The difference between the equipartition values of C_p for X(g) and N_2(g) is ca. 6 cal/deg-mole. Show from the above information what can be concluded about n and any other aspects concerning the structure of X.

15. (15 min) The heats of combustion of $(CH_2)_3$, carbon, and H_2 are -500.0, -94.0, and -68.0 kcal/mole, respectively (where burned to carbon dioxide and liquid water). The heat of formation of $CH_3CH=CH_2$ is 4.9 kcal/mole. (a) Calculate the heat of formation of cyclopropane $(CH_2)_3$. (b) Calculate the heat of isomerization of cyclopropane to propylene.

16. (12 min) One mole of NaCl is dissolved in sufficient water to give a solution containing 12 per cent NaCl by weight. The ΔH for this reaction is 774.6 cal at 20°C and 700.8 cal at 25°C. The heat capacity of solid NaCl is 12 cal/deg-mole and, for water, 18 cal/deg-mole. Calculate the heat capacity of the solution in cal/deg-g.

17. (12 min) (a) The equipartition value of γ $(= C_p/C_v)$ for ozone is 1.15; assuming ideal gas behavior, is the molecule linear or nonlinear?

(b) A lead-silver alloy has a C_v of 0.0383 cal/deg-g. What is the composition of the alloy? (Atomic weights: Pb, 207, Ag, 107).

18. (18 min) Given the following data:

(ethyl benzene) $-CH_2-CH_3(\ell) + 3H_2(g) =$ (ethylcyclohexane) (ℓ)

$\Delta H_{298°K} = -48.3$ kcal

$$\text{(styrene)} \quad \text{CH}=\text{CH}_2(\ell) + 4\text{H}_2(g) = \text{ethylcyclohexane} \quad (\ell)$$

$$\Delta H_{298°K} = -74.65 \text{ kcal}$$

The heat of combustion of ethylcyclohexane to water vapor and CO_2 is -1238.23 kcal/mole at 298°K, and the heats of formation of water vapor and of CO_2 are -58.32 and -94.05 kcal/mole, respectively, at 298°K. Calculate (a) the heat of hydrogenation of styrene to ethylbenzene, and (b) the heat of formation of ethylbenzene.

19. (12 min) For the process $Na_2CO_3 \cdot 10H_2O$ + water = solution, $\Delta H = 16.2$ kcal. We propose to utilize this effect to cool beverage cans (e.g., beer) by equipping the cans with an outer jacket containing this salt, and by adding water to this reservoir when cooling is desired (see Fig. 6-1). As a typical case, 0.2 mole

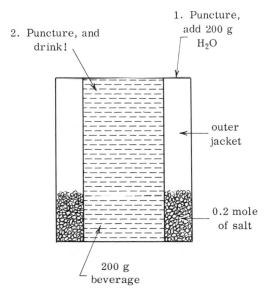

Figure 6-1

(60 g) of salt are used, the jacket holds 200 g of water, and the inner container holds 200 g of beverage (99.99%water); the initial temperature is 20°C, heat capacities are: water = 1 cal/deg-g, solution = 0.8 cal/deg-g, solid salt = 0.20 cal/deg-g, and container = 10 cal/deg. Calculate the temperature to which the beverage would be cooled.

20. (9 min) Calculate or estimate (to the nearest whole number) the following heat capacities in cal/deg-mole: (a) C_p for H_2 at 25°C, (b) C_V for NaCl(s) at 300°C, (c) C_p for Ag(s) at 25°C, (d) γ (equipartition) for CH_4, (e) γ for argon at 1000°C.

21. (19 min) Given that:

heats of combustion at 298°K: $CH_2{=}CHCN(g)$ -488.67 kcal
                                 $C(graphite)$ $-\ \ 94.05$
                                 $H_2(g)$ $-\ \ 68.33$

heats of formation at 298°K: $HCN(g)$ 31.00
                                C_2H_2 54.19

[In the combustion of acrylonitrile, nitrogen ends up as $N_2(g)$.]

(a) Calculate $\Delta H_{298°K}$ for the reaction $HCN(g) + C_2H_2(g) =$ $CH_2{=}CHCN(g)$, and (b) calculate the difference between ΔH and ΔE for this reaction.

22. (11 min) For the process $(NH_4)_2C_2O_4(s) + H_2O(\ell)$ = solution of 1 mole of each $\Delta H_{298°K} = 0.8$ kcal. C_p values are: $(NH_4)_2C_2O_4(s)$, 20 cal/deg-mole; $H_2O(\ell)$, 1 cal/deg-g; the solution of 1 mole of each, 40 cal/deg. If 1 mole of ammonium oxalate and 1 mole of water, both at 25°C, are mixed in an insulated vessel, what will be the temperature of the resulting solution?

23. (18 min) Given the following data: Heat of combustion of ethyl acetate $(CH_3COOC_2H_5)(\ell)$ to give $CO_2(g)$ and $H_2O(\ell)$: -536.9 kcal/mole at 25°C. Heats of formation, per mole at 298°K: $CH_3COOH(\ell)$: -116.7; $C_2H_5OH(\ell)$: -66.3; $CO_2(g)$: -94.0; $H_2O(g)$: -57.8. Heat of vaporization of water at 298°K is 10.5 kcal/mole. Calculate ΔH and ΔE at 298°K for the reaction

$$CH_3COOH(\ell) + C_2H_5OH(\ell) = CH_3COOC_2H_5(\ell) + H_2O(g)$$

24. (12 min) Given, for the reaction $CO(g) + H_2O(g) = CO_2(g) +$ $H_2(g)$, that $\Delta H_{298°K} = -10$ kcal, and the following heat capacities (C_p) per mole:

CO: $6.60 + 1.0 \times 10^{-3}$ T H_2: $6.6 + 1.0 \times 10^{-3}$ T

H_2O: $7.3 + 2.0 \times 10^{-3}$ T CO_2: $7.3 + 3.0 \times 10^{-3}$ T

Calculate ΔH for the above reaction at 1000°K.

25. (30 min) Given the following information:

heats of formation per mole at 298°K: $C_2H_5OH(\ell)$ −66.0 kcal
                                          $CO_2(g)$ −94.0
                                          $H_2O(\ell)$ −68.3

heats of combustion, at 298°K, to
give $H_2O(\ell)$ and/or $CO_2(g)$:   CO   −68 kcal
                                          $CH_4(g)$ −212

heat capacities C_p in cal/deg-mole: CH_4 = 5.0, CO_2 = 7.0,
                                           $C_2H_5OH(\ell)$ = 32.

(a) Calculate $\Delta H_{298°K}$ for the reaction $3CH_4(g) + CO_2(g) = 2C_2H_5OH(\ell)$.

(b) Calculate $\Delta E_{298°K}$ for the reaction in (a).

(c) Calculate $\Delta H_{-100°C} - \Delta H_{298°K}$ for reaction in (a).

26. (16 min) Given the values of ΔH at 25°C and 1 atm for the reactions:

(1) $C_2H_6(g) + \frac{7}{2}O_2(g) = 2CO_2(g) + 3H_2O(\ell)$ $\Delta H = -372.8$ kcal
(2) $H_2(g) + \frac{1}{2}O_2(g) = H_2O(\ell)$ $\Delta H - - 68.3$
(3) $2C(\text{graphite}) + 3H_2(g) = C_2H_6(g)$ $\Delta H = - 20.2$
(4) $2C(\text{graphite}) + 2H_2(g) = C_2H_4(g)$ $\Delta H = $ 12.6

(a) Calculate ΔH for the hydrogenation of ethylene at 25°C:

$$C_2H_4(g) + H_2(g) = C_2H_6(g)$$

(b) Calculate the heat of combustion of ethylene at 25°C.

(c) Calculate ΔE for the reaction in (a), making and stating any reasonable assumptions that are necessary.

27. (5 min) Given the following data: $C_2H_6(g,25°C) + \frac{7}{2}O_2(g,25°C) = 2CO_2(g,25°C) + 3H_2O(g,25°C)$, $\Delta E = -262.6$ kcal.

C_V in cal/deg-mole: C_2H_6 8.0 H_2O 6.2
                              O_2 4.8 CO_2 5.7

Calculate the maximum temperature achieved when 0.1 mole of ethane is exploded with 1 mole of oxygen in a bomb calorimeter. The reactants are initially at 25°C (make any reasonable assumptions necessary to complete the calculation).

Answers

1. The only process that involves C(s) is the heat of formation of CH_4, so start with it:

$$C(s) + 2H_2 = CH_4 \qquad \Delta H_1 = -17.9$$

now add $\quad CH_4 + 2O_2 = CO_2 + 2H_2O \qquad \Delta H_2 = -192.2$

then add $\quad 4H_2O = 4H_2 + 2O_2 \qquad \Delta H_3 = 4 \times 57.8$

This gives the desired equation so $\Delta H = -17.9 - 192.2 + 231.2 = \underline{21.3 \text{ kcal}}$. Within slide rule accuracy, $\Delta E = \Delta H - \Delta n_g RT = 21.3 - 1.98 \times 298/1000 = \underline{20.7 \text{ kcal}}$.

2. C(s): assume Dulong and Petit's law, $6 \cong C_p$;* $H_2O(g)$: assuming 20% of vibrational heat capacity, $C_p = R + (3R/2)(\text{trans.}) + (3R/2)(\text{rot.}) + 0.2(3R)(\text{vib.})$ or $C_p = 4.6R = \underline{9.1 \text{ cal/deg-mole}}$; $CO_2(g)$: (linear molecule) $C_p = R + (3R/2)(\text{trans.}) + (2R/2)(\text{rot.}) + 0.2(4R)(\text{vib.}) = 4.3R = \underline{8.5 \text{ cal/deg-mole}}$; $H_2(g)$: $R + (3R/2)(\text{trans.}) + (2R/2)(\text{rot.}) + 0.2(R)(\text{vib.}) = 3.7R = \underline{7.3 \text{ cal/deg-mole}}$.

3. (a) Start with the reaction written backwards:

$$10H_2O + 8CO_2 + 2Cl_2 = 13O_2 + 4C_2H_5Cl \quad \Delta H_1 = 1229.6 \text{ kcal}$$

Then get in the 4 moles of C_2H_6 needed by adding the combustion of 4 moles:

$$4C_2H_6 + 14O_2 = 8CO_2 + 12H_2O \qquad \Delta H_2 = -4 \times 341 \text{ kcal}$$

Now get in the desired 4 moles of HCl:

$$2Cl_2 + 2H_2 = 4 HCl \qquad \Delta H_3 = -4 \times 21 \text{ kcal}$$

To make things come out, add:

$$2H_2O = O_2 + 2H_2 \qquad \Delta H_4 = 2 \times 57.8 \text{ kcal}$$

$4C_2H_6 + 4Cl_2 = 4C_2H_5Cl + 4HCl \qquad \Delta H = 1229.6 - 1364 - 84 + 115.6 = -103 \text{ kcal}$

(b) $\Delta H_{398°K} = \Delta H_{298°K} + \Delta C_p \Delta T = -1229.6 + (10 \times 100)/1000 = \underline{-1230.6 \text{ kcal}}$.

(c) $\Delta E = \Delta H - \Delta n_g RT = -1229.6 - 3RT = \underline{-1231.4 \text{ kcal}}$.

---

*Actually, one should recognize that for C(s) the value at 25°C will be about 20% of 6 or about 1.5.

4. For O_2 and Cl_2: C_p = R + (3R/2)(trans.) + (2R/2)(rot.) + 0.2(R)(vib.) = 3.7R = $\underline{7.3\ cal/deg\text{-}mole}$ (assuming 20% of equipartition vibrational C_v). CO_2 and H_2O: see Problem 2. C_2H_5Cl: C_p = R + (3R/2)(trans.) + (3R/2)(rot.) + 0.2(18R)(vib.) = 7.6R = $\underline{15\ cal/deg\text{-}mole}$.

5. (a) Heat of formation of $H_2O(\ell)$: $-57.8 + 9.4 = \underline{-67.2\ kcal}$.

(b) We want acetic acid on the left, so begin with the reverse of its formation:

$$C_2H_4O_2 = 2C(s) + 2H_2 + O_2 \qquad \Delta H_1 = 116.4\ kcal$$

We want CH_4 on the right, so add the reverse of its combustion:

$$CO_2 + 2H_2O = CH_4 + 2O_2 \qquad \Delta H_2 = 192.7\ kcal$$

Now, eliminate C(s) using the formation of CO_2:

$$2C(s) + 2O_2 = 2CO_2 \qquad \Delta H_3 = -2 \times 94.0\ kcal$$

To make things come out, add the formation of H_2O:

$$2H_2 + O_2 = 2H_2O \qquad \Delta H_4 = -2 \times 57.8\ kcal$$

$$\overline{C_2H_4O_2 = CH_4 + CO_2 \qquad \begin{array}{l} \Delta H = 116.4 + 192.7 - 188 \\ \quad\ \ - 115.6 = \underline{5.5\ kcal} \end{array}}$$

(c) $\Delta H_T = \Delta H_{298°K} + \Delta C_p \Delta T$. ΔC_p = 9.0 + 7.5 − 12.5 = 4.0. Hence ΔH_T = 0 = $-4000 + 4\Delta T$ or ΔT = 1000° and T = 1298°K.

6. (a) H_2: no vib. at $-150°C$, so C_p = R + (3R/2)(trans.) + (2R/2)(rot.) = 3.5R $\cong$ $\underline{7}$.

(b) N_2: at 25°C take 20% of equipartition vibrational heat capacity, so C_p = R + (3R/3)(trans.) + (2R/2)(rot.) + 0.2(R)(vib.) = 3.7R $\cong$ $\underline{7.4}$ $\cong$ 7.

(c) He: C_p = R + (3R/2)(trans.) = 2.5R $\cong$ 5.

(d) NaBr: assume Dulong and Petit's law, but remember there are 2 moles of atoms so $C_p \cong C_V = \underline{12}$.

(e) Pb: assume Dulong and Petit's law, $C_p \cong C_V = \underline{6}$.

(f) C_2H_5OH: C_p = R + (3R/2)(trans) + (3R/2)(rot.) + 0.2(21R)(vib.) = 8.2R $\cong$ $\underline{16}$.

7. There is a real short-cut here. Any standard reaction in which all species except the one of interest are the same behaves like a heat of formation or combustion. A ΔH of reaction involving such species is simply given by the appropriate sum or difference of the ΔH's of the standard reactions. Here, H_{TC} has this property; moreover H_{TC} is zero for CH_4. The desired ΔH is then simply $2H_{TC}(C_2H_6) + H_{TC}(C_3H_8) = 2 \times 15.6 + (-20.9) = \underline{10.3\ cal.}$ (Check the answer the long way, if you don't believe me!)

8. (a) $\Delta H_{298°K}$ is simply the heat of formation of $H_2O(g)$ or -58 kcal. $\Delta E = \Delta H - \Delta n_g RT = -58 - (-\frac{1}{2})RT/1000 = \underline{-57.7\ kcal.}$ (Δn_g is determined by the stoichiometry of the reaction that takes place.)

(b) $\Delta H_{598°K} = \Delta H_{298°K} + \Delta C_p \Delta T = -58 + (-2.25)200/1000 = \underline{-58.45\ kcal.}$

(c) The maximum temperature is that obtained by applying the ΔE of reaction to heating up the products, here $H_2O(g) + 9.5O_2(g)$; so $57,700 = C_v \Delta T = (5.5 + 9.5 \times 4.5)\Delta T = 69.2\ \Delta T$ or $\Delta T = 1200°$, $T = \underline{1225°C.}$

9. (a) $C_p = R + (3R/2)(trans.) = 2.5R \cong \underline{5.}$

(b) Probably only about 20% of the Dulong and Petit maximum of 6, since Be atoms are light and the temperature is small. $C_p \cong C_v \cong 0.2 \times 6 \cong \underline{1.2.}$

(c) Allow maybe 30% of equipartition vibrational heat capacity, $C_p = R + (3R/2)(trans.) + (2R/2)(rot.) + 0.3(R)(vib.) = 3.8R \cong \underline{7.}$

(d) At 25°C allow about 20% of equipartition vibrational heat capacity, $C_p = R + (3R/2)(trans.) + (3R/2)(rot.) + 0.2(18R)(vib.) = 7.6R \cong \underline{15.}$

(e) Allow the full Dulong and Petit value (heavy atoms, high temperature), so $C_p \cong C_v = \underline{6.}$

(f) allow 20% of vibrational heat capacity, $C_p = R + (3R/2)(trans.) + (3R/2)(rot.) + 0.2(3R)(vib.) = 4.6R \cong \underline{9.}$

10. (a) The molar heat of combustion of graphite is the same as the heat of formation of CO_2; per gram it would be $-94/12 = \underline{-7.82\ kcal.}$

(b) The answer must be the same as for (a), plus the energy added by the water gas reaction, so $-7.82 - 32/12 = \underline{-10.5\ kcal.}$

(c) $\Delta E = \Delta H - \Delta n_g RT = 32 - RT/1000 = \underline{31.43\ kcal.}$

(d) $\Delta H_{600°K} = \Delta H_{298°K} + \Delta C_p \times 302 = 32 + 4.5 \times 302/1000 = \underline{33.4\ kcal.}$

(e) We take the bond energy for the O—H bond to be half the ΔH for the reaction $H_2O = 2H + O$. This reaction is the sum of:

$$\begin{array}{lll} H_2O = H_2 + \frac{1}{2}O_2 & \Delta H_1 = 58\ kcal \\ H_2 = 2H & \Delta H_2 = 103\ kcal \\ \frac{1}{2}O_2 = O & \Delta H_3 = \frac{1}{2}34 = 17\ kcal \end{array}$$

or 178/2 = 89 kcal. Strictly, this should be one-half the ΔE, so subtract 0.5 kcal to get 88.5 kcal.

11. Ar(g): only translation so 3R/2 or 3.

H_2(g): allow 20% of equipartition vibrational heat capacity, so
C_V = (3R/2)(trans.) + (2R/2)(rot.) + 0.2(R)(vib.) = 2.7R $\cong$ 5.

CO_2(g): C_V = (3R/2)(trans.) + (2R/2)(rot.) + 0.2(4R)(vib.) = 3.3R $\cong$ 6.

N_2(g): same as for H_2.

Ag(s): heavy atoms, soft, so assume equipartition Dulong and Petit value: 6.

C(s): light atoms, hard, so guess that about 20% of D and P value: 1.

C_6H_6(g): C_V = (3R/2)(trans.) + (3R/2)(rot.) + 0.2(30R)(vib.) = 9R = 18.

H_2O(g): C_V = (3R/2)(trans.) + (3R/2)(rot.) + 0.2(3R)(vib.) = 3.6R $\cong$ 7.

H_2O(ℓ): C_V = 18. (You should know that the specific heat of water is about 1 cal/deg-g!)

12. We want C_2H_5OH on the left, so write the formation in reverse:

$$C_2H_5OH = 2C + 3H_2 + \tfrac{1}{2}O_2 \qquad \Delta H_1 = 66 \text{ kcal}$$

Bring in CH_3—O—CH_3 by adding its combustion, also in reverse:

$$2CO_2 + 3H_2O = CH_3\text{—}O\text{—}CH_3 + 3O_2 \qquad \Delta H_2 = 348 \text{ kcal}$$

Now add the formation of H_2O and the combustion of C:

$$2C + 2O_2 = 2CO_2 \qquad \Delta H_3 = -94 \times 2 \text{ or } -188 \text{ kcal}$$

$$3H_2 + \tfrac{3}{2}O_2 = 3H_2O \qquad \Delta H_4 = -3 \times 68 = -204 \text{ kcal}$$

The desired ΔH is then 66 + 348 − 188 − 204 = 22 kcal.
   (b) $\Delta E = \Delta H - \Delta n_g RT = -10 - RT/1000 = -10.6$ kcal.

13. (a) The formation reaction is H_2(g) + Br_2(g) = 2HBr(g). The molecules are all diatomic and there are the same number on both sides, so ΔC_p = 0. ΔH at 125°C is therefore also −9 kcal/mole.
   (b) After the reaction, there are 2 moles of HBr and 98 of Br_2 or 100 moles of diatomic gas—the C_V of the mixture is then

$100(7 - 2) = 500$. The increase in temperature is then $9000 = 500 \, \Delta T$ or $\Delta T = 18$ (note ΔE and ΔH are both -9000); T is $25 + 18 = \underline{43°C.}$

14. The heat capacity of N_2 is made up of R (for C_p) + $(3R/2)$(trans.) + $(2R/2)$(rot.) + R(vib.). At 0°C only translation and rotation are to be considered, so X must also have only two degrees of rotational freedom, i.e., X must be linear. However, the extra 6 cal/deg-mole at equipartition means that X has three more vibrational degrees of freedom than N_2, which means one more atom. X is therefore a linear triatomic molecule.

15. The heat of combustion of $(CH_2)_3$: $(CH_2)_3 + \frac{9}{2}O_2 = 3CO_2 + 3H_2O$ is related to its heat of formation: $\Delta H_c = 3H_{CO_2} + 3H_{H_2O} - H_{(CH_2)_3}$ (H denotes heat of formation), so $H_{(CH_2)_3} = 500.0 - 3 \times 94 - 3 \times 68 = \underline{14 \text{ kcal.}}$ (Note that the heat of combustion of carbon is also the heat of formation of CO_2; likewise, the heat of combustion of H_2 is the same as the heat of formation of water.)

For the isomerization, $\Delta H_1 = H_{CH_3CH=CH_2} - H_{(CH_2)_3} = 4.9 - 14.0 = \underline{-9.1 \text{ kcal.}}$

16. Take 100 g of solution as a basis—the process is then:

12 g NaCl + 88 g H_2O = 100 g solution

$(12/58.2 = 0.205$ moles)

Per mole of NaCl, ΔC_p is given by the change in ΔH per degree, i.e., $(700.8 - 774.6)/5$ or -14.7. Per 12 g or 0.205 moles, $\Delta C_p = -3.01$. Then $-3.01 = C_p$(solution) $- 2.5$ (C_p of NaCl) $- 88$ (C_p of H_2O) or, C_p(solution) $= 87$ or, per gram, $\underline{0.87 \text{ cal/deg-g.}}$

17. (a) If linear, the equipartition C_v would be $(3R/2)$(trans.) + $(2R/2)$(rot.) + $(4R)$(vib.) or 6.5R, and γ would then be $7.5/6.5 = 1.15$. If nonlinear, C_v would be $(3R/2)$(trans.) + $(3R/2)$(rot.) + $(3R)$(vib.) or 6R and γ is then $7/6 = 1.17$. The molecule is therefore <u>linear.</u>

(b) Assuming 6 cal/deg-mole as the Dulong and Petit value, the average molecular weight of the alloy must be $6/0.0383 = 157$. In terms of mole fractions N, then: $157 = N_{Ag} \, 107 + N_{Pb} \, 207 = 107 + 100N_{Pb}$ or $N_{Pb} = \underline{0.50.}$

18. (a) Subtracting the two reactions gives:

C_8H_8(styrene) + H_2 = C_8H_{10} (ethylbenzene)

$\Delta H = -74.65 - (-48.3) = \underline{-26.4 \text{ kcal}}$

(b) For the combustion of ethylcyclohexane:

$C_8H_{16} + 12O_2 = 8CO_2 + 8H_2O \qquad \Delta H_C = -1238.23 \text{ kcal}$

$\Delta H_C = 8H_{CO_2} + 8H_{H_2O} - H_{C_8H_{16}}$
$\qquad = -8 \times 94.05 - 8 \times 58.32 - H_{C_8H_{16}}$

from which $H_{C_8H_{16}} = 1238.23 - 8 \times 152.37 = 19.27 \text{ kcal.}$
From the first reaction given,

$-74.65 - 48.3 = H_{C_8H_{16}} - H_{C_8H_{10}} \quad$ or

$H_{C_8H_{10}} = 48.3 + 19.3 = \underline{67.6 \text{ kcal}}$

19. For 0.2 mole of salt, q_p will be $0.2 \times 16,200$ or 3,240 cal. This heat is then abstracted from the final system, whose heat capacity will be: 0.8×260 (solution) + 1×200 (beverage) + 10 (container) = 418 cal/deg. The ΔT will then be $3240/418$ = 7.8 so the final temperature is 12.2°C.

20. (a) Assume 20% of equipartition vibrational heat capacity:
C_p = R + (3R/2)(trans.) + (2R/2)(rot.) + (0.2R)(vib.) = 3.7R $\cong$ $\underline{7.}$
   (b) Take Dulong and Petit value (but for 2 moles of atoms):
$\underline{12.}$
   (c) Take Dulong and Petit value: $\underline{6.}$
   (d) C_V = (3R/2)(trans.) + (3R/2)(rot.) + (9R)(vib.) = 12R;
γ = 13/12 = $\underline{1.08 \cong 1.}$
   (e) C_V = 3R/2; γ = 5/3 = $\underline{1.66 \cong 2.}$

21. (a) We want acrylonitrile on the right, so write its combustion in reverse:

$3CO_2 + \frac{3}{2}H_2O + \frac{1}{2}N_2 = CH_2{=}CHCN + 3\frac{3}{4}O_2$

$\Delta H_1 = 488.67 \text{ kcal}$

C_2H_2 must be on the left, so write its formation in reverse:

$C_2H_2 = 2C + H_2 \qquad \Delta H_2 = -54.19$

Also,

$HCN = \frac{1}{2}H_2 + C + \frac{1}{2}N_2 \qquad \Delta H = -31.00$

To tidy up, add the combustion of the proper number of moles of C and H_2:

$$3C + 3O_2 = 3CO_2 \qquad \Delta H_3 = -3 \times 94.05$$

$$\tfrac{3}{2} H_2 + \tfrac{3}{4} O_2 = \tfrac{3}{2} H_2O \qquad \Delta H_4 = -\tfrac{3}{2} 68.33$$

The sum gives the desired reaction, for which ΔH is then:

$$488.67 - 54.19 - 282.15 - 102.50 - 31.00 = \underline{18.83 \text{ kcal}}$$

(b) Since $\Delta H = \Delta E + \Delta n_g RT$, then in this case $\Delta H - \Delta E = (-1)RT = \underline{-0.59 \text{ kcal.}}$

22. When the dissolution reaction occurs, 800 cal are absorbed. The total heat capacity of the solution is 40 cal/deg, so there will be a 20-deg drop, i.e., the final temperature will be 5°C. (The data for the salt and for water were superfluous.)

23. The combustion reaction for $CH_3COOC_2H_5$ is

$$CH_3COOC_2H_5 + 5O_2 = 4CO_2 + 4H_2O \qquad \Delta H = -536.9 \text{ kcal}$$

Then $-536.9 = 4H_{CO_2} + 4H_{H_2O} - H_{ester}$ or $H_{ester} = 536.9 - 649.2 = -112.3$ kcal. [Note that H for $H_2O(\ell)$ is required here.] Then ΔH for the desired reaction is

$$\Delta H = H_{ester} + H_{H_2O} - H_{CH_3COOH} - H_{C_2H_5OH}$$

$$= -112.3 - 57.8 - (-116.7) - (-66.3) = \underline{12.9 \text{ kcal}}$$

$$\Delta E = \Delta H - \Delta n_g RT = 12.9 - RT = \underline{12.3 \text{ kcal}}$$

24. The basic equation is

$$\Delta H_{1000°K} = \Delta H_{298°K} + \int_{298}^{1000} \Delta C_p \, dT$$

On combining the equations for C_p, $\Delta C = 0 + 10^{-3} T$. The integral then becomes $(10^{-3}/2)(1000^2 - 298^2) = (10^{-3} \times 9.1 \times 10^5)/2 = 460$, so $\Delta H_{1000°K} = -10 + 0.46 = \underline{-9.54 \text{ kcal.}}$

25. (a) It is probably quickest to get the heat of formation of CH_4 first. The combustion reaction is $CH_4 + 2O_2 = CO_2 + 2H_2O$ and $\Delta H_c = H_{CO_2} + 2H_{H_2O} - H_{CH_4}$, whence $H_{CH_4} = 212 - 94.0 - 2 \times 68.3 = 212 - 230.6 = -18.6$ kcal. Then ΔH for the desired reaction is: $\Delta H = 2H_{C_2H_5OH} - 3H_{CH_4} - H_{CO_2}$ or

$$\Delta H = -2 \times 66.0 - (-3 \times 18.6) - (-94.0) = \underline{17.8 \text{ kcal}}$$

(b) $\Delta E = \Delta H - \Delta n_g RT = 17.8 - (-4)RT/1000 = \underline{20.2 \text{ kcal.}}$
(c) $\Delta H_{173°K} = \Delta H_{298°K} + \Delta C_p \, \Delta T$. $\Delta C_p = 2 \times 32 - 3 \times 5 - 7 = 42$ cal/deg, so the desired difference is $42(-125) = \underline{-5250 \text{ cal.}}$

26. (a) The simplest way is just to take the difference between (3) and (4), i.e., the desired ΔH is $\Delta H_3 - \Delta H_4 = -20.2 - 12.6 = \underline{-32.8}$ kcal. (b) Reaction (1) plus reaction (a) plus the reverse of reaction (2) gives the desired heat of combustion, so $\Delta H_c = -372.8 + (-32.8) - (-68.3) = \underline{-337.3 \text{ kcal.}}$ (c) $\Delta E = \Delta H - \Delta n_g RT$ if the gases are ideal. Then $\Delta E = -32.8 - (-1)RT/1000 = \underline{-32.2 \text{ kcal.}}$

27. The reaction will use 0.35 mole O_2, leaving 0.65, and produces 0.2 mole CO_2, 0.3 mole H_2O. Neglecting the heat capacity of the calorimeter and assuming the C_V values do not change with temperature and that the reaction does go to completion, the total C_V for the mixture after reaction will be: $0.65 \times 4.8 + 0.2 \times 5.7 + 0.3 \times 6.2 = 6.13$. ΔT is then given by

$$0.1 \times 262,000 = 6.13 \Delta T \quad \text{or} \quad \Delta T = 4280 \quad \text{or} \quad T = 4300°C$$

7 Second law
of thermodynamics

Comments

The combined first and second law statement and the use of
H, A, F, and S are given a going over in this chapter. In many
cases, ideal gases are involved, so that the relationships you have
to use are not very complicated. The main difficulty will be in
seeing what to do rather than how to do it. A good deal of attention is paid to irreversible processes, and it is important to remember that S is a state function, so that ΔS does not depend on
path. On the other hand, to calculate ΔS from the data, it may be
necessary to make use of the relationship $\Delta S = q_{rev}/T$, which
means that you will want to formulate a set of reversible steps
that take you from the given initial to the given final condition.

The criteria for equilibrium must be kept in mind. Two of the
more useful ones are that dS is zero for a reversible process
occurring in an isolated system and that dF is zero for a reversible process at constant T and P. Also, the Carnot cycle is made

use of a good deal, as are applications of it to heat engines and heat pumps.

Since E, A, H, F, and S are state functions, they each have a total differential, usually expressed in terms of those variables most convenient for the particular quantity. The total differentials, in turn, give rise to a number of cross-differential or Euler relationships (see Appendix), and there is now considerable scope for derivations of partial differential equations. A number of problems are of this type.

Equations and concepts

Definitions: $H = E + PV$, $A = E - TS$, $F = H - TS$.

Combined First and Second Law Statements:

$$dE = T\,dS - P\,dV \qquad \text{so} \qquad (\partial E/\partial S)_V = T, \quad (\partial E/\partial V)_S = -P$$

$$dH = T\,dS + V\,dP \qquad\qquad\qquad (\partial H/\partial S)_P = T, \quad (\partial H/\partial P)_S = V$$

$$dA = -S\,dT - P\,dV \qquad\qquad\qquad (\partial A/\partial T)_V = -S, \quad (\partial A/\partial V)_T = -P$$

$$dF = -S\,dT + V\,dP \qquad\qquad\qquad (\partial F/\partial T)_P = -S, \quad (\partial F/\partial P)_T = V$$

Entropy in Terms of q: $dS = dq_{rev}/T$ or $dS = C\,d\ln T$ where $C = $ heat capacity. Thus $\Delta S = \int C_p\,d\ln T$ for a constant pressure process and $\Delta S = \int C_V\,d\ln T$ for a constant volume process (both should be reversible).

Ideal Gas:

$$dS = C_V\,d\ln T + R\,d\ln V$$

$$\Delta S = \int C_V\,d\ln T \quad \text{for a constant-volume process}$$

$$\Delta S = \int R\,d\ln V = R\ln V_2/V_1 \quad \text{for a constant-temperature process}$$

$$\Delta S = \int C_V\,d\ln T + R\ln V_2/V_1 \quad \text{for any process}$$

Note that the change need not be reversible here, since an irreversible change from V_1 and T_1 to V_2 and T_2 can always be replaced by two reversible steps consisting of an isothermal change from V_1 to V_2 followed by an isochoric change from T_1 to T_2, and the over-all ΔS is again given by the above equation.

An alternative form is: $\Delta S = \int C_p \, d \ln T - R \ln P_2/P_1$.
If the ideal gas is monatomic, we have:

$$\Delta S = \tfrac{3}{2} R \ln T_2/T_1 + R \ln V_2/V_1 = \tfrac{5}{2} R \ln T_2/T_1 - R \ln P_2/P_1$$

Reversible Adiabat: ΔS is zero for a reversible adiabatic change. For an ideal gas it follows that:

$$C_V \ln T_2/T_1 = -R \ln V_2/V_1$$

$$C_p \ln T_2/T_1 = R \ln P_2/P_1$$

Carnot Cycle, Heat Engines, and Heat Pumps: The two basic equations for a carnot cycle operating between an upper temperature T_2 and a lower temperature T_1 are

$$w = q_1 + q_2$$

$$q_1/T_1 + q_2/T_2 = 0 \qquad (\text{i.e., } \Delta S_1 + \Delta S_2 = 0)$$

In the case of a heat engine, we want w in terms of q_2, so eliminate q_1:

$$w = -(T_1/T_2)\, q_2 + q_2 = q_2\left(\frac{T_2 - T_1}{T_2}\right)$$

In the case of a refrigerator, we want q_1 in terms of w, so eliminate q_2:

$$w = q_1 - (T_2/T_1)\, q_1 \qquad \text{or} \qquad q_1 = w\left(\frac{T_1}{T_1 - T_2}\right)$$

The quantity in parentheses is negative, but w is negative and q_1 is positive, so the signs come out all right.

Euler Relationships: If $dz = M \, dx + N \, dy$ is a total differential, then:

$$(\partial M/\partial y)_X = (\partial N/\partial x)_y$$

Thus

$$(\partial T/\partial V)_S = -(\partial P/dS)_V \qquad \text{etc.}$$

Problems

1. (10 min) A refrigerator operates at 50% of ideal efficiency, i.e., the ideal work is 50% of the actual work. If it operates between 0°C and 25°C, calculate the work to freeze 1 kg of ice (heat of fusion 80 cal/g) and the heat discharged at 25°C.

2. (12 min) Calculate (or give with explanation) ΔH and ΔS when a 1-kg bar of copper at 100°C is placed in 2 kg of water at 0°C in an insulated container maintained at 1 atm pressure. Heat capacities: Cu, 0.1 cal/deg-g; $H_2O(\ell)$, 1 cal/deg-g.

3. (7 min) Calculate ΔF for the process of Problem 2. Actually there is insufficient information, so explain what additional information is needed, and set up the equations to show clearly how you would make the calculations.

4. (9 min) Derive from the first and second laws and related definitions:

$$(\partial S/\partial V)_T = (\partial P/\partial T)_V$$

5. (21 min) One-tenth mole of liquid ether in an ampule is placed in a 10-liter flask maintained at 35°C and filled with 0.4 mole of nitrogen gas at 1 atm pressure. By means of a mechanical arrangement, the ampule is broken in situ, and the ether evaporates completely. The process is then:

0.1 ether $(\ell, 35°C) + 0.4N_2$ (10 liters, 35° C)

= mixture of gases (10 liters, 35°C)

(The normal boiling point of ether is 35°C, and the heat of vaporization is 6.0 kcal/mole.)

(a) Calculate the final pressure of ether. (b) Calculate or explain the value of ΔH, ΔS, and ΔF for the nitrogen gas. (c) Calculate or explain the value of ΔH, ΔS, and ΔF for the ether.
(3 min extra): Calculate or explain the value of ΔS for the complete system, flask plus thermostat, when the process occurs.

6. (6 min) Show what per cent T_1 is of T_2 for a heat engine whose ideal efficiency is 10%.

7. (12 min) One mole of an ideal monatomic gas is taken from the

state (22.4 liters, 273°K, S = 20 cal/deg) to the state (2 atm, 303°K).
Calculate ΔE, ΔH, ΔS, and ΔF for this change.

8. (12 min) (a) Derive $(\partial S/\partial V)_E = P/T$. (Hint: make use of the
total differential for E expressed as a function of S and V.)
(b) Verify the above equation for an ideal gas, i.e., evaluate
$(\partial S/\partial V)_E$ directly.

9. (9 min) Derive from the first and second laws of thermodynamics and related definitions

$$(\partial T/\partial P)_S = (\partial V/\partial S)_P$$

10. (10 min) Figure 7-1 shows a carnot cycle as often depicted in
texts. The same cycle may, alternatively, be given as a plot of S
vs. T, as is done in Fig. 7-2.

(a) Indicate which are the corresponding steps in the two fig-
ures. Do this by labeling the arrows in Fig. 7-2 with A, B, C, and
D.

(b) An ideal heat engine operating between T_1 = 273°K and T_2

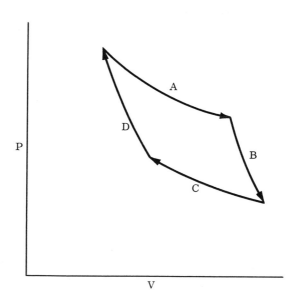

Figure 7-1

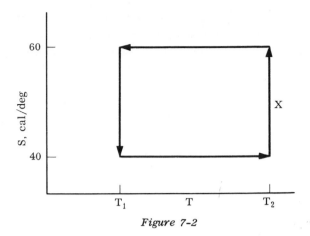

Figure 7-2

produces 1000 cal of work per cycle. The entropy changes that the working fluid goes through are shown in Fig. 7-2. Calculate q_1 and q_2 for one cycle, and T_2.

11. (10 min) Give a process for which (a) $\Delta E = 0$, (b) $\Delta H = 0$, (c) $\Delta A = 0$, (d) $\Delta F = 0$, and (e) $\Delta S = 0$. State all necessary conditions or restrictions clearly.

12. (12 min) It has been possible to supercool small drops of water to $-40°C$. Such drops are unstable, of course, and eventually nucleation occurs and ice crystals form. Assume that such a drop is thermally isolated so that, when spontaneous ice formation occurs, it does so adiabatically (and isobarically). C_p is 1 cal/deg-g for water (ℓ) and 0.5 cal/deg-g for water (s), and the heat of fusion of water is 80 cal/g at 0°C. Calculate the final temperature of the drop after the spontaneous process has occurred, and ΔH and ΔS for the process, in cal/g.

13. (9 min) Calculate ΔH and ΔF for the process

$$CH_3OH(\ell, 64°C, 1\ atm) = CH_3OH(g, 64°C, 0.5\ atm)$$

(The normal boiling point of CH_3OH is 64°C, and the heat of vaporization is 260 cal/g.)

14. (15 min) A home-owner is fortunate enough to possess an ideally operating refrigerator; nonetheless he feels it is using too much power and calls in a repair man, who moves the machine

back from the wall to get better air circulation around the hot
coils. The home-owner now finds his power consumption to be
halved. Assuming that the machine operated between 0°C and an
upper temperature T_2, and after adjustment, operated between
0°C and 30°C, calculate (a) the watts/hr needed (after adjustment)
to convert 1 kg water at 0°C to 1 kg ice at 0°C and (b) the original
upper temperature T_2. (1 cal = 4.2 joules or watt-sec, heat of
fusion of water is 80 cal/g.)

15. (7 min) Show that $(\partial H/\partial P)_S = V$, using the first and second
laws of thermodynamics and related definitions.

16. (7 min) One mole of an ideal, monatomic gas initially at 27°C
is allowed to expand into an evacuated flask of such size that the
volume is increased tenfold. Calculate ΔF for the process.

17. (10 min) Derive from the first and second laws of thermodynamics and related definitions:

$$\partial(A/T)/\partial T = -E/T^2$$

18. (13 min) A reversible heat engine absorbs heat q_2 at 900°K,
per cycle, and evolves heat q_1 at 300°K. Its work output is used
to run a hoist, and, owing to friction in the pulleys, 10% of w is
converted into heat at 300°K. For the system engine plus pulleys,
the <u>total</u> heat evolved is 12,000 cal per cycle. (a) Calculate q_1, q_2,
and w. (b) Calculate ΔS per cycle, for the system engine plus
pulleys.

19. (6 min) Show from the first and second laws of thermodynamics and related definitions that $(\partial A/\partial T)_V = -S$.

20. (10 min) One mole of an ideal, monatomic gas initially at STP
expands isothermally and <u>irreversibly</u> to 44.8 liters, under conditions such that w = 100 cal. Calculate ΔS and ΔF.

21. (12 min) Given the process:

   0.20 mole O_2 (g, 0.2 atm) + 0.8 mole N_2 (g, 0.8 atm)

   = mixture (g)

all at 25°C, which is carried out by having the oxygen and nitrogen initially in separate flasks, and then by opening the stopcock

connecting the two flasks. (a) Calculate the final P. (b) Calculate q, w, ΔE, ΔS, and ΔF for the process. (c) Calculate the reversible q and w for the isothermal process returning the mixture to its initial state.

22. (18 min) One gram of water enclosed in a vial is placed in an evacuated flask maintained at 25°C. By means of a lever, the vial is broken so that the water is free to vaporize and, when equilibrium is reached, one-half the water has vaporized. The vapor pressure of water at 25°C is 24 mm Hg, and the heat of vaporization is 590 cal/g. Calculate q, w, ΔH, ΔF, and ΔS for this process.

23. (12 min) A home-owner has the idea of using an extra refrigerator to cool his living room during the summer. He therefore sets up the machine in the middle of the room, leaving the refrigerator door open to get the benefit of its cooling coils. Room temperature is 25°C, and it may be assumed that the refrigerator is operating between 25°C and 0°C. The machine ordinarily is capable of freezing 1 kg of ice per hr with these operating temperatures. Calculate the temperature change in the living room, i.e., the new temperature, after 1 hr of operation of the refrigerator. Assume ideal operation, and that the heat capacity of the room is 100 kcal/deg. The heat of fusion of water is 80 cal/g.

24. (15 min) One mole of liquid water is allowed to expand into an evacuated flask of volume such that the final pressure is 0.3 atm. The bulb containing the liquid and the flask are thermostated so that a constant temperature of 100°C is maintained. It is found that 11,000 cal of heat are absorbed when this process occurs. Calculate or explain what the values are for w, ΔE, ΔH, ΔS, and ΔF. Neglect PV quantities for liquid water.

25. (7 min) Derive from the first and second laws and related definitions the relationship:

$$(\partial A/\partial V)_T = -P$$

26. (15 min) Derive from the first and second laws and related definitions:

$$(\partial V/\partial T)_P = -(\partial S/\partial P)_T$$

27. (20 min) One mole of a perfect monatomic gas initially at volume V_1 = 5 liters, pressure P_1, and temperature T_1 = 298°K experiences the following reversible changes: (1) Isothermal compression to one half the volume, the new volume and pressure being $V_2 = \frac{1}{2}V_1$, and P_2. (2) Cooling at constant volume, until the pressure is returned to the original value of P_1, the final temperature being T_2. These changes are shown schematically in Fig. 7-3. Notice that process C, reduction in volume at constant pressure P_1, is equivalent to the sum of steps A and B.

(a) Calculate P_1, P_2, and T_2. Also q, w, ΔE, ΔH, ΔS, and ΔF for A and B separately.

(b) Are the magnitudes (without regard for sign) of ΔE, q, and w for step C greater than, less than, or equal to the values of these quantities for the sum of steps A and B?

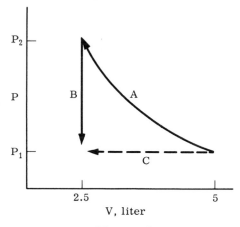

Figure 7-3

28. (12 min) One mole of an ideal monatomic gas initially at 10 atm pressure and 0°C is allowed to expand against a constant external pressure of 1.0 atm. Conditions are such that the final volume is 10 times the initial volume; the final gas pressure equals the external pressure.

(a) Calculate the initial and final volume and the final temperature.

(b) Calculate q, w, ΔE, ΔH, ΔS, and ΔF for the process.

29. (19 min) One mole of water vapor at 100°C is compressed to 2 atm. It is sufficiently dust free so that it supersaturates; after a while, however, condensation occurs and goes to completion, since T and P are kept constant. The process is thus $H_2O(g, 100°C, 2 atm) = H_2O(\ell, 100°C, 2 atm)$. Data: heat capacities: C_p for the vapor is 7 cal/deg-mole, and is 18 cal/deg-mole for the liquid. Heat of vaporization under these conditions: 11 kcal/mole. It is permissible to assume the vapor to be ideal and liquid water to be incompressible at a molar volume of 18 cc. Calculate ΔH, ΔF, and ΔS for the process.

30. (10 min) For a certain ideal heat pump, which operates between 0°C and t°C, it takes 200 cal of work to deliver 2000 cal of heat to the house that it is heating. (a) What is the value of t? (b) How many calories of heat are absorbed at 0°C?

31. (10 min) The four steps of the Carnot cycle are often given in terms of a P-V diagram. Draw the corresponding S vs T diagram, i.e., draw the paths corresponding to the four steps for a Carnot cycle operating with an ideal gas (reversibly) between T_2 and T_1. Label the nature of each step, i.e., whether isothermal or adiabatic. Show by arrows the direction along each path (the first step is to be an isothermal expansion at T_2).

32. (19 min) One mole of an ideal monatomic gas is contained in a piston and cylinder at 300°K and 10 atm. The pressure is suddenly released to 2 atm, so that the gas expands adiabatically at a constant pressure of 2 atm. (a) Explain whether ΔS for this expansion should be positive, negative, or zero. (b) Calculate ΔE and ΔS. To speed your calculation, 288 cal of work are done by the gas in this expansion.

33. (10 min) The refrigerating machine of an eastern ice plant operates between 0°C and 25°C by freezing river water at 0°C and evolving heat at 25°C. In an efficiency test, the owner finds that in a given 8-hr shift, 100 kg of ice are produced (it's a small plant), and 16,000 kcal of heat are evolved at 25°C. Calculate the fractional efficiency, i.e., the ratio of the amount of reversible work necessary to freeze the ice to the actual amount of work necessary to freeze it. (Heat of fusion of water is 80 cal/g.)

34. (19 min) Give one example each of processes for which (a) ΔF is 0 and ΔS is positive, (b) ΔF is negative and ΔS is positive, and (c) ΔF is positive and ΔS is negative. The initial and final states for each process need be detailed only to the extent necessary to make it definite that the desired type of ΔS and ΔF value will apply.

35. (19 min) One mole of ice at 0°C is placed in a Dewar flask and 10 moles of water at 25°C is added. The ice melts, and cools the water. The heat of fusion of water is 1420 cal/mole. (a) Write the equation for the above process. (b) What is ΔH for the process? (c) Calculate the final temperature of the water. (d) Calculate ΔS for the process.

36. (3 min) An <u>isolated</u> system comprises 1 mole of ideal gas, a heat reservoir at T_1, a machine, and a source of energy for the machine. The gas, at T_1, first expands freely to twice its initial volume; it is then compressed by the machine (at T_1) back to the initial volume; the gas again is allowed to expand freely to twice the initial volume. What is the <u>minimum</u> ΔS for the system at the end of these three steps?

37. (18 min) One mole of He is heated from 200°C to 400°C at a constant pressure of 1 atm. Given that the absolute entropy of He at 200°C is 32.3 cal/deg-mole, and assuming that He is a perfect gas, calculate ΔF, ΔH, and ΔS for this process. ΔF comes out negative; does this mean that the process is spontaneous? Explain.

38. (16 min) A flask of 2.24-liter volume contains 1 mole of an ideal, monatomic gas at 10 atm pressure. The flask is placed inside a piston and cylinder arrangement, as shown in Fig. 7-4. The space around the flask is evacuated, the piston being held

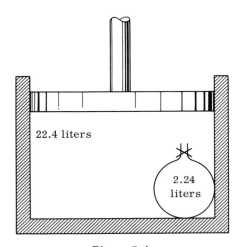

22.4 liters

2.24 liters

Figure 7-4

back by a catch. The piston and cylinder are of non-heat-conduct-
ing material and all changes inside may be taken to be adiabatic.
The total volume of the cylinder space is 22.4 liters.

(a) The flask is broken by means of a mechanical device, so
that the gas it contains expands adiabatically and irreversibly,
filling the space in the cylinder. (b) The catch on the piston is
released, and the gas is now compressed adiabatically and reversibly back to the original volume of 2.24 liters.

Calculate q, w, ΔE, and ΔS for the processes (a) and (b).

39. (12 min) The element Krypton exists in nature as a mixture
of about 10% Kr^{82}, 70% Kr^{84}, and 20% Kr^{86}. Calculate ΔS and ΔF
at 25°C for the process:

$$1 \text{ mole Kr} \begin{bmatrix} \text{natural mixture,} \\ \text{1 atm, 25°C} \end{bmatrix}$$

$$= 0.1 \text{ mole } Kr^{82}(1 \text{ atm, 25°C}) + \text{mixture of} \begin{pmatrix} 0.7 \text{ moles } Kr^{84} \\ 0.2 \text{ moles } Kr^{86} \\ \text{at 1 atm, 25°C} \end{pmatrix}$$

Answers

1. Here, we want w in terms of q_1: $w = q_1 - (T_2/T_1)q_1 =$
$-80,000 \times 25/273 = -7,350$ cal. The actual work will be twice
this: $-14,700$ cal. The heat discharged at 25°C will be 80,000
plus 14,700 = 94,700.

2. Since the system is adiabatic at constant pressure, $\Delta H = 0$.
ΔS, however, is the sum of the entropy changes in the copper and
the water. First, the final temperature is given by $1000 \times$
$0.1(100-t) = 2000 \times 1 \times t$, or $t = 4.77$°C. For the copper:

$$\Delta S = C_p \ln T_2/T_1 = 1000 \times 0.1 \times 2.3 \log 277.9/373$$

$$= -28.7 \text{ cal/deg.}$$

for the water:

$$\Delta S = 2000 \ln(277.9/273.1) = 2000 \ln(1 + 0.018)$$

$$\cong 2000 \times 0.018 = 36 \text{ cal/deg.}$$

The net ΔS is then $-28.7 + 36 = 7$ cal/deg.

3. Since the initial and final states are not at the same temperature, ΔF must be assembled as follows: For the copper, ΔF =
$\Delta H_{Cu} - (T_2 S_2 - T_1 S_1)_{Cu}$; and for the water, $\Delta F = \Delta H_{H_2O} -$
$(T_2 S_2 - T_1 S_1)_{H_2O}$. ΔF net is the sum (the ΔH's will cancel).
The additional information needed is then the absolute entropy of
Cu and of H_2O at some particular temperature, from which the
values at the desired temperatures can be calculated using the
given heat capacities, i.e., $S_2 = S_1 + \int_{T_1}^{T_2} C_p d \ln T$.

4. We have a derivative by V with T constant equal to one by T
with V constant...clearly a Euler or cross-differentiation equation, so one looks for a total differential equal to S dT + P dV. A
little reflection produces:

$$-dA = S\, dT + P\, dV \text{ (from } dE = T\, dS - P\, dV \text{ and A}$$

$$= E - TS) \quad \text{Q.E.D.}$$

5. (a) The final ether pressure must be: $(0.1/0.4) \times 1$ atm =
0.25 atm.
     (b) The nitrogen suffers no change in pressure or tempera-
ture. We assume ideal gas behavior, so ΔH, ΔS, and ΔF are
zero.
     (c) For the ether, $\Delta H = 0.1 \times 6$ or 0.6 kcal. (This is essen-
tially a constant-pressure process.) To get ΔS and ΔF, write
the evaporation in two steps:

   0.1 ether(ℓ) = 0.1 ether(g, 1 atm) $\Delta S_1 = 600/308 =$
        1.95 cal/deg; $\Delta F_1 = 0$

   0.1 ether(g, 1 atm) = 0.1 ether(g, 0.25 atm) $\Delta S_2 =$
        0.1 R ln P_1/P_2

   $\Delta S_2 = 0.1 \times 1.98 \times 2.3 \log 4 = 0.28$ cal/deg

   $\Delta F_2 = 0.1$ RT ln $P_2/P_1 = -89$ cal

Then ΔS = 2.23 cal/deg, $\Delta F = -89$ cal.
     (Overtime) ΔS for the thermostat system is q/T or
$-600/308 = -1.95$ cal/deg, so the over-all ΔS is 0.28 cal/deg.

6. We want the equation w = $q_2 - q_2 T_1/T_2$. If $w/q_2 = 0.1$, then
$(1 - T_1/T_2) = 0.1$, or $T_1/T_2 = 0.9$ so T_1 is 90% of T_2.

7. First, complete the identification of initial and final
states:

Initial: V = 22.4 liters   Final: V = 12.4 liters
          T = 273°K   T = 303°K
So   P = 1 atm   P = 2 atm
          S = 20 cal/deg-mole

Since the gas is ideal, $\Delta E = C_V \Delta T = (3R/2) \times 30 = \underline{90 \text{ cal}}$; $\Delta H = C_p \Delta T = (5R/2) \times 30 = \underline{150 \text{ cal}}$.

For ΔS, the general equation could be used, but since ΔF also is wanted, it is better to write out explicitly the two steps:

(1) 22.4 liters, 273°K, 1 atm = 24.8 liters, 303°K, 1 atm

$$\Delta S_1 = C_p \ln T_2/T_1 = (5R/2) \ln 1.11 =$$

$$0.53 \text{ cal/deg (so } S_{final} = 20.53)$$

$$\Delta F_1 = \Delta H_1 - (T_2 S_2 - T_1 S_1) = 150 -$$

$$(303 \times 20.53 - 273 \times 20) = -600 \text{ cal}$$

(2) 24.8 liters, 303°K, 1 atm = 12.4 liters, 303°K, 2 atm

$$\Delta S_2 = R \ln P_1/P_2 = 1.98 \times 2.3 \log \tfrac{1}{2} = -1.37 \text{ cal/deg}$$

$$\Delta F_2 = RT \ln P_2/P_1 = 417 \text{ cal}.$$

Over-all, then, $\Delta S = 0.53 + (-1.37) = -0.84$ cal/deg, $\Delta F = -600 + 417 = \underline{-183 \text{ cal}}$.

8. (a) Following instructions (i.e., the hint), write $dE = (\partial E/\partial S)_V \, dS + (\partial E/\partial V)_S \, dV$. The desired partial derivative follows, on dividing by dV at constant E:

$$0 = (\partial E/\partial S)_V (\partial S/\partial V)_E + (\partial E/\partial V)_S$$

or

$$(\partial S/\partial V)_E = -(\partial E/\partial V)_S /(\partial E/\partial S)_V$$

The two partial derivatives can be evaluated by comparing with the first law equation $dE = T \, dS - P \, dV$, i.e., $(\partial E/\partial S)_V = T$ and $(\partial E/\partial V)_S = -P$. Substitution then yields the equation to be derived.

(b) For an ideal gas, E is a function of T only, so the partial derivative becomes $(\partial S/\partial V)_T$. Since $dS = R \, d \ln V = R \, dV/V$ for an isothermal process with an ideal gas, $dS/dV = (\partial S/\partial V)_T = R/V = P/T$. Q.E.D.

9. We have a derivative by P with S constant equal to one by S with P constant, so this is clearly a Euler or cross-differentiation relationship. We look for something equal to

T dS + V dP, and a little reflection yields dH = T dS + V dP
(from dE + T dS − P dV and H = E + PV).

10. Step (a) is isothermal and at the higher temperature, so it
must correspond to the step marked X in Fig. 7-2; the other
labels follow in counterclockwise order.
   (b) For the cycle $q_1/T_1 + q_2/T_2 = 0 = \Delta S_1 + \Delta S_2$. From
Fig. 7-2, $\Delta S_1 = -20$ and $\Delta S_2 = 20$, so $q_1 = -20\ T_1$ and $q_2 =$
$20\ T_2$. The work, w $= q_1 + q_2 = 1000$ cal, so $-20 \times 273 +$
$20 T_2 = 1000$ and $T_2 = 323°K; \; q_2 = \underline{-6460\ cal.}$

11. (a) $\Delta E = 0$ for any isochoric adiabatic process ($q_v = 0$).
(b) Similarly, $\Delta H = 0$ for any isobaric adiabatic process ($q_p = 0$).
(c) Since dA $= -S\ dT - P\ dV$, it will be zero for any reversible
constant T and V process. (d) Since dF $= -S\ dT + V\ dP$, ΔF
will be zero for any reversible constant T and P process.
(e) Since dS $= q_{rev}/T$, ΔS will be zero for any reversible adiabatic process.

12. It is first necessary to decide whether the drop ends up entirely as ice (at t $\le$ 0°C) or whether it only partly freezes (and
so is at 0°C). A little reflection suggests that the 80 cal/g liber-
ated if it all froze should be more than enough to raise the temperature to 0°C, and that the drop will therefore not entirely
solidify. To check this, set up the two reversible steps and work
out the heat balance (clearly q_p and also ΔH are zero here):

$\underline{1\ g}$ (1) $H_2O(\ell, -40°C)$ $= H_2O(\ell, 0°C)$ $\Delta H_1 = 40$ cal/g
      (2) $xH_2O(\ell, 0°C)$ $= xH_2O(s, 0°C)$ $\Delta H_2 = -80x$

Since $\Delta H_1 + \Delta H_2 = 0$, x must be 0.5 g.
   The fact that x is a physically possible answer confirms the
guess as to which happens. Then $\Delta S_1 = C_p \ln T_2/T_1 = 1 \times$
2.3 log (273/233) $= 0.159$ cal/deg. $\Delta S_2 = q/T = -40/273 =$
-0.146. ΔS net is then $\underline{0.013\ cal/deg.}$

13. Set up a reversible path as follows:

(1) $CH_3OH(\ell, 64°C, 1\ atm) = CH_3OH(g, 64°C, 1\ atm)$
    $\Delta H_1 = 260 \times 32 = 8310$ cal/mole
    $\Delta F_1 = 0$
(2) $CH_3OH(g, 64°C, 1\ atm) = CH_3OH(g, 64°C, 0.5\ atm)$
    $\Delta H_2 = 0$
    $\Delta F_2 = RT \ln P_2/P_1 = 1.98 \times 337 \times 2.3 \log \frac{1}{2} = -460$ cal.

Over-all then, $\Delta H = \underline{8310\ cal/mole,}$ $\Delta F = \underline{-460\ cal/mole.}$

14. (a) Use the equation $w = q_1 - (T_2/T_1)q_1 = 80{,}000 \times$
$(1 - 303/273) = -8800$ cal (per hr). In joules/sec, $8800 \times$
$4.2/3600 = \underline{10.1 \text{ watts.}}$
   (b) The original work must have been $-17{,}600$ cal for the same
job, hence $1 - T_2/T_1 = -17{,}600/80{,}000 = -0.22$ so $T_2/T_1 = 1.22$
and $T_2 = 333°K$ or $60°C$ (inspection of the formula for w would
have told you that to double w, the temperature difference must
be doubled, and hence be $60°$ instead of $30°$).

15. These types of relationships generally come from one of the
versions of the combined first and second laws. Try $dH = T\ dS + V\ dP$; dividing by dP with S constant yields the desired partial
derivative.

16. Since the gas is ideal, there is no temperature change, and the
equivalent reversible process is an isothermal expansion to 10
times the volume or $1/10$ the pressure. $\Delta F = RT \ln P_2/P_1 = 1.98 \times$
$2.3 \times 300 \log 1/10 = \underline{-1370 \text{ cal.}}$

17. It is necessary to recognize that the partial derivative must
be at constant V: $\partial(A/T)/\partial T = (1/T)(\partial A/\partial T)_V - A/T^2$ but $dA = -S\ dT - P\ dV$ so $(\partial A/\partial T)_V = -S$ and $\partial(A/T)/\partial T = -S/T - A/T^2 = -(1/T^2)(TS + A) = -E/T^2$.

18. (a) First, $0.1w = |q_1| = 12{,}000$ cal. Also, $w = q_1 - (T_2/T_1)q_1 = (600/300)|q_1| = 2|q_1|$. (It is easier to use the magnitude of q_1 and
argue intuitively that it is then to be added to $0.1w$.) Then $0.2|q_1| + |q_1| = 12{,}000$ and $|q_1| = 10{,}000$ or $q_1 = \underline{-10{,}000 \text{ cal.}}$ Next, $q_2 = -(T_2/T_1)q_1 = -(900/300)q_1 = \underline{30{,}000 \text{ cal.}}$ Finally, $w = q_1 + q_2 = \underline{20{,}000 \text{ cal.}}$
   (b) Since the engine is reversible, $\Delta S = 0$, per cycle, for it.
Its surroundings also receive the frictional heat, which is 2000 cal
from part (a), at $300°K$, which produces an entropy of $2000/300 = 6.67$ cal/deg per cycle.

19. Try various versions of the combined first and second laws.
In fact, the one for dA suggests itself: $dA = -S\ dT - P\ dV$ (from
$dE = T\ dS - P\ dV$ and $A = E - TS$). Division by T with V constant gives the required partial differential.

20. (Since the gas is ideal and the process is isothermal, $\Delta E = 0$,
so $q = w = 100$ cal.) Actually, all that is needed is the knowledge
that the final state is $273°K$ and 44.8 liters (so $P = 0.5$ atm). Hence

$\Delta S = R \ln V_2/V_1 = 1.98 \times 2.3 \log 2 = 1.37$ cal/deg, and $\Delta F = RT \times \ln P_2/P_1 = 1.98 \times 273 \times 2.3 \log 0.5 = -374$ cal.

21. (a) The volume of 0.2 mole at 0.2 atm is the same as that of 0.8 mole at 0.8 atm, so the two flasks must have been equal in volume. We end up with 1 mole of gas in twice the volume of one flask, so the final pressure must be 0.5 atm.

(b) The final partial pressures must be 0.4 for N_2 and 0.1 for O_2. Then for the O_2: $\Delta S = 0.2R \ln V_2/V_1$ and for the N_2: $\Delta S = 0.8R \ln V_2/V_1$ or ΔS total is $R \ln V_2/V_1 = 1.98 \times 2.3 \log 2 = \underline{1.37}$ cal/deg. Similarly, ΔF total is $RT \ln P_2/P_1 = 1.98 \times 298 \times \overline{2.3 \log \frac{1}{2}}$ ($P_2/P_1 = \frac{1}{2}$ for each gas) or $\Delta F = -409$ cal. From the nature of the operation no work is performed, so $\underline{w = 0}$. The gases are ideal so their energies do not change with volume, hence $\underline{\Delta E = 0}$. Finally, it follows that $\underline{q = 0}$.

(c) Since ΔE is zero (the gases being ideal), $q = w$. Also, $q_{rev} = T \Delta S$ or $q = w = 298(-1.37) = \underline{-409}$ cal.

22. The process is evidently:

$$\tfrac{1}{2} \text{ g } H_2O \; [\ell, \; 25°C \text{ (and 24 mm Hg)}] = \tfrac{1}{2} \text{ g } H_2O$$

$$(g, \; 25°C, \; 24 \text{ mm Hg})$$

Then $q = 590/2 = 295$ cal, $w = 0$ (no external work is done). We assume q is q_v, so $\Delta E = 295$ cal. The corresponding reversible process would simply involve placing the vial in a piston and cylinder at 25°C, and slowly expanding until half the liquid vaporized, so that for this process $q = q_p = q_v + P \Delta V = 295 + (1/36)$ moles $\times$ $RT = 312$ cal (neglecting the volume of liquid). ΔH is then 312 cal. 312 is the q_{rev} so $\Delta S = 312/298 = 1.05$ cal/deg. ΔF is zero since we have a reversible constant T and P process. Answers based on $\Delta H = 295$ cal were equally accepted, in which case q would be 278 cal.

23. Here $w = q_1 - (T_2/T_1) q_1 = -80,000 \times 25/273 = -7,350$ cal (per hr). ($q_1 = 80,000$ and $q_2 = -87,350$ cal.) The home-owner is evidently in for a surprise, as the net effect is that the work of running the refrigerator appears as heat! The room heats up by 7,350 cal/hr or $7,350/10^5 = 0.0735$ deg/hr.

24. No external work is done, so $w = 0$ and $q = q_v = \Delta E = \underline{11,000}$ cal. $\Delta H = \Delta E + \Delta(PV) = 11,000 + P_g V_g = 11,000 + RT = \underline{11,740}$ cal. To get the other quantities, set up the reversible steps:

(1) $H_2O(\ell, 100°C) = H_2O(g, 100°C, 1 \text{ atm})$
   $\Delta S_1 = q/T = 11,740/373 = 31.5 \text{ cal/deg.}$
   $\Delta F_1 = 0$
(2) $H_2O(g, 100°C, 1 \text{ atm}) = H_2O(g, 100°C, 0.3 \text{ atm})$
   $\Delta S_2 = R \ln V_2/V_1 = 1.98 \times 2.31 \log(1/0.3) = 2.37 \text{ cal/deg}$
   $\Delta F_2 = RT \ln P_2/P_1 = -886 \text{ cal}$

Then ΔS total is $\underline{33.9 \text{ cal/deg}}$ and ΔF total is $\underline{-886 \text{ cal.}}$

25. Try various versions of the combined first and second laws. In fact, the one for dA suggests itself: $dA = -S \, dT - P \, dV$ (from $dE = T \, dS - P \, dV$ and $A = E - TS$). Division by dV with T constant yields the desired partial differential.

26. We have a differential by T with P constant equal to one by P with T constant, which suggests a Euler or cross-differential relationship. We therefore look for a relationship involving $V \, dp - S \, dT$ and a little reflection yields $dF = -S \, dT + V \, dP$ (from $dE = T \, dS - P \, dV$, and $F = H - TS$, $H = E + PV$).

27. (a) From the ideal gas law, $P_1 = RT_1/V_1 = 4.89$ atm. After the isothermal compression to half the volume, pressure must be doubled, so $P_2 = 9.78$ atm. To halve this pressure by cooling, $T_2 = T_1/2 = 149°K$.

   Step 1: Since it is isothermal, $\Delta E = \Delta H = 0$. $q = w = RT \times \ln V_2/V_1 = 1.98 \times 298 \times 2.3 \log \frac{1}{2} = \underline{-408 \text{ cal.}}$ $\Delta S = R \ln V_2/V_1 = -1.36 \text{ cal/deg}$ and $\Delta F = RT \ln P_2/P_1 = \underline{408 \text{ cal.}}$

   Step 2: Since it is isochoric, $w = 0$. $q = \Delta E = C_V \Delta T = (3R/2) \times (-149) = \underline{-442 \text{ cal.}}$ $\Delta H = C_p \Delta T = (5R/2)(-149) = \underline{-740 \text{ cal.}}$ $\Delta S = C_V \ln T_2/T_1 = (3R/2)2.31 \log \frac{1}{2} = -2.06 \text{ cal/deg}$. Since $\Delta F = \Delta H - (T_2 S_2 - T_1 S_1)$, it cannot be obtained without a knowledge of the absolute entropies and these are not given.

   (b) ΔE is independent of path and must be the same. Since the area under step 3 in the P—V plot of Fig. 7-5 is less than under steps 1 plus 2, w must be smaller in magnitude for step 3. Since $\Delta E = q - w$, q must likewise be smaller

28. (a) V_1 is 2.24 liters hence V_2 is 22.4 liters. Since the final pressure equals the external pressure of 1 atm, the final temperature must be 0°C. The over-all process is then isothermal, hence $\Delta E = \Delta H = 0$.

   (b) The work done is $P \Delta V = 1 \text{ atm} \times (22.4 - 2.24) = 20.2$ lit-atm or $\underline{493 \text{ cal.}}$ Since ΔE is zero, $q = w = \underline{493 \text{ cal.}}$ $\Delta S = R \ln V_2/V_1 = 1.98 \times 2.3 \log 10 = \underline{4.55 \text{ cal/deg}}$ and $\Delta F = RT \ln P_2/P_1$ ($P = P_{int}$) = $-1.98 \times 273 \times 2.3 \log 0.1 = \underline{-1240 \text{ cal.}}$

29. The process is at constant P, so $q = q_p = \Delta H = \underline{-11,000 \text{ cal.}}$ Now set up equivalent reversible steps:

(1) $H_2O(g, 100°C, 2 \text{ atm}) = H_2O(g, 100°C, 1 \text{ atm})$
   $\Delta H_1 = 0$
   $\Delta S_1 = R \ln V_2/V_1 = 1.37 \text{ cal/deg}$
   $\Delta F_1 = RT \ln P_2/P_1 = -509 \text{ cal}$
(2) $H_2O(g, 100°C, 1 \text{ atm}) = H_2O(\ell, 100°C, 1 \text{ atm})$
(3) $H_2O(\ell, 100°C, 1 \text{ atm}) = H_2O(\ell, 100°C, 2 \text{ atm})$

Since the liquid is incompressible and V_L is small, ΔH_3, ΔS_3, and ΔF_3 are small and may be neglected.

For process (2) then, ΔH_2 must be $-11,000 = q_2$, hence $\Delta S_2 = -11,000/373 = -29.5 \text{ cal/deg}$. ΔF_2 is zero, as we have a constant T and P reversible process. Over-all, then: $\Delta H = \underline{-11,000 \text{ cal}}$, $\Delta S = \underline{-28.1 \text{ cal/deg}}$, $\Delta F = \underline{-509 \text{ cal}}$.

30. Use the equation $w = -(T_1/T_2) q_2 + q_2$ where $w = -200 \text{ cal}$, $q_2 = -2000$, so $1 - T_1/T_2 = 0.1$, $T_1/T_2 = 0.9$, and $T_2 = 303°K$ or $\underline{t = 30°C}$. Since $w = q_1 + q_2$, then $q_1 = -200 + 2000 = \underline{1800 \text{ cal.}}$

31. The desired plot is shown in Fig. 7-5. The arrows marked A and C represent isothermal steps, and those marked B and D indicate adiabatic steps.

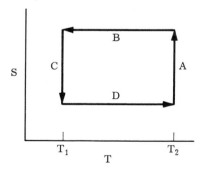

Figure 7-5

32. (a) This is an irreversible process for which $q = 0$; therefore $\Delta S > 0$. (b) Since $q = 0$, $\Delta E = C_V \Delta T = -w$ or $(3R/2) \times \Delta T = -288$ and $\Delta T = -97°$, so $T_2 = 203°K$, and therefore $V_2 = 8.32$ liters. Since $\Delta S = C_p \ln T_2/T_1 - R \ln P_2/P_1$, $\Delta S = (5R/2)2.3 \times \log(203/300) - 1.98 \times 2.3 \log 2/10 = -1.92 + 3.19 = \underline{1.27 \text{ cal/deg.}}$

33. q_1 is 8000 kcal and q_2 is $-16,000$ kcal; the plant is therefore expending 8000 cal of work. The ideal q_2 would be $-(T_2/T_1)q_1$ or $-8,720$ kcal, and a corresponding work of 720 kcal. The efficiency is thus 9%.

34. (a) We want a reversible process at constant T and P, with q positive, e.g., $H_2O(\ell, 100°C, 1$ atm$) = H_2O(g, 100°C, 1$ atm$)$.

(b) The isothermal expansion of an ideal gas. $\Delta S = R \ln V_2/V_1$, and so is positive, and $\Delta F = RT \ln P_2/P_1$, and so is negative.

(c) If in process (a), the water (g, 100°C, 1 atm) is then compressed slightly (assuming no condensation, i.e., supersaturation), then the over-all ΔF will be positive, and the large positive ΔS for the first step will overbalance the small negative ΔS for the second.

35. (a) The process is: $H_2O(s, 0°C, 1$ atm$) + 10H_2O(\ell, 25°C, 1$ atm$) = 11H_2O(\ell, t°C, 1$ atm$)$. (b) Since the system is insulated, $q_p = 0 = \Delta H$. (c) To get t, set up the heat balance:

(1) $H_2O(s, 0°C) = H_2O(liq, 0°C)$ $q_1 = 1420$ cal.
     $\Delta S_1 = 1420/273 = 5.2$ cal/deg
(2) $H_2O(\ell, 0°C) = H_2O(\ell, t°C)$ $q_2 = 18t$
(3) $10H_2O(\ell, 25°C) = 10H_2O(\ell, t°C)$ $q_3 = -180(25 - t)$

(d) Since $q_1 + q_2 + q_3 = 0$, we get $1420 + 18t = 180(25 - t)$ or $t = 15.5°C$. Then $\Delta S_2 = C_p \ln T_2/T_1 = 18 \times 2.3 \log(289/273) = 1.08$ cal/deg. And $\Delta S_3 = 180 \times 2.3 \log(289/298) = -180 \ln(1 + 0.031) = -5.42$ cal/deg. ΔS over-all is then $5.2 + 1.08 - 5.42 = 0.86$.

36. Consider first the gas only: Step 1 plus step 2 returns it to the initial state, so $\Delta S_1 = 0$. Step 3 (as does step 1) involves $\Delta S = R \ln 2 = 1.36$ cal/deg. For the rest of the system: In step 2, $w = RT \ln P_2/P_1 = 1.98 \times T_1 \times 2.3 \log 2 = 1.36 T_1 = q$, since the gas suffers no energy change. Therefore $1.36T_1$ cal are delivered to the heat reservoir, and it gains $1.36(T_1/T_1)$ entropy or 1.36 cal/deg. The minimum total ΔS is then 2×1.36 cal/deg.

37. $\Delta S = C_p \ln T_2/T_1 = (5R/2) \times 2.3 \log(673/473) = 1.75$ cal/deg. Then $\Delta S_2 = 32.3 + 0.8 = 34.1$ cal/deg; $\Delta H = C_p \Delta T = (5R/2)200 = 990$ cal. Then $\Delta F = \Delta H - (T_2S_2 - T_1S_1) = 990 - (673 \times 34.1 - 473 \times 32.3) = -6560$ cal. The process need not be spontaneous; if ΔF is negative for a process at constant T and P, then it is spontaneous.

38. (a) The work is evidently zero: $w_a = 0$. Since $q_a = 0$, it then follows that $\Delta E_a = 0$. $\Delta S_a = R \ln (22.4/2.24) = 1.98 \times 2.3 \times 1 = 4.57$ cal/deg. In step (b) we are dealing with a reversible adiabatic compression, so $q_b = 0$ and $\underline{\Delta S_b = 0}$. Then $C_V \ln T_2/T_1 = -R \times$ $\ln V_2/V_1$, so $\log T_2/T_1 = -\frac{2}{3} \log(2.24/22.4) = 0.67$ and $T_2/T_1 = 4.68$. From the initial conditions, $T_1 = 273°K$, and does not change during step (a), so $T_2 = 1280°K$. ΔE is then $C_V \Delta T = (3R/2)(1280 - 273) = \underline{3000 \text{ cal.}}$ The work is then $\underline{w = -3000 \text{ cal.}}$

39. Since the Kr^{84} and Kr^{86} are not separated, their mixture may be treated as a single species, and the process can be rewritten as:

$$1 \text{ mole } (10\% \text{ A}, 90\% \text{ B}) = 0.1A + 0.9B$$

ΔS is then $-\Delta S = -R(0.1 \ln 0.1 + 0.9 \ln 0.9) = 0.642$ or $\Delta S = -0.642$ cal/deg. Since ΔH is zero, $\Delta F = -T \Delta S = \underline{192 \text{ cal.}}$

8   *Liquids and their*
simple phase equilibria

Comments

We now consider the application of the combined first and second laws of thermodynamics to simple phase equilibria. The general cross-differentiation equation $(\partial P/\partial T)_V = (\partial S/\partial V)_T$ becomes the Clapeyron equation $dP/dT = \Delta H/T \, \Delta V$ when applied to the equilibrium between two phases, since ΔS can now be written as $\Delta H/T$, and it is not necessary to retain the partial differential form. If one of the two phases is an ideal gas, then further approximations lead to the very useful Clausius-Clapeyron equation. These two relationships, plus some semiempirical rules such as Trouton's rule, are presented to you in this chapter in quite a variety of disguises.

The present chapter is an appropriate one in which to introduce surface tension, its manifestations, and its determination. The Laplace equation is fundamental to this topic of capillarity, and its use will be required over and over again in the problems

111

that follow. Watch for variations such as the case of maximum
bubble pressure, and the rise of a liquid between parallel plates.

Be careful in your choice of units. ΔH will sometimes be
needed in cc-atm/mole units and pressure differences in capillarity situations will generally be in dynes/cm^2, not atm.

Equations and concepts

Clapeyron Equation: $dP/dt = \Delta H/T\,\Delta V$

Clausius-Clapeyron Equation:

$$d \ln P/dT = \Delta H/RT^2$$

$$\ln P_2/P_1 = \frac{\Delta H}{R}(1/T_1 - 1/T_2)$$

$$\ln P = \text{constant} - \Delta H/RT, \quad \text{or} \quad P = P^0\, e^{-\frac{\Delta H}{R}(1/T - 1/T^0)}$$

Effect of Mechanical Pressure on Vapor Pressure:

$$RT \ln P'/P = \int V\, dP_{mech}$$

Semiempirical Rules and Laws:

Trouton's rule: $\Delta H_v/T_b = 21$ cal/deg-mole where T_b denotes the normal boiling point and ΔH_v, the heat of vaporization
per mole. Another observation is that the normal boiling point of
a liquid is often about two-thirds of its critical temperature.

Law of Rectilinear Diameters: The sum of the densities of a liquid
and its equilibrium vapor is a constant, independent of temperature. A more realistic version is that the sum varies linearly
with temperature.

Capillarity:

Laplace equation: $\Delta P = \gamma(1/R_1 + 1/R_2)$ where ΔP is the
pressure difference across a curved surface, γ is the surface
tension, and R_1 and R_2 are the two radii of curvature. The signs
are such that the surface is convex toward the low-pressure side;
thus the pressure inside a spherical drop or soap bubble is

greater inside than outside. For surfaces that are sections of a sphere, the Laplace equation becomes

$$\Delta P = 2\gamma/r$$

where r is the radius of the sphere.

Capillary rise: $\Delta P = \rho gh = 2\gamma/r$ where r is the radius of the capillary and h, the height of rise. For a nonzero contact angle, the equation becomes:

$$\Delta P = \rho gh = 2\gamma \cos \theta/r$$

Drop-weight method: $W_{ideal} = 2\pi r\gamma$. This is known as Tate's law, and actual drop weights will differ from the ideal weight by a substantial correction factor f, so that

$$W_{actual} = 2\pi r\gamma f$$

This correction factor can be expressed as a graphical function of $(r/V)^{1/3}$ where V is the drop volume. Note that in the case of a liquid that wets the tube, r is the outside radius.

Maximum bubble-pressure method: $P = P_{hyd} + 2\gamma/r$. P_{hyd} is the hydrostatic pressure as determined by the depth of immersion of the tube out of which bubbles are formed.

Problems

1. (21 min) The normal boiling point of pyridine is 114°C. At this temperature, its vapor density is 2.5 g/liter, and the density of the liquid is 0.8000 g/cc. At a certain higher temperature T', the liquid has expanded to where its density is 0.7900 g/cc. Calculate, or estimate with explanation (a) the heat of vaporization of pyridine, (b) the boiling point of pyridine on a mountain top where atmospheric pressure is 740 mm Hg instead of 760 mm Hg, and (c) the vapor density of pyridine at the temperature T'.

2. (7.5 min) Water, which wets glass, rises in a given capillary to a height h. If, as shown in Fig. 8-1, the capillary is broken off, so that its length above the surface is only h/2, will the water then flow over the edge? Explain your answer in terms of specific detailed analysis of just what happens. Use sketches.

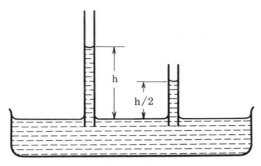

Figure 8-1

3. (18 min) A certain liquid of molecular weight 60 has a critical temperature of 400°C. Its melting point is 15.000°C as normally measured and is 14.980°C at its triple point (where the system is subjected only to its own low vapor pressure). The solid and liquid densities are 0.85 and 0.80 g/cc, respectively. Calculate, using empirical or semiempirical relationships where necessary, ΔH_V, ΔH_S, ΔH_f, and the vapor pressure at the triple point.

4. (14 min) The semilog plots for the vapor pressures of liquids A and B are shown in Fig. 8-2. (a) Calculate ΔH_V for liquid A. (b) Liquids A and B cannot both have the same Trouton constant. Explain how this can be concluded from the data. Give a brief argument as to which liquid should be considered the more associated.

5. (4.5 min) The law of rectilinear diameters (in its simplest form as illustrated in Fig. 8-3) is not compatible with the van der Waals statement that $V_c = 3b$. Show why this statement is true.

6. (12 min) A capillary tube of radius 0.1 mm is inserted through the two-layer system shown in Fig. 8-4. The capillary rise of the water–benzene meniscus is 4.0 cm. The glass–water–benzene contact angle is 40° (cos θ = 0.76), and the densities of water and of benzene are 1.00 and 0.80, respectively. Calculate the interfacial tension between water and benzene.

7. (18 min) The vapor pressure of liquid A is 50 mm Hg at 46°C; this vapor pressure is 0.50 mm greater than that of solid A at the same temperature. At 45°C, the vapor pressure of the liquid

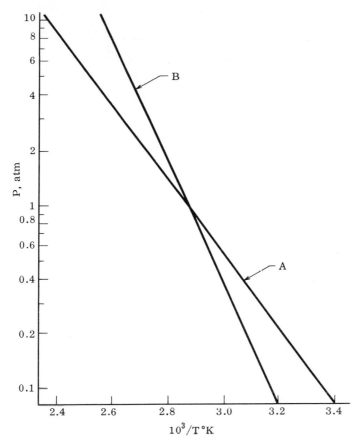

Figure 8-2

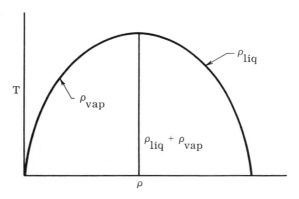

Figure 8-3

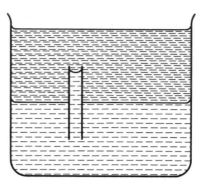

Figure 8-4

is 1.00 mm Hg greater than that of the solid. ΔH_V is 9.0 kcal.
(a) Estimate the melting point of A. (b) Calculate the heat of
fusion of A, and its heat of sublimation.

8. (12 min) A length of uniform-bore capillary tubing is bent in
an S shape, and one end is immersed in a liquid of surface tension
25 dynes/cm and density 0.80 g/cc. The radius of the capillary
is 0.050 cm; the liquid wets it.

   After immersing one end of the capillary, some of the same
liquid is added to the other end until the pressure of the trapped
air is sufficient to force the meniscus back down to the level of
the liquid in the container. This final situation is illustrated in
Fig. 8-5. If the external air pressure is 1 atm (10^6 dynes/cm^2),
calculate or explain what the values of P_1, P_2, P_3, P_4, and P_5
must be.

9. (18 min) The vapor pressure of CCl_4 increases by 4% per degree around 25°C. Calculate ΔH_V and the normal boiling point of
CCl_4. List all the assumptions and approximations involved in the
derivation of the equation used to obtain ΔH_V.

10. (6 min) ΔH is 0.07 kcal for the transition S(rhombic) =
S(monoclinic). Monoclinic sulfur is in equilibrium with rhombic
at 1 atm pressure and 115°C, and at 100 atm pressure the two are
in equilibrium at 120°C. Show which of the two forms is the more
dense.

11. (6 min) (a) Liquid A has half the surface tension and twice

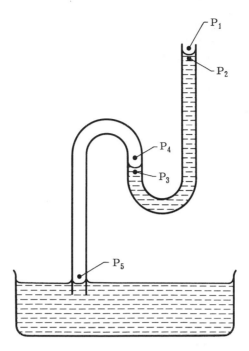

Figure 8-5

the density of liquid B, at 25°C. If the capillary rise is 1.0 cm for liquid A, then, in the same capillary, the rise will be (0.25, 0.5, 1.0, 2, 4, 10 cm, none of these). (b) Given the same data as in (a), the maximum bubble pressure for liquid A will be (0.25, 0.5, 1.0, 2, 4, 10, none of these) times that for liquid B, using the same tube for both liquids.

12. (12 min) The vapor pressure of a certain liquid, which obeys Trouton's rule, increases by 15 mm Hg per degree at temperatures around its normal boiling point. Calculate the heat of vaporization and the normal boiling point of this liquid.

13. (9 min) A thin-walled tube 0.10 cm in diameter is lowered into a dilute aqueous detergent solution until its open end is 10 cm below the surface. The maximum air pressure just insufficient for bubbles to grow and break away is found to be 11.6 cm, as read on a <u>water</u> manometer. Calculate the surface tension of this solution.

14. (9 min) Explain whether the melting point of a solid substance A will be raised or lowered by pressure, given that solid A does <u>not</u> float on liquid A. Illustrate your explanation by suitable equations.

15. (15 min) In the drop–weight method for surface tension determination, the actual weight W of a drop is equal to the ideal weight W_i multiplied by a correction factor Ψ where Ψ is a function of $r/V^{1/3}$. Here, r is the radius of the tip, and V, the volume of the actual drop. For $r/V^{1/3}$ = 0.5, it has been found that Ψ = 0.65.

(a) Give the equation relating W_i to the surface tension of the liquid. (b) Calculate what size of tip (i.e., r value) should be used for a liquid of γ = 26, and density equal to 0.8 g/cc, in order that $r/V^{1/3}$ will in fact be 0.5. Using this tip size and the above liquid, what will be the actual weight of the drop?

16. (15 min) The heat of vaporization of water is 9.7 kcal/mole, whereas that for liquid A is 7.0 kcal/mole. The vapor pressure of water and of A are the same at 150°C. (a) Plot P vs 1/T on a semilog plot, for water and for A. (The plots may be approximate, but it must be clear how they were obtained.) (b) Determine from the plot the normal boiling point of liquid A. (c) Which of the two liquids more nearly obeys Trouton's rule? (On a problem such as this, the appropriate graph paper would be available.)

17. (30 min) The following data are given for <u>p</u>-chloro aniline:

mol. wt.: 127   v.p. at the m.p.: 5.0 mm Hg
normal m.p.: 70°C   v.p. at 100°C: 20.0 mm Hg
ΔH_f = 4700 cal/mole   densities at the m.p.: solid   1.45 g/cc
                                               liquid 1.15 g/cc

(a) Calculate the heat of vaporization. (b) State the assumptions and approximations involved in the equations(s) used in (a). (c) Estimate the normal boiling point and the heat of sublimation. State whether the m.p. under 100 atm pressure would be greater or less than 70°C (explain). (d) Air at 1 atm and 100°C is bubbled through the liquid (also at 100° C) at the rate of 3.8 moles/hr. Assuming the effluent air to be saturated with vapor, how long will it take for 12.7 g of the liquid to be evaporated? (Effluent gas also at 1 atm.)

18. (10 min) Two vertical, parallel plates, 0.1 cm apart are

partly lowered into a liquid density 1.10, which wets the plates
(see Fig. 8-6). Derive the formula for the capillary rise of the
liquid. If the rise is 1.30 cm, what is the surface tension? (Assume that the plates are wide enough that end effects can be neglected.)

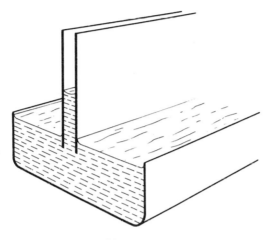

Figure 8-6

19. (18 min) The melting point of glacial acetic acid is 16°C at 1
atm pressure. Calculate the melting point under its own vapor
pressure (essentially zero pressure). The heat of fusion is 2700
cal/mole, densities for liquid and solid acetic acid are 1.05 and
1.10 g/cc, respectively, and the molecular weight is 60. Set up
the appropriate equation and insert the proper data so as to obtain an equation whose only unknown is the desired quantity.

The normal boiling point of acetic acid is 118°C. Show how to
estimate the heat of sublimation of solid acetic acid from this
and the other data given (obtain a numerical answer).

20. (12 min) A metal cylinder has a small pin hole in the bottom.
The hole is smooth and circular, and 0.04 mm in diameter. Calculate the depth to which the container can be filled with water
before the water will start dripping out through the hole. $\gamma = 72$,
density = 1.0; assume that water fails to wet the metal so that
the sequence of drop shapes is that shown in Fig. 8-7. Sketch the
shape of the meniscus or nascent drop when the container is filled
to the maximum depth possible before dripping occurs.

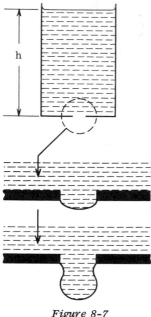

Figure 8-7

21. (12 min) The surface tension of ben-zophenone is 45 ergs/cm^2 at 50°C, and its normal boiling point is 300°C. Cal-culate or estimate (a) the heat of vapor-ization, (b) the vapor pressure at 100°C (set up the equation and insert numbers), and (c) the maximum bubble pressure of an air bubble blown in the liquid at 50°C, using a 0.5-cm-diameter tube.

22. (15 min) Water and chloroform have the normal boiling points of 100°C and 60°C, and the respective heats of vapor-ization are 12.0 and 7.0 kcal/mole. Cal-culate the temperature at which the two liquids will have the same vapor pres-sure.

23. (15 min) It is desired to calculate the vapor pressure of an equilibrium mixture of solid and liquid benzene which is under 100 atm of inert gas pres-sure. The information available includes ΔH_f and ΔH_v, the molar heats of fusion and vaporization at the melting point (under normal pressure), which is T_1; the densities of the solid and liquid ρ_1 and ρ_2; the molecular weight M; the normal boiling point of the liquid T_2; and general constants such as R. Set up equations for calculating this vapor pressure. Make clear what equations you would use, the sequence of their use, and the actual data needed.

24. (15 min) One commonly used method of measuring surface tension consists of placing a cylindrical tube so that its opening is just below the surface of the liquid in question, and slowly bubbling an inert gas through the liquid (see Fig. 8-8). A manom-eter connected to the tube permits the measurement of the dif-ference in pressure between the gas in the tube and atmospheric pressure. Show that the gas pressure is a maximum when the radius R of the bubble is equal to the radius r of the tube. (A brief logical argument is wanted, based on the laws governing sur-face tension effects.) Assuming the proposition to be correct, cal-culate the surface tension of the liquid if the maximum pressure difference is 0.30 mm Hg, given that the temperature is 25°C, the

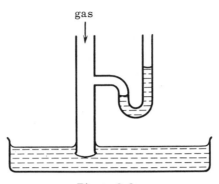

Figure 8-8

density of the liquid is 1.5 g/cc, that of mercury is 13.6 g/cc, and the radius of the tube is 0.10 cm.

25. (12 min) The vapor pressure of acetonitrile is changing at the rate of 0.030 atm/deg in the vicinity of its normal boiling point, which is 80°C. Calculate the heat of vaporization.

26. (12 min) The straight-line plots of ln P vs 1/T are sketched in Fig. 8-9 for various liquids obeying the simple Clausius-Clapeyron equation. These lines all meet at 1/T equal to zero; show that this behavior is required by Trouton's rule.

27. (4.5 min) The vapor pressure of liquid A is 20 mm Hg and that of liquid B is 40 mm Hg, both measured at 40°C. The normal boiling point of A is 120°C, whereas that of B is 140°C. The heat

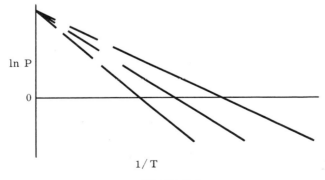

Figure 8-9

of vaporization of A is 11.3 kcal/mole. The heat of vaporization of B is (5.65 kcal/mole, 11.3 kcal/mole, 22.6 kcal/mole, less than 11.3 kcal/mole, greater than 11.3 kcal/mole, about the same, indeterminate because of insufficient data).

28. (12 min) The straight-line plot of ln P vs 1/T for the vapor pressure of a certain liquid whose normal boiling point is 27°C extrapolates to $P = 10^5$ atm at infinite temperature. Using the Clausius-Clapeyron equation, calculate from these data the heat of vaporization of the liquid.

29. (12 min) A length of glass tubing is suspended vertically so that both ends are open. If a liquid which wets the glass is added slowly, a hanging column of liquid forms, as in Fig. 8-10. Eventually enough liquid will be added so that a drop detaches.

Assuming the liquid to be water (surface tension 72 dynes/cm) and the diameter of the tube to be 0.1 cm, calculate the maximum weight of liquid that the tube can hold before a drop falls. (Make reasonable simplifying assumptions.)

30. (24 min) For a certain substance the change in entropy on melting is 3 cal/deg per cc of solid which melts. The melting point under 1 atm pressure is 6°C, and the densities of the solid and liquid are 0.90 and 0.85 g/cc, respectively. Calculate the melting point under 10^4 atm pressure.

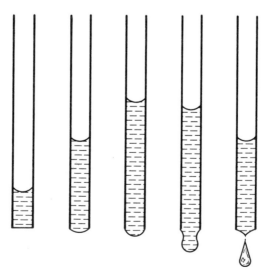

Figure 8-10

Also, the vapor pressure vs. temperature curve for the solid and the liquid, at 1 atm pressure, are sketched in Fig. 8–11. Show qualitatively how these two curves should look for the solid and liquid under 100 atm pressure (the pressurization is done by means of inert gas pressure, so these vapor pressure curves can be obtained experimentally). (The curves should be of the correct shape, relative position, etc.)

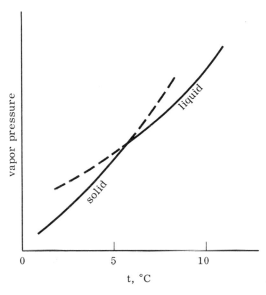

Figure 8-11

Answers

1. (a) Using Trouton's rule, $\Delta H_V = 21 \times 387°K = $ _8.13 kcal._

(b) From the Clausius-Clapeyron equation, $d \ln P / dT = \Delta H / RT^2$ or $dP/dT = \Delta H \times P/RT^2$. As an approximation, take P to be 750 mm Hg, so $dP/dT = 8130 \times 750/1.98 \times 387^2 = 20.5$ mm Hg/deg. The temperature at which P is 740 mm Hg is then reduced by 20/20.5 or by _1.0°_. More exactly:

$$\log 760/740 = \frac{\Delta H}{2.3 \, R}\left(\frac{1}{T'_b} - \frac{1}{T'_b}\right)$$

which gives _0.98°_.

(c) From the law of rectilinear diameters, the sum of the liquid and vapor densities should be invariant. At 114°C it is 800 + 2.5 g/liter. The vapor density at T′ is then 802.5 − 790 or <u>12.5 g/liter.</u>

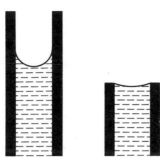

Figure 8-12

2. The water will not flow over the edge! As shown in Fig. 8-12, the meniscus will rise to the end of the capillary, then flatten to a point where its radius of curvature is just half of what it would normally be; the pressure drop across the meniscus is then in hydrostatic balance with the pressure drop along the column of liquid.

3. (a) The heat of vaporization can be estimated as follows: The normal boiling point is about 2/3 of the critical temperature, so is 2 × 673/3 or about 450°K. By Trouton's rule, ΔH_V is then 21 × 450 or <u>9.4 kcal.</u>

(b) The heat of fusion is given by the Clapeyron equation: $dP/dT = \Delta H_f / T_f \Delta V$. The molar volumes of the liquid and solid are 60/0.8 and 60/0.85 or 75 and 70.7 cc/mole, respectively, so ΔV is 4.3 cc/mole. ΔH_f is then $\dfrac{(1 \text{ atm} - 0)}{(15.000 - 14.980)}$ 288 × 4.3 or $\Delta H_f = 6.2 \times 10^4$ (in cc-atm units!) or $6.2 \times 10^4/41.3 = $ <u>1.5 kcal.</u> ΔH_s is the sum of ΔH_V and ΔH_f or <u>10.9 kcal.</u> Finally, the vapor pressure at the triple point is given by the Clausius-Clapeyron equation:

$$\log 760/P = \frac{9{,}400}{2.3 \times 1.98} (1/288 - 1/450)$$

or log 760/P = 2.57; P = <u>2.05 mm Hg.</u>

4. (a) From the Clausius-Clapeyron equation, $d \ln P/d(1/T) = -\Delta H/R$, so the slope of the line for liquid A can be used directly. It is: $[\log 1 - \log 0.1]/[2.9 - 3.4] \times 10^{-3}$ or about −2000. ΔH_V is then 2000 × 2.3 × 1.98 = <u>9.2 kcal.</u>

(b) The simplest way of showing this is by writing the integrated form of the Clausius Clapeyron equation: ln P = const. − $\Delta H/Rt$. By Trouton's rule, when P = 1 atm, $\Delta H/T$ = 21, so the constant of integration must be 21/R. It is thus the same for all liquids, or in other words, all liquids should show the same intercept at $1/T = 0$. This is clearly not the case here, so Trouton's rule cannot be valid in this instance.

(c) Liquid B has the higher heat of vaporization (steeper slope) and hence is probably the more associated.

5. In its simplest form, the law of rectilinear diameters states that the sum of liquid and equilibrium vapor densities is a constant. For a liquid around its boiling point, the vapor density is so small that this sum is essentially just the liquid density. Then, according to the LRD, at the critical temperature, the liquid and vapor densities are equal, and each must then be half the density of the liquid around its boiling point. In other words, the critical volume is predicted to be twice (not three times) that of the liquid and hence only twice that of the volume of 1 mole of molecules (to which b is supposed to correspond).

6. The relevent equation is: $\Delta \rho g h = 2 \gamma \cos \theta / r$, so the interfacial tension γ is:

$$\gamma = \frac{(1.00 - 0.80) \times 980 \times 4 \times 0.01}{2 \times 0.76} = \underline{5.1 \text{ dynes/cm}}$$

7. (a) At the melting point, liquid and solid must have the same vapor pressure. If the difference is 1 mm at 45°, 0.5 mm at 46°, it should be close to zero at $\underline{47°C}$.

(b) The most efficient way to get at the heat of fusion is probably from the Clausius–Clapeyron equation: $dP/dT = \Delta H \times P/RT^2$. For the vapor at 46°C, then $\lfloor dP/dT \rfloor_V = 9000 \times 50/1.98 \times 319^2 = 2.2$ mm/deg. Since the vapor pressure of the solid is increasing 0.5 mm/deg faster than is that of the liquid, $\lfloor dP/dT \rfloor_S = 2.7$ mm/deg. The heat of sublimation of the solid is then

$$\Delta H_S = \frac{2.7 \times 1.98 \times 320^2}{52.7} = \underline{10.35 \text{ kcal}}$$

The heat of fusion is then $\Delta H_S - \Delta H_V = \underline{1.35 \text{ kcal}}$.

8. We need the value of ΔP, the pressure drop across the meniscus; this is given by $\Delta P = 2\gamma/r = 2 \times 25/0.05 = 1000$ dynes/cm². We can now reason as follows: P_1 is just atmospheric pressure, 10^6 dynes/cm². P_2, just under the meniscus, must be 1000 dynes/cm² less or 0.999×10^6. P_5, just above the bottom meniscus, must be 1.001×10^6 and, neglecting the hydrostatic drop in air pressure, will be equal to P_4. P_3 must be 1000 less, or equal to 1.000×10^6 dynes/cm^2.

9. We use the Clausius-Clapeyron equation in the form:

$$dP/dT = P \times \Delta H_V / RT^2$$

If P increases by 4% per degree, then $(dP/P)/dT$ is 0.04, so $\Delta H_V = 0.04 \times 1.98 \times 298^2 = \underline{7.04 \text{ kcal.}}$

The normal boiling point can be estimated from Trouton's rule: $T_b = 7040/21 = \underline{335°K.}$ The assumptions and approximations involved in the derivation of the Clausius-Clapeyron equation are as follows. (1) First and second laws of thermodynamics; (2) equilibrium between liquid and vapor; (3) neglect molar volume of liquid in comparison with that of vapor; (4) assume ideal behavior for the vapor.

10. By the Clapeyron equation, $dP/dt = \Delta H/T \Delta V$. Since dP/dT is positive, in this case, ΔV must have the same sign as ΔH, i.e., is positive for $V_m - V_r$. Therefore rhombic sulfur has the smaller molar volume and is the more dense.

11. For capillary rise, $\rho gh = 2\gamma/r$ or h is proportional to γ/ρ. If liquid B has twice the surface tension and half the density of liquid A, the two ratios will combine to give <u>four</u> times the height of capillary rise for liquid B. (b) The maximum bubble pressure, ΔP, is given by $\Delta P = 2\gamma/r$. It will therefore be twice as much for liquid B as for liquid A.

12. We use the Clausius-Clapeyron equation in the form

$$(dP/P)/dT = \Delta H/RT^2$$

where $(dP/P)dT$ is the fractional increase in vapor pressure per degree and, in this case, is $(15/760)/1 \text{ deg} = 0.0198$. Since Trouton's rule is obeyed, $\Delta H/T_b = 21$, hence $0.0198 = 21/T_b R$ or $T_b = 537°K$. The heat of vaporization is then $\Delta H = 21 \times 537 = \underline{11.3 \text{ kcal.}}$

13. In the bubble-pressure method, the maximum pressure due to meniscus curvature occurs when the nascent bubble has a minimum radius of curvature, which, for small tubes, is that of the tube itself. ΔP is then $2\gamma/r$, where r is 0.05 cm in this case. The height h of water corresponding to this pressure is ρgh, so

$h = 2 \times \gamma/1.0 \times 980 \times 0.05 = 0.0408\gamma$. The total pressure is the above, plus the hydrostatic head at the level of immersion, i.e., $11.6 = 10 + 0.0408\gamma$ or $\gamma = 1.6/0.0408 = \underline{39.3 \text{ dynes/cm}}$.

14. According to the Clapeyron equation, $dP/dT = \Delta H/T\,\Delta V$. If the solid is more dense than the liquid, its molar volume is less, so ΔV must be positive for the process: solid $\rightleftharpoons$ liquid. Since ΔH_f is always positive, the right-hand side of the Clapeyron equation must be positive and hence also dP/dT. The melting point is therefore raised on application of pressure.

15. (a) By Tate's law, $W_i = 2\pi r \gamma$.

(b) If $r/V^{1/3}$ is to be 0.5, then $V = r^3/0.125$ and $W = \rho Vg = 0.8gr^3/0.125$. But $W = 2\pi r \gamma \Psi = 2\pi r \gamma \times 26 \times 0.65$, so we have the equation $2\pi r \gamma \times 26 \times 0.65 = 0.8r^3g/0.125$, whence $r^2 = 0.017$ and $r = \underline{0.148 \text{ cm}}$. $W = 2\pi r \gamma = 2\pi \times 0.148 \times 26 = 24.1$ or, in grams, $\underline{W = 0.0246}$.

16. (a) We know P_w is 1 atm at 373°K; by the Clausius-Clapeyron equation, $\log P_2/P_1 = (\Delta H/2.3R)(1/T_1 - 1/T_2)$, the vapor pressure at 150°C will be: $\log P_2 = \dfrac{9700}{2.3 \times 1.98}(2.69 - 2.36) \times 10^{-3} = 0.70$ or $P_2 = 5$ atm.

(b) Since the plot will be a straight line (see Fig. 8-13), we now draw it between the two points. For liquid A, the point at 150°C is the same, and at 100°C its vapor pressure is given by:

$$-\log \frac{P_1}{5} = \frac{7000}{2.3 \times 198} \times 0.33 \times 10^{-3} = \frac{7}{9.7} \times 0.7 = 0.5$$

or $\quad P_1 = 0.32 \times 5 = 1.6$ atm

The line for liquid A can then be located. Extension of the line, gives a normal boiling point of $10^3/T = 2.86$ or $T = \underline{351°K}$.

(c) $\Delta H/T_b$ is $9700/373 = 26$ for water and $7000/340 = 20$ for liquid A, so $\underline{\text{liquid A}}$ is the closer to obeying the Trouton rule value of 21.

17. (a) The heat of vaporization is given by the Clausius-Clapeyron equation: $\log 20/5 = \dfrac{\Delta H}{2.3 \times 1.98}(1/343 - 1/373)$ or $\Delta H = 0.60 \times 2.3 \times 1.98/0.24 \times 10^{-3} = \underline{11.4 \text{ kcal}}$.

(b) The assumptions and approximations involved in the derivation of the Clausius-Clapeyron equation are: (1) First and second laws of thermodynamics, (2) molar volume of liquid negligible compared to that of the vapor, (3) vapor behaves ideally, (4) ΔH does not vary with temperature, and (5) (optional) liquid and vapor are in equilibrium.

(c) From Trouton's rule, the normal boiling point would be $T_b = 11,400/21 = \underline{543°K.}$ The heat of sublimation is the sum of ΔH_f and ΔH_v or $4.7 + 11.4 = \underline{16.1 \text{ kcal.}}$ From the Clapeyron equation, $dP/dT = \Delta H_f / T \Delta V$. Since the solid is more dense, its molar volume is less than that for the liquid and ΔV is positive for the process; solid $\rightleftharpoons$ liquid. Since ΔH is also positive for this process, dP/dT must be positive, and the melting point under 100 atm pressure will be $\underline{\text{greater}}$ than 70°C.

(d) The mole fraction of vapor in the effluent gas will be 20/760 or 0.0263, or the ratio of moles of air to moles of vapor will be 37.4 Now 12.7 g of liquid corresponds to 0.1 mole; hence 3.74 moles of air are needed, and air must be bubbled through for $\underline{1 \text{ hr.}}$

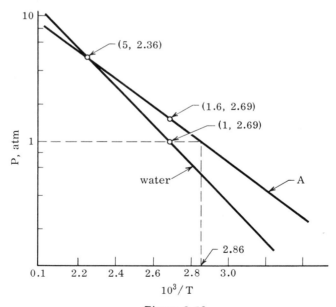

Figure 8-13

18. The only difference between this case and that for capillary rise in a cylindrical capillary is that one of the radii of curvature is infinite, i.e., $\Delta P = \gamma(1/R_1 + 1/R_2)$ where $1/R_2$ is now zero.

Hence $\rho gh = \gamma/r$ (assuming $R_1 = r$, the half-distance between plates). In this present case, $\gamma = r\rho gh = 0.05 \times 1.10 \times 980 \times 1.30 = \underline{70 \text{ dynes/cm}}$.

19. The Clapeyron equation applies here:

$$dP/dT = \Delta H/T\, \Delta V$$

Solving for dT, or ΔT: $\Delta T = \Delta P \times T \times \Delta V/\Delta H$ where ΔP is -1 atm, T is $289°K$, ΔH is $2700 \times 41.5 = 1.13 \times 10^5$ cc-atm and $\Delta V = V_\ell - V_s = 60(1/1.05 - 1/1.10)$. From Trouton's rule, the normal boiling point is related to ΔH_v by $\Delta H_v/T_b = 21$, hence $\Delta H_v = 21 \times 391 = 8200$ cal/mole. $\Delta H_s = \Delta H_f + \Delta H_v = 8200 + 2700 = \underline{10,900 \text{ cal/mole}}$.

20. The analysis is similar to that for the maximum bubble-pressure method. For any height less than the maximum, the hydrostatic head ρgh must be just balanced by an equal ΔP across the meniscus, where ΔP will be given by the Laplace equation, $\Delta P = 2\gamma/R$ (R is the radius of curvature of the drop, assumed to be a section of a sphere). h will be a maximum when R is a minimum, and this will occur when the nascent drop is just hemispherical, with radius equal to that

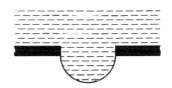

Figure 8-14

of the hole, as shown in Fig. 8-14. Then $\rho gh_{max} = 2\gamma/r$, or $h_{max} = 2 \times 72/1 \times 980 \times 0.002 = \underline{73 \text{ cm}}$.

21. (a) From Trouton's rule, $\Delta H_v = 21T_b = 21 \times 573 = \underline{12 \text{ kcal}}$.
(b) Using the Clausius-Clapeyron equation:

$$\log P_{373}/P_{573} = \frac{12,000}{2.3 \times 1.98}(1/573 - 1/373)$$

where $P_{573} = 1$ atm.
(c) By the Laplace equation, $\Delta P = 2\gamma/R$, and the situation in the maximum bubble-pressure case is that ΔP is a maximum when the bubble is just hemispherical, so that R has the minimum value of r, the radius of the tube. $\Delta P_{max} = 2 \times 45/0.25 = \underline{360 \text{ dynes/cm}^2}$.

22. Using the Clausius-Clapeyron equation, for water:

$$\ln P/1 = \frac{12,000}{R} (1/373 - 1/T)$$

and for chloroform:

$$\ln P/1 = \frac{7000}{R} (1/333 - 1/T)$$

T is to be such that the two P's are the same, so, equating the left-hand sides:

$$12,000(1/373 - 1/T) = 7000(1/333 - 1/T)$$

from which

$$5000/T = 11.0 \quad \text{or} \quad \underline{T = 454°K}$$

23. First, we determine the temperature of the freezing mixture under 100 atm pressure, using the Clapeyron equation $\Delta P/\Delta T = \Delta H/T\,\Delta V$, where ΔH is the heat of fusion, and ΔV is given by $\Delta V = M(1/\rho_2 - 1/\rho_1)$; T is approximately the melting point T_1. T is then $T_1 + \Delta T$. Next, use the Clausius-Clapeyron equation to calculate the vapor pressure of the liquid at this temperature.

$$\ln P/1 = \frac{\Delta H_V}{R} (1/T_2 - 1/T)$$

where T is the above temperature. Finally, it is necessary to recognize that the liquid at T is under 100 atm pressure so that its free energy is increased by $\int V\,dP$. That is, $RT \ln P'/P = \int V\,dP = (M/\rho_2) \times 100$ atm, where P is the vapor pressure obtained from the Clausius-Clapeyron equation and P' is the desired final answer.

24. The pressure is given by the Laplace equation $\Delta P = 2\gamma/R$, where R is the radius of the bubble (if a section of a sphere); for ΔP to be a maximum, R must be at a minimum, and this will indeed be true when the bubble is just hemispherical, as illustrated in Fig. 8-15. At this point, R = r, so the proposition is correct. For the particular case then, $\Delta P = \rho_{Hg}\,gh = 13.6 \times 980 \times 0.03 = 400$ dynes/cm². Then $\gamma = 400 \times 0.1/2 = \underline{20 \text{ dynes/cm.}}$

Figure 8-15

25. The Clausius-Clapeyron equation is best used here in the form:

$$(dP/P)/dT = \frac{\Delta H}{RT^2}$$

where $(dP/P)/dT$ is given a 0.030 (P is 1 atm at the normal boiling point). Then $\Delta H = 0.030 \times 1.98 \times 353^2 = \underline{7.4 \text{ kcal/mole.}}$

26. The integrated form of the Clausius-Clapeyron equation may be written $\ln P = \text{const} - \Delta H/RT$. According to Trouton's rule, when $P = 1$ atm, $\Delta H/T = 21$; hence the constant equals $21/R$, i.e., $\ln P = 21/R - \Delta H/RT$. Thus all liquids are supposed to have a common intercept at $1/T = 0$.

27. Using the Clausius-Clapeyron equation,

$$\ln 760/20 = \frac{\Delta H_A}{R} (1/313 \quad 1/393)$$

and

$$\ln 760/40 = \frac{\Delta H_B}{R} (1/313 - 1/413)$$

Clearly the ΔH's will not be related by any simple factor. Qualitatively, the vapor pressure of A is less than that of B at 40°C, whereas at 140°C it must be greater than that of B (since this is the boiling point of B, but above the boiling point of A). Therefore the vapor pressure of A changes more rapidly with temperature than does that of B, and the ΔH_v of B must be less than that of A.

28. The integrated form of the Clausius-Clapeyron equation is $\ln P = A - \Delta H/RT$, and, evidently, $A = \ln 10^5$, so the equation becomes:

$$\log 1/10^5 = -\Delta H/R \times 300 \times 2.3$$

The $\Delta H = \underline{6820 \text{ cal.}}$

29. Perhaps the easiest way to see the answer is to note that the hydrostatic pressure just inside the bottom surface will be a maximum when the incipient drop is just hemispherical, and will then be equal to $2\gamma/r$. The pressure just underneath the meniscus will be $-2\gamma/r$, so the total change in hydrostatic head will be $4\gamma/r$. This can be equated to ρhg, so h = 4 × 72/1 × 980 × 0.05 = <u>5.9 cm.</u>

30. For 1 g solid, the volume changes from 1.11 cc to 1.18 cc, so ΔV is 0.07 cc. Per cc of solid, ΔV is then 0.9(1/0.85 − 0.9) = 0.06 cc. From the Clapeyron equation, $\Delta P/\Delta T = \Delta S/\Delta V$ = (3/0.06) × (41) = 2050 atm/deg, so for $\Delta P = 10^4$ atm (or, better, 99 atm), $\Delta T = 4.9°$.

The effect of mechanical pressure will be to raise both vapor pressure curves (RT ln $P'/P = \int V\ dP_{mech}$), but evidently the crossing point must shift to the right (see Fig. 8-16), so the vapor-pressure curve for the liquid must be raised more than that for the solid (as the $\int V\ dP_{mech}$ predicts).

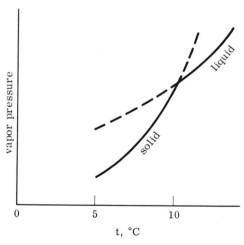

Figure 8-16

9 *Solutions*

Comments

This chapter is concerned primarily with solutions of non-electrolytes. You will become acquainted with Raoult's law, both as a limiting law and as an ideal law. In this second capacity, the Raoult's law statement that $P_i = N_i P_i^o$ is taken to apply to all components of a solution, at all compositions. As a limiting law, the statement: $P_A = N_A P_A^o$, approaches validity only in the limit of N_A approaching unity, but now applies to nonideal solutions. For such solutions a second limiting law, Henry's law, applies in the limit of N_A approaching zero; this second limiting behavior may be written $P_A = k_A N_A$. You are expected to keep these two limiting laws in mind in drawing partial pressure vs. composition diagrams.

Such diagrams may show just the plot of total vapor pressure vs. solution composition; this will be a straight line connecting the two P° values if the solution is ideal, and will otherwise be

curved and may have a minimum or a maximum. A second curve
may now be included, which gives the plot of vapor pressure vs.
equilibrium vapor composition. The combined plot takes on the
character of a phase diagram in that it shows a liquid, a vapor,
and a two-phase region; a system whose gross composition and
vapor pressure is such as to locate a point in the two phase region will consist of some vapor and some liquid. Furthermore,
the relative amounts of the two phases can be obtained by a simple graphical method of making a material balance calculation,
known as the "lever principle."

Vapor-pressure diagrams may be converted to boiling point
ones, and vice versa. Many of the problems deal with these inter-
conversions, and it is helpful to remember that the two types of
diagrams for a given system resemble each other if one is turned
upside down. Thus a system showing a maximum in its vapor pressure diagram will show a minimum in its boiling point diagram.
Qualitatively, positive deviation from ideality is interpreted on a
molecular basis as being due to a tendency toward immiscibility
of the two components. In terms of intermolecular forces, this
amounts to saying that A—A and B—B type forces are greater
than A—B type forces. The increasing degree of manifestation of
this tendency leads to maximum vapor-pressure (and minimum
boiling-point) diagrams and, finally, to the limiting case of complete immiscibility. At this extreme, we get into steam-distilla-
tion-type problems.

Conversely, negative deviation from ideality is interpreted
qualitatively as due to a tendency toward association or compound formation. Increasing degree of this tendency leads to minimum vapor-pressure (and maximum boiling-point) diagrams.

Finally, you will find a small introduction to partial molar
quantities via a few problems involving partial molar volumes.

Equations and concepts

Ideal Solutions:

Raoult's law: $P_i = N_i P_i^\circ$. For two components, $P_{total} = P_A +$
$P_B = N_A P_A^\circ + N_B P_B^\circ = P_B^\circ + N_A (P_A^\circ - P_B^\circ)$.

Vapor Composition: $Y_i = P_i/P_{total}$. For two components,

$$Y_A = \frac{N_A P_A^\circ}{P_B^\circ + N_A (P_A^\circ - P_B^\circ)} \text{ and } Y_B = 1 - Y_A$$

There is no volume change and no heat of mixing in the case of ideal solutions.

Nonideal Solutions: Raoult's law and Henry's law are now limiting laws. Thus,

$$P_A \to N_A P_A^\circ \quad \text{as} \quad N_A \to 1$$

and

$$P_A \to N_A k_A \quad \text{as} \quad N_A \to 0$$

where k_A is the Henry's law constant. Remember that, if k_A/P_A° is greater than unity, then for a two component solution, k_B/P_B° will also be greater than unity, and similarly, if k_A/P_A° is less than unity, k_B/P_B° will be less than unity. That is, both components will show the same direction of deviation from ideality.

Regular Solutions: The effective mole fraction of a component may be written as $a_i = P_i/P_{total}$ where a denotes activity or effective composition. In the case of a nonideal solution, a_i will not be equal to N_i and we may write $a_i = f_i N_i$ where f_i is called the activity coefficient.

So-called regular solutions show a symmetric behavior of the activity coefficients, and for a two-component solution this is given by:

$$\log f_A = -\alpha N_B^2 \quad \text{and} \quad \log f_B = -\alpha N_A^2$$

where α has the same value in both equations.

Immiscible Liquids: Each component contributes its full vapor pressure to the total vapor pressure. For two-component systems, it then follows that $Y_A = P_A^\circ/(P_A^\circ + P_B^\circ)$. In the case of steam distillation, $P_W^\circ + P_X^\circ = 1$ atm, and P_W° is known from the boiling temperature, and hence so is P_X°, and therefore Y_X for the vapor.

"Lever Principle": If a two-component system of over-all composition N_A is partitioned into n_ℓ moles of composition N_A' and n_v moles of vapor of composition Y_A, then

$$\frac{n_\ell}{n_\ell + n_v} = \frac{Y_A - N_A}{Y_A - N'_A}$$

In the case of diagrams showing both the liquid- and vapor-composition lines, the differences $(Y_A - N_A)$ and $(Y_A - N'_A)$ may be read off the graph directly and may in fact be measured in arbitrary units by means of a ruler since their ratio is dimensionless. If composition is in weight fraction, the lever principle gives the weight fraction of the system present as liquid, that is,

$$\frac{w_\ell}{w_\ell + w_v} = \frac{W_{A(vapor)} - W_{A(gross)}}{W_{A(vapor)} - W_{A(liquid)}}$$

where W denotes weight-fraction composition.

Problems

1. (15 min) Liquids A and B form nonideal solutions, and the total vapor pressure vs. composition (for a given temperature) is plotted in Fig. 9-1.

(a) Draw on the graph qualitatively (but carefully) the separate vapor pressure vs. composition plots for each component, i.e., P_A and P_B.

(b) Add also to the graph the probable appearance of the vapor-composition line.

(c) Sketch in a separate diagram the probable appearance of the boiling-point diagram for this system.

2. (26 min) Liquids A and B form ideal solutions. A mixture of the vapors which is 40 mole % in A is contained in a piston and cylinder arrangement which is kept at a certain constant temperature T. The system is then slowly compressed. Given that P°_A and P°_B are 0.4 and 1.2 atm, respectively, at T, calculate the total pressure at which liquid first begins to condense out and also the composition of this liquid. Calculate the composition of that solution whose normal boiling point is T.

3. (10 min) Using the vapor-pressure plots in Fig. 9-2, calculate the normal boiling point of (a) pure liquid A and B, (b) a solution of $N_A = 0.25$ and (c) a solution of $N_A = 0.75$. [Your answers to (b) and (c) need be correct only to a few degrees, provided the procedure is clear.] (Assume ideal solutions.)

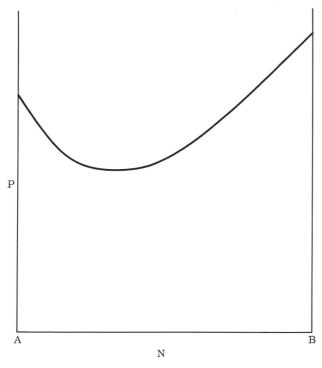

Figure 9-1

(d) Calculate the vapor compositions for the solutions in (b) and (c) when at their normal boiling points, and make a semi-quantitative plot of the boiling-point diagram. Label the phases present in each phase region. (Assume ideal solutions.)

(e) Calculate the normal boiling points of mixtures (b) and (c), assuming now that A and B are completely immiscible.

4. (4 min) Give a brief chemical or molecular explanation of why, if one component of a nonideal binary solution shows negative deviation from ideality in its variation of partial pressure with composition, the other component will do likewise.

5. (10 min) The graph of Fig. 9-3 gives the average molar volume V for the system ethyl iodide–ethyl acetate, as a function of N, the mole fraction of ethyl iodide. Calculate or obtain graphically the partial molar volumes $\overline{V}_1$ and $\overline{V}_2$ for ethyl iodide and ethyl acetate, respectively, for a solution of composition $N_1 = 0.75$. Calculate ΔV for the process: 3 ethyl iodide + ethyl acetate = solution.

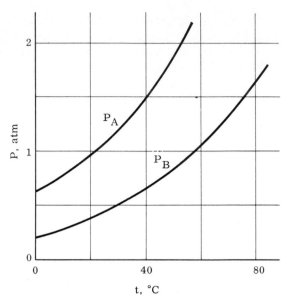

Figure 9-2

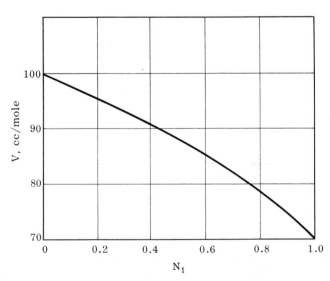

Figure 9-3

6. (9 min) The vapor-pressure diagram for the chloroform–iso-propyl ether system is such as to suggest that there is a tendency toward compound formation. Sketch the probable appearance of the two partial-pressure and the total vapor-pressure curves at 60°C. At this temperature, the vapor pressures of chloroform and of isopropyl ether are 700 mm Hg and 800 mm Hg, respectively. Although the curves need only be qualitative, pay attention to their general shape.

7. (10 min) Liquids A and B form ideal solutions. They are isomeric so that their molecular weights are the same (and hence weight and mole fractions). A solution of composition N_A is found to have a vapor pressure of 650 mm Hg at 50°C. It is then distilled (with no reflux) until half has been collected as conden-sate. The condensate has a composition $N'_A = 0.60$, and the residual liquid a composition $N''_A = 0.40$ and a vapor pressure of 600 mm Hg at 50°C. Calculate N_A, P°_A, and P°_B.

8. (12 min) Liquids A and B form ideal solutions. The vapor pressure of a mixture of 1 mole of A and 2 of B is 0.5 atm at 70°C. Addition of 3 more moles of A raises the vapor pressure of the solution at 70°C to 0.7 atm. Calculate or estimate graph-ically (use Fig. 9-4) the values of P°_A and P°_B. If some of the vapor in equilibrium with the first solution were completely condensed, calculate what its vapor pressure would be at 70°C.

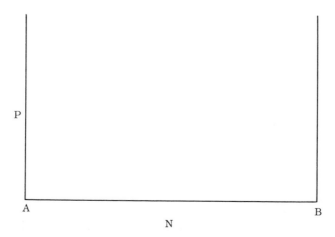

P

A N B

Figure 9-4

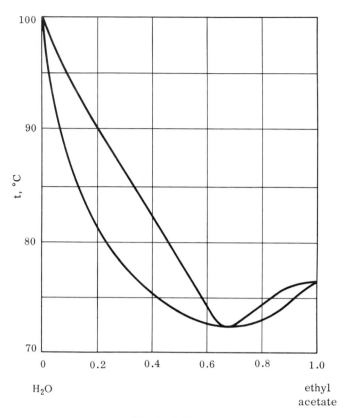

Figure 9-5

9. (18 min) Figure 9-5 shows the ethyl acetate-water system. A solution of mole fraction 50% is boiled in an open beaker until the boiling point rises by 5°C. Calculate or make clear how you obtain graphically (a) the composition of the solution when the boiling was stopped and the initial and final boiling points, (b) the average composition of the distillate (if the vapors had been collected and condensed), (c) the moles of ethyl acetate remaining in the liquid when the boiling was stopped, assuming that the initial mixture contained 1 mole of ethyl acetate, (d) the composition of the last drop of liquid had the boiling been continued, and (e) the probable appearance of the vapor-pressure diagram for this system.

10. (12 min) Water and CCl_4 are completely immiscible; their vapor pressures are shown in Fig. 9-6 as a function of temperature. A <u>gaseous</u> mixture of water and CCl_4 (i.e., a mixture of the

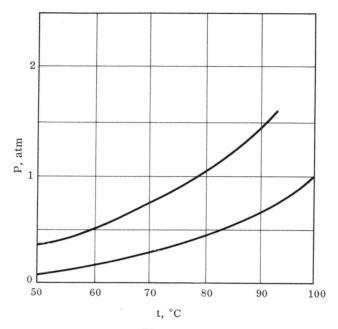

Figure 9-6

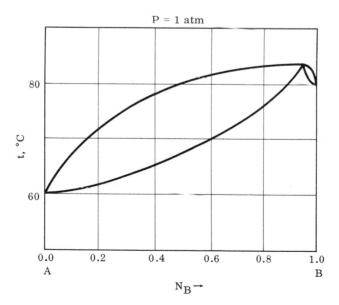

Figure 9-7

vapors) at 1 atm constant total pressure is cooled from 100°C. At
80°C pure liquid water begins to condense out.

Estimate, by means of the graph, the mole fraction of water in
the vapor mixture and the temperature to which the mixed vapor
must be cooled before liquid CCl_4 begins to condense out.

11. (9 min) The boiling point diagram for two miscible liquids is
shown in Fig. 9-7. (a) On boiling a 50 mole % solution in an open
container, what will be the composition of the first vapor and of
the last vapor? (b) If the solution is heated in a closed system at
1 atm constant pressure, what will be the liquid composition when
half the solution is vaporized? What will be the temperature?

12. (9 min) Liquids A and B form an ideal solution. At 50°C, the
total vapor pressure of a solution consisting of 1 mole of A and
2 moles of B is 250 mm Hg; on addition of 1 more mole of A to
the solution, the vapor pressure increases to 300 mm Hg. Calculate P_A° and P_B°.

13. (7.5 min) The molar volume of pure methanol is 40 cc/mole.
Also, the volume of a solution containing 1000 g of water and n
moles of methanol is given by: $V = 1000 + 35n + 0.5n^2$. Calculate the partial molar volume $\overline{V}$ for methanol for m (molality) =
0 and for m = 1. Calculate also ΔV for the process: $55.5H_2O +
CH_3OH$ = solution.

14. (15 min) Toluene and xylene form an ideal solution. At 20°C
the vapor pressures of pure toluene and xylene are 22 and 5 mm
Hg, respectively. Make a graph showing how the vapor pressure
of a solution should vary with composition. Show, on the same
graph, the approximate appearance of the plot of equilibrium vapor
compositions and explain how one particular point on this plot is
calculated.

If the force of attraction between a toluene and a xylene
molecule were less than in the ideal case, i.e., the toluene–xylene
pair were less strongly attracted than the toluene–toluene and
xylene–xylene pairs, show grapically the changes qualitatively to
be expected in the above plot.

15. (7.5) Liquids A and B form ideal solutions. What can be deduced about the relationships of (a) the density and (b) the enthalpy of a solution to the densities and enthalpies of the pure
liquids?

16. (20 min) Liquids A and B form an ideal solution, and their normal boiling-point diagram is shown in Fig. 9-8. A solution consisting of 0.4 mole of A and 0.6 mole of B is heated to 50°C in a closed system at 1 atm pressure; as a result n_V moles of vapor of composition Y_B and n_ℓ moles of liquid of composition N_B are present. Some of this vapor is withdrawn, condensed, and the vapor pressure of the condensate was found to be 1.20 atm at 50°C; there is a little bit of vapor phase in equilibrium with the condensate and a sample of this vapor was found to have the composition $Y'_B = 0.85$.

(a) Calculate Y_B and N_B. (b) Calculate n_V and n_ℓ and the per cent of B in the vapor phase. (c) Using the available data, construct the liquid- and vapor-composition lines in the vapor-pressure diagram for 50°C (the vapor line may be sketched in if one or two points are determined) and state the values for P°_A and P°_B.

17. (10 min) Liquids A and B are miscible, and at 50°C, the vapor pressures of A and B show a negative deviation from Raoult's law. (a) Draw the vapor-pressure vs composition diagram (Fig. 9-9)

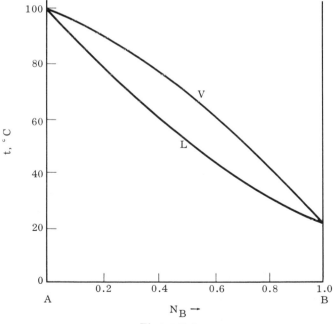

Figure 9-8

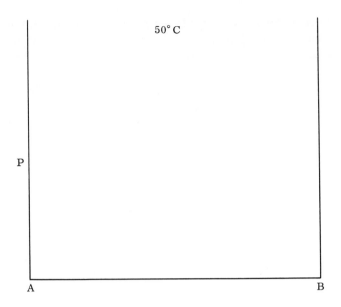

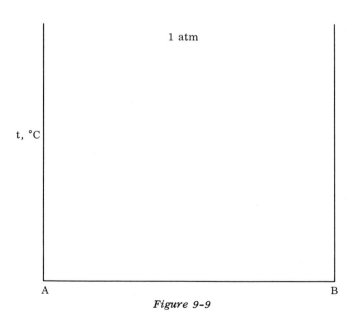

Figure 9-9

for 50°C, giving the curves for the partial pressure of each component, the total pressure line, and the vapor-composition line.
(b) Draw the boiling-point diagram in Fig. 9-9, giving the liquid-
and the vapor-composition lines.

A is lower boiling than B. Although the graphs are necessarily qualitative, care is to be exercised that the lines are of the proper shape.

18. (10 min) When a mixture of water and chlorobenzene (mutually immiscible) is distilled at an external pressure of 740.2 mm Hg, the mixture is found to boil at 90.3°C, at which temperature the vapor pressure of pure water is 530.1 mm Hg. Calculate the per cent by weight of chlorobenzene in the distillate. (Molecular weight is 112.)

19. (9 min) A and B form ideal solutions; at 50°C, P_A° is one-half P_B°. A solution containing 0.2 mole of A and 0.8 mole of B has a normal boiling point of 50°C. Calculate P_A° and P_B° at 50°C.

20. (18 min) Liquids A and B form an ideal solution. A certain solution contains 25 mole % of A, whereas the vapor in equilibrium with the solution at 25°C contains 50 mole % of A. The heat of vaporization of A is 5 kcal/mole; that of B is 7 kcal/mole.

(a) Calculate the ratio of the vapor pressure of pure A to that of pure B at 25° C.

(b) Calculate the value for this same ratio at 100°C. (It is not necessary to obtain a final numerical answer to (b); set up the equations and substitute in numbers so that the desired ratio is the only unknown.)

21. (12 min) The boiling-point diagram for two liquids A and B is shown in Fig. 9-10. A solution with $N_B = 0.4$ is boiled in an open beaker until the composition of the vapor coming off is $Y_B = 0.4$.

(a) Show on the graph the temperature at which the solution first boils.

(b) Show on the graph the composition of the first vapor coming off.

(c) Similarly show the boiling point when the vapor reaches the above stated composition of $Y_B = 0.4$.

(d) Show on the graph the composition of the final liquid. Give in all cases the approximate numerical values to the answers requested.

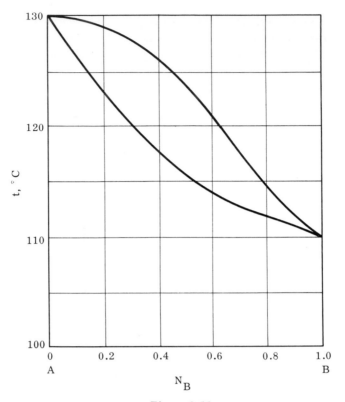

Figure 9-10

22. (18 min) Two-tenths mole of a solution of composition N_B is placed in a 2-liter vessel at 25°C. The vessel initially is evacuated so that, on introduction of the solution, partial evaporation occurs yielding residual solution of composition N'_B and equilibrium vapor of composition Y_B (still at 25°C). The equilibrium vapor is withdrawn and condensed. The normal boiling point of this condensate is 45°C.

By means of the graphs in Fig. 9-11, calculate (a) the composition of the final condensate, (b) the value of N'_B, (c) the total vapor pressure of this residual solution at 25°C, (d) the total moles of equilibrium vapor, and (e) the value of N_B.

23. (15 min) Two solutions of A and B are available. The first is known to contain 1 mole of A and 3 moles of B, and its total vapor pressure is 1.0 atm. The second is known to contain 2 moles of A and 2 moles of B; its vapor pressure is greater than 1 atm, but it

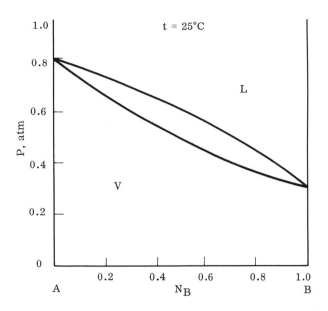

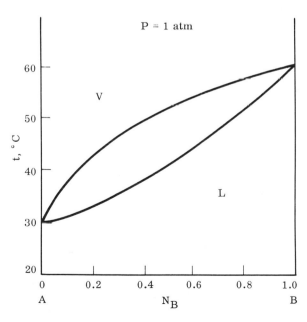

Figure 9-11

is found that this total vapor pressure may be reduced to 1 atm by
the addition of 6 moles of C. The vapor pressure of pure C is
0.80 atm. Assuming ideal solutions, and that all these data refer
to 25°C, calculate the vapor pressures of pure A and of pure B.

24. (21 min) Given that liquids A and B form ideal solutions and
that the vapor pressures of the pure liquids at 80°C are 100 and
600 mm Hg, respectively, plot the total vapor pressure of solutions at 80°C vs. their mole fraction. Calculate several vapor
compositions and, by means of these points, draw on your diagram
a semiquantitative vapor-composition curve.

A solution containing 40 mole % of B is placed in a previously
evacuated container of such size that, at 80°C, one-third of the
liquid vaporizes. Calculate the compositions of the final liquid
and vapor phases.

Solution of N_B = 0.6 is evaporated in an open container at a
constant temperature of 80°C until the total vapor pressure falls
to 80% of its initial value (i.e., by 20%). What is the final liquid
composition, and roughly how many moles of liquid remain after
the evaporation to this point, assuming that initially there was
1 mole of liquid?

25. (16.5 min) One mole of a 50 mole % solution of propyl alcohol
in ethyl alcohol is distilled until the boiling point of the solution
rises to 90°C. The condensate is allowed to accumulate in a cooled
receiver and, after being mixed to insure uniformity, its vapor
pressure is found to be 1066 mm Hg when measured at 90°C. The
vapor pressures of pure ethyl and propyl alcohols are 1190 and
574 mm Hg at 90°C, respectively. Assuming that the solutions and
vapors are ideal, calculate (a) the mole fraction of ethyl alcohol
in the 90°C-boiling liquid in the distilling flask, (b) the mole fraction of ethyl alcohol in the distillate, and (c) the number of moles
of ethyl alcohol that were distilled.

26. (12 min) Liquids A and B form nonideal, but regular, solutions; P_A° and P_B° are 0.75 atm and 1.50 atm at 25°C, respectively.
If for a solution of N_A = 0.50, P_A at 25°C is 0.25 atm, calculate
the activity coefficient of species A and the value of P_B.

Answers

1. The curves for P_A and P_B are shown on Fig. 9-12. The main
points are that they should show a negative deviation from ideality,

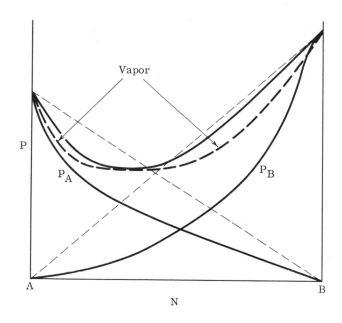

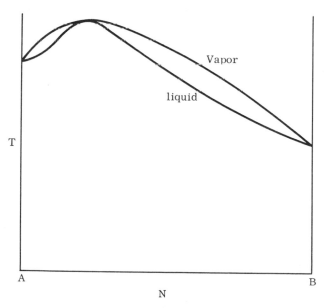

Figure 9-12

and should approach the Raoult's law line at one end and a Henry's law line at the other. The vapor-composition line should touch the liquid composition line at the point of minimum pressure. The boiling-point diagram is expected to be a maximum boiling-point type, with the vapor line now above the liquid-composition line, and touching it at the maximum. Also, the boiling point of A should appear higher than that of B.

2. At the beginning of condensation, the vapor will still be essentially 0.4 mole fraction in A, hence $P_A/P_{total} = 0.4$. But $P_{total} = P_A^o N_A + P_B^o N_B = 0.4N_A + 1.2N_B = 1.2 - 0.8N_A$. The first equation then becomes: $0.4N_A/(1.2 - 0.8N_A) = 0.4$, from which $\underline{N_A = 0.67}$. P_{total} is then $1.2 - 0.8 \times 0.67 = \underline{0.67 \text{ atm}}$. If the solution is boiling at T, then $P_{total} = 1$ atm. Hence $N_A = (1.2 - 1)/0.8$ or $\underline{N_A = 0.25}$.

3. (a) The normal boiling points are simply those temperatures at which the vapor pressures are 1 atm, namely, about $\underline{22°C}$ for A and $\underline{58°C}$ for B.

(b) The equation $1 \text{ (atm)} = P_A^o \times 0.25 + P_B^o \times 0.75$ must be satisfied; with a few trials, an approximate solution is found at about $\underline{45°C}$, with $P_A^o = 1.7$ and $P_B^o = 0.75$.

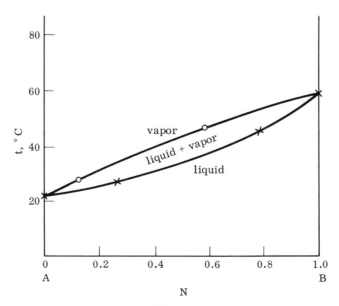

Figure 9-13

(c) The equation is now $1 = 0.75P_A^\circ + 0.25P_B^\circ$, for which a solution is found at about 27°C, with $P_A^\circ = 1.2$ and $P_B^\circ = 0.5$.

(d) The mole fractions of A in the vapor are given by $Y_A = P_A/1$ or about 0.42 and 0.9 for solutions (b) and (c), respectively. These various values are located in Fig. 9-13 to provide an approximate boiling-point plot.

(e) If A and B are immiscible, one now seeks a solution to: 1 (atm) $= P_A^\circ + P_B^\circ$, which is found at approximately 10°C.

4. Negative deviation is considered to be due to the presence of some degree of association, i.e., to a situation where the forces between A molecules or between B molecules are less than those between A and B molecules. Clearly, the situation is symmetric; if A is partially involved in association with B, B is similarly involved. Both partial pressures should then show a negative deviation from ideality.

5. The average molar volume is the total volume divided by the number of moles, and it turns out (see your text) that the partial molar volumes are very easily obtained from the plot of V against mole fraction. One simply locates the tangent at the particular composition, and the two partial molar volumes are then given by the two intercepts. On doing this, one obtains the intercepts $\overline{V}_1 = 108$ and $\overline{V}_2 = 73$ cc/mole. For the process:

3 ethyl iodide + ethyl acetate = solution

the volumes are:

$$3 \times 70 \quad + \quad 100 \quad = 4 \times V \text{ of a solution of}$$
$$N_1 = 0.75 \quad \text{or} \quad 4 \times 81$$

ΔV is then $324 - 310$ or 14 cc.

6. Negative deviation is expected if there is a tendency toward compound formation. The partial-pressure plots of Fig. 9-14 should show an approach to Raoult's law at one end and to Henry's law at the other.

7. By material balance in A, we can write $N_A = (N_A' + N_A'')/2$ since if there were 1 mole of solution, after distillation there was 0.5 mole of condensate and 0.5 mole of residual liquid. Then $N_A = (0.6 + 0.4)/2 = 0.5$.

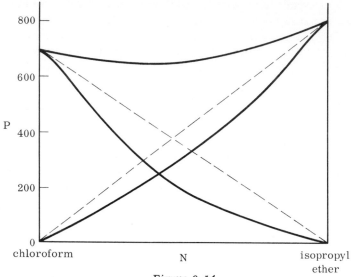

Figure 9-14

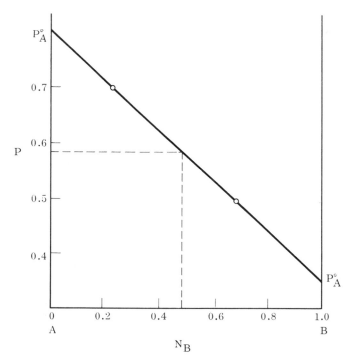

Figure 9-15

We have the total vapor pressure of the original and residual solutions, hence

$$650 = 0.5P_A^\circ + 0.5P_B^\circ \quad \text{and} \quad 600 = 0.4P_A^\circ + 0.6P_B^\circ$$

On solving these equations simultaneously, $P_A^\circ = 900$ mm Hg and $P_B^\circ = 400$ mm Hg.

8. P_A° and P_B° may be obtained graphically quite easily (see Fig. 9-15). For ideal solutions the total vapor pressure vs. mole fraction plot is a straight line, and we have the two points: $N_A = \frac{1}{3}$, $P = 0.5$ atm, and $N_A = \frac{2}{3}$, $P = 0.7$ atm. The intercepts of the straight line so defined give $P_A^\circ = 0.8$ and $P_B^\circ = 0.35.$ The vapor composition in equilibrium with the first solution is $Y_A = P/P_{total} = 0.33 \times 0.8/0.5 = 0.53$. From the graph, P for a liquid of this composition would be about 0.58 atm.

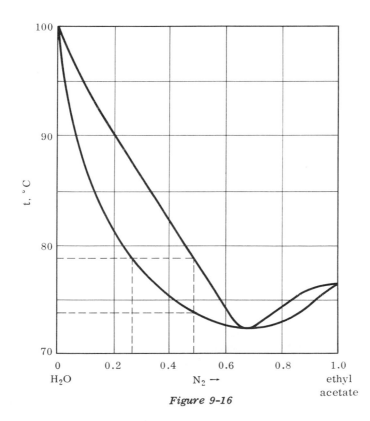

Figure 9-16

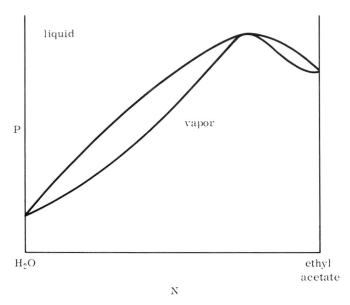

Figure 9-17

9. (See Fig. 9-16.) (a) The initial boiling point is given by the liquid line at 50%, i.e., 74°C; the final boiling point, of course, is
then 79°C. At 79°C, the liquid line gives a composition of about
$N_2 = 0.25$.

(b) The initial vapor composition is given by the vapor line as
0.6, and the final one as about 0.45. The average value is then
about 0.53.

(c) By material balance in ethyl acetate:

initial moles = moles left + moles vapor

$$0.5 \times 1 \quad = \; 0.25 \times n \; + \; 0.53(1 - n)$$

from which n, the moles of liquid left, is about 0.1. The moles
of ethyl acetate remaining is then about 0.025.

(d) The composition of the last drop of liquid is pure water
(we are boiling away in an open system).

(e) The general appearance of the vapor pressure diagram is
sketched in Fig. 9-17.

10. From the graph, the vapor pressure of water at 80°C is

0.5 atm; since the total pressure of the vapor mixture is 1 atm, the partial pressure of the CCl_4 must then also be 0.5 atm. The vapor is thus <u>50 mole %</u> in composition. At the point where CCl_4 begins to condense out, we have both liquid phases present, and must now look for a temperature at which the sum of the liquid vapor pressures is 1 atm. Inspection of the graph gives about <u>65°C</u>.

11. (a) The 50% composition line intercepts the liquidus line at about 68°C, and the horizontal line drawn over to the vapor-composition curve intersects it at about <u>$N_B = 0.1$</u>. The last vapor composition will be that of the maximum boiling point, or about <u>$N_B = 0.95$</u>.

   (b) On half vaporization in a closed system, the temperature must be such that the tie line is bisected by the system composition line, and, as indicated in Fig. 9-18, this occurs at about <u>75°C</u>. The liquid composition is <u>$N_B = 0.75$</u>.

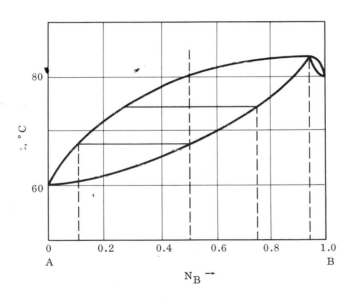

Figure 9-18

12. The two conditions yield two equations:

$$250 = \tfrac{1}{3}\, P_A^\circ + \tfrac{2}{3}\, P_B^\circ \quad \text{and} \quad 300 = \tfrac{1}{2}\, P_A^\circ + \tfrac{1}{2}\, P_B^\circ$$

Simultaneous solution yields P_B° = <u>150 mm Hg</u> and P_A° = <u>450 mm Hg</u>.

13. $\overline{V} = (\partial V/\partial n)_{H_2O} = 35 + n$; n is so defined that, when n = 0, m = 0, and when n = 1, m = 1, so the two $\overline{V}$ values are $\underline{35}$ and $\underline{36 \text{ cc/mole}}$, respectively. For the process

$$55.5 \text{ H}_2\text{O} + \text{CH}_3\text{OH} = \text{solution (m = 1)}$$

the volumes are: 1000   40   (1000 + 35 + 0.5)

so $\Delta V = 1035.5 - 1040 = \underline{-4.5 \text{ cc.}}$

14. As shown in Fig. 9-19, the liquid-composition line is simply the straight line connecting the two P° values. The vapor-composition line is curved, and must lie below the liquid line. As an illustration, the vapor composition in equilibrium with liquid of toluene mole fraction 0.2 will be $Y_T = 0.2 \times 22/(0.2 \times 22 + 0.8 \times 5) = 0.53$. In this case a positive deviation from ideality is expected, and the qualitative appearance of the vapor-pressure diagram is as shown in Fig. 9-19.

15. In an ideal solution, volumes are additive, so $V_{soln} = n_A V_A + n_B V_B$. The density of a solution is then given by

$$\rho_{soln} = \frac{W}{V} = \frac{n_A M_A + n_B M_B}{n_A V_A + n_B V_B}$$

where V_A and V_B can in turn be replaced by M_A/ρ_A and M_B/ρ_B.

(b) The relationship for enthalpies is simple: $H_{soln} = n_A H_A + n_B H_B$.

16. (a) The original solution was 0.6 mole fraction in B and, from the boiling-point diagram, a tie line drawn at 50°C is intersected by this composition line. The ends of the tie line give liquid compositions $\underline{N_B = 0.53}$ and $\underline{Y_B = 0.70}$.

(b) From the lever principle,

$$n_v = \frac{0.6 - 0.53}{0.7 - 0.53} = \underline{0.41}, \text{ so } n_\ell = \underline{0.59}.$$

(c) We have the following information regarding the vapor-pressure diagram for 50°C: First, liquid of composition 0.53 is in equilibrium with vapor of composition 0.7 at 50°C, with the vapor pressure equal to 1 atm. Second, on condensing this vapor,

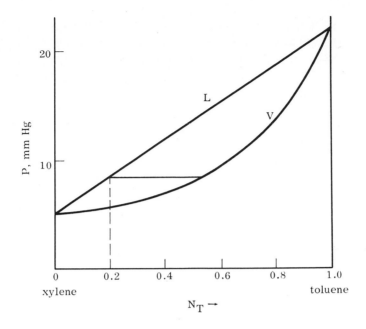

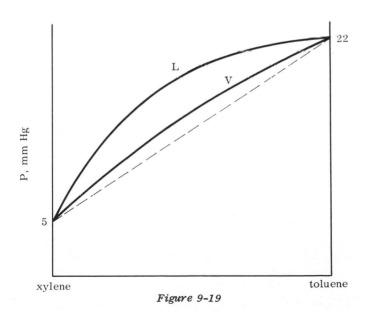

Figure 9-19

so that one now has liquid of composition 0.70, the vapor pressure
at 50°C is 1.20 atm, and the vapor composition is now 0.85. The
vapor pressure vs. liquid-composition plot is simply a straight
line, which can now be drawn through the two points; the inter-
cepts give $P_A^\circ \cong 0.4$ and $P_B^\circ \cong 1.5$ The vapor-composition curve
can finally be sketched in (Fig. 9-20) since two points on it are
known.

17. The answers are shown in the graphs (Fig. 9-21). Points to
note are: (a) Since A is lower boiling, it must have the higher
vapor pressure at 50°C (in all probability). (b) The partial pressure curves must approach the Raoult's law line as pure liquid is
approached in composition, and must approach a Henry's law line
at the other extreme of composition. (c) The boiling-point diagram should look somewhat like the vapor pressure one if the
latter is viewed upside down.

(The answer need not show a maximum boiling system, but
the deviation must be in that direction.)

18. The chlorobenzene must be supplying 740.2 − 530.1 or 210.1
mm Hg vapor pressure and the ratio of moles of it to moles of
water in the distillate must then be 210.1/530.1 or 0.40. Per
100 g of water, or 5.55 moles, there will then be 0.4 × 5.55 or
2.2 moles of chlorobenzene and hence 2.2 × 112 or 246 g. The
weight % chlorobenzene will then be 246/346 or 0.71 (71%).

19. We can write immediately: 1 (atm) = $0.2P_A^\circ + 0.8P_B^\circ$ and,
further, $1 = 0.2 \times P_B^\circ/2 + 0.8P_B^\circ$ so $P_B^\circ = 1/0.9 = 1.11$ atm. P_A°
must then be 0.55 atm.

20. (a) We can write $Y_A/Y_B = P_A/P_B$ where Y denotes mole
fraction in the vapor phase; in this case $Y_A = Y_B$. Then $1 = P_A/P_B = 0.25P_A^\circ/0.75\ P_B^\circ$ or $P_A^\circ/P_B^\circ = 3$.

(b) For a solution of the same composition, but at 100°C, we
can write:

$$\ln P_A'/P_A = \ln P_A'^\circ/P_A^\circ = \frac{\Delta H_A}{R}(1/298 - 1/373)$$

and similarly for component B. If the two equations are then subtracted, one obtains:

$$\ln R'/R = \frac{(\Delta H_A - \Delta H_B)}{R}(1/298 - 1/373)$$

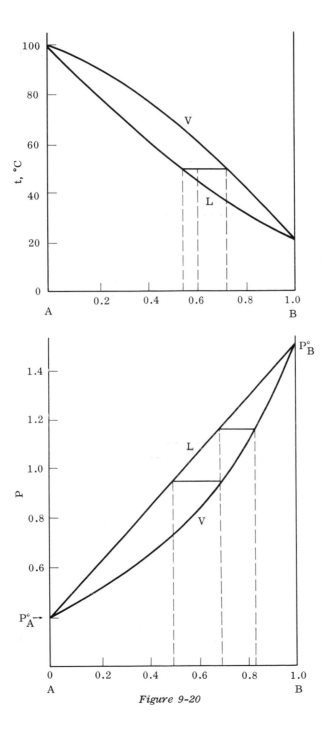

Figure 9-20

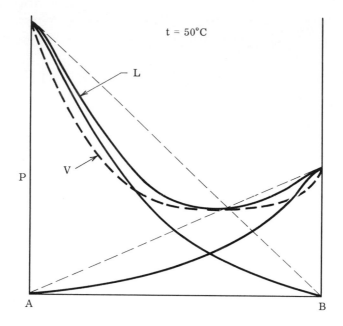

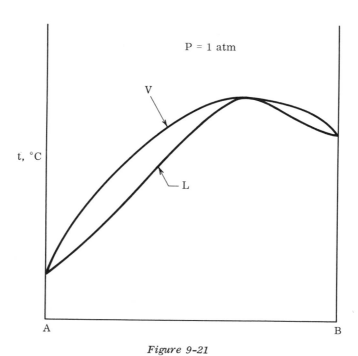

Figure 9-21

where R denotes the ratio P_A/P_B. Insertion of R = 3, and of values for R (gas constant) and the ΔH's completes the solution.

21. The various graphical solutions are indicated in Fig. 9-22. Numerical answers are: (a) 118°, (b) N_B = 0.7, (c) 126°, and (d) N_B = 0.12.

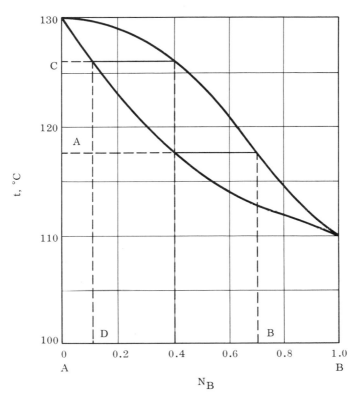

Figure 9-22

22. (a) By marking off the 45°C line in Fig. 9-23, one reads off 0.6 as the mole fraction in B of the condensate. (b) As vapor, before condensation, the tie line shows it was in equilibrium at 25°C with liquid of composition N_B' = 0.8. (c) The tie line in (b) is located at P = 0.45 atm. (d) The moles of this vapor that were present must be n = PV/RT = 0.45 × 2/0.082 × 298 = 0.037. (e) By material balance, e.g., the lever principle, N_B is given by:

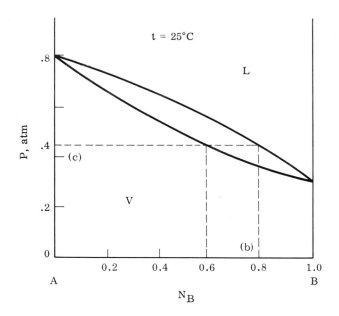

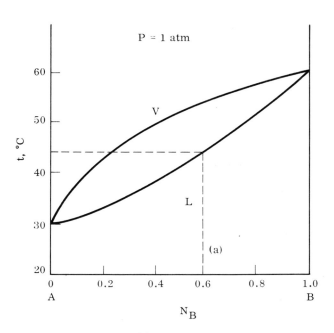

Figure 9-23

$$0.037/0.2 = (0.8 - N_B)/(0.8 - 0.6) \quad \text{or}$$

$$N_B = 0.8 - 0.037 = \underline{0.763}$$

23. The data provide the following two expressions for total pressure:

$$1 = \tfrac{1}{4}P_A^\circ + \tfrac{3}{4}P_B^\circ \quad \text{or} \quad 4 = P_A^\circ + 3P_B^\circ$$

and

$$1 = \tfrac{1}{5}P_A^\circ + \tfrac{1}{5}P_B^\circ + \tfrac{3}{5}P_C^\circ \quad \text{or} \quad 5 = P_A^\circ + P_B^\circ + 2.4$$

On solving these two equations simultaneously, one obtains $P_B^\circ = \underline{0.7 \text{ atm}}$ and $P_A^\circ = \underline{1.9 \text{ atm}}$.

24. The liquid line in Fig. 9-24 is obtained simply by drawing a straight line connecting the two P° values. A few vapor compositions may be calculated from the equation $Y_B = P_B/P_{total}$. Thus for $N_B = 0.2$, $P_B = 120$ and from the graph, $P_{total} = 200$, hence $Y_B = 0.6$. Similarly, for $N_B = 0.4$, one finds $Y_B = 240/300 = 0.80$, and for $N_B = 0.6$, $Y_B = 360/400 = 0.90$. These points then allow a rough curve of vapor composition to be drawn in.

Since $\tfrac{1}{3}$ of the $N_B = 0.4$ solution evaporates, one looks for that tie line which will, by the lever principle, predict this proportioning. As shown on the graph, the ends of this line give liquid and vapor compositions of approximately 0.3 and 0.75 mole fraction in B, respectively.

The initial vapor pressure at 80°C is read off the graph as 400 mm Hg, and at 80% of this value, or 320 mm Hg, the liquid composition is read off the graph to be about $N_B = \underline{0.45}$. The initial and final vapor compositions similarly can be read off the graph as approximately 0.92 and 0.90, giving an average value of about 0.91. By the lever principle, i.e., by material balance, the moles of liquid remaining must then be about

$$n_\ell = (0.91 - 0.6)/(0.91 - 0.45) = \underline{0.67}$$

25. (a) We have to assume that by boiling point is meant normal boiling point, i.e., P = 1 atm. Then $760 = 1190N_E + 574N_P = 574 + 616N_E$, so $N_E = \underline{0.30}$. (b) Similarly for the distillate,

$1066 = 574 + 616N_E$, $N_E = \underline{0.80}$. (c) By material balance, the moles of distillate $= (0.5 - 0.3)/(0.8 - 0.3) = 0.40$ (using the lever principle). The moles of ethanol in the distillate is then $0.40 \times 0.80 = \underline{0.32}$.

26. The ideal vapor pressure for component A would be $0.5 \times 0.75 = 0.375$, so the activity coefficient of A is $f_A = 0.25/0.375 = \underline{0.67}$. We then have

$$\log f_A = -\alpha N_B^2 = -\alpha(0.5)^2 = \log f_B$$

In this particular case, since $N_A = N_B = 0.5$, it follows that $f_A = f_B$, so $f_B = 0.67$. The ideal vapor pressure for B would be $0.5 \times 1.5 = 0.75$, so the actual value will be $0.75 \times 0.67 = \underline{0.50}$.

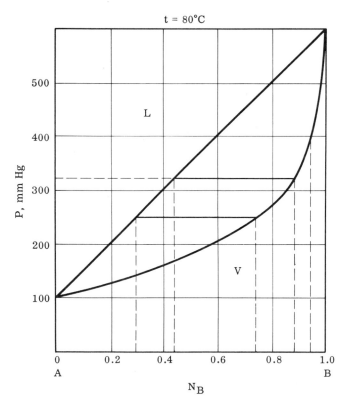

Figure 9-24

10   *Colligative properties*

Comments

Vapor-pressure lowering, boiling-point elevation, freezing-point depression, and the osomotic-pressure effects form a natural group.   These phenomena have in common the situation consisting of an equilibrium between two phases in which two components (in the simplest case) are present in one phase, but only one of them is present in the second phase.

In the case of vapor-pressure lowering and boiling-point elevation, one of the components is nonvolatile. In that of freezing-point depression, the solid phase consists of one component only. Osmotic pressure develops if there is present a membrane permeable only to one of the components.

With binary systems in general, it is entirely arbitrary as to which component is designated as solvent. Thus a 50 mole % solution of water in alcohol could equally well be described as a 50 mole % solution of alcohol in water.   Ordinarily one would be

165

inclined to name as solvent that component present in the larger
amount. Thus we would speak of a 40 mole % solution of water in
alcohol.

For the purpose of dicussing colligative-property effects,
however, it is convenient to adapt a special definition of solvent
as that component which is present in both phases. The solute
component is then that which is present in only one of the phases.
Thus, in the case of the 40 mole % solution of water in alcohol,
the freezing-point-depression effect relates to the equilibrium
between the solution and ice (since on cooling it would be ice, not
solid alcohol, that would freeze out first). The solvent is therefore water, not alcohol. On the other hand, if we were dealing
with the osmotic pressure of this solution, and had a membrane
permeable only to alcohol, so that alcohol would be the species
present in both phases, then, for the purpose of dealing with
osmotic effect, alcohol would be the solvent.

It is important to keep in mind that the colligative-property
equations are all derived by considering the equilibrium of a
species between two phases, and that that species or component
will be designated as solvent. The subscript one, as in N_1, then
will always refer to solvent as defined in the above manner.

Another aspect of this matter occurs in relating solubility to
freezing-point depression. If we saturate a liquid A with a solid
B, we then speak of the equilibrium concentration of B in the
liquid as the solubility of B. Implicitly, A is considered to be
the solvent. However, the same equilibrium can also be thought
of as having been reached by taking a solution of this particular
composition, cooling it to the temperature in question, and ob-
serving that solid B just begins to freeze out. This is now a freezing-point-depression experiment; B is the component present in
both phases, and from the colligative-property point of view, B is
therefore the solvent. You will find several problems requiring
you to relate solubility to freezing-point depression, or vice
versa.

It will generally be assumed that the solutions are ideal.
These are, after all, quiz problems, and it would usually have
been asking too much in the time allowed to expect the student
to handle nonideality corrections. It is not very difficult, however, to obtain the activity coefficient of the solvent from vapor-
pressure data, and you should be able to do this. The principal
potential source of confusion lies in the concept of standard state,
and it might help to review briefly here just what the operational
definition of activity coefficient is.

We can start with the chemical potential or partial molar free energy of a component of an ideal gas mixture, i.e., $\mu_i(g) = \mu_i^\circ(g) + RT \ln P_i$. If now this species is in equilibrium with a solution, its chemical potential must be the same in the two phases, so $\mu_i(\ell) = \mu_i(g)$. If the solution were ideal, we could use Raoult's law to write $P_i = N_i P_i^\circ$ so that the expression for the chemical potential becomes

$$\mu_i(\ell) = \mu_i^\circ(g) + RT \ln N_i P_i^\circ = \mu_i^\circ(\ell) + RT \ln N_i$$

It is convenient to retain this form for nonideal solutions, so we invent the activity a_i as the effective mole fraction of the component; thus $P_i = a_i P_i^\circ$. As a further matter of convenience, we retain mole fraction as the composition variable, and simply say that $a_i = f_i N_i$, where f_i is a correction factor and is known as the activity coefficient. Thus

$$\mu_i(\ell) \equiv \mu_i^\circ(\ell) + RT \ln f_i N_i$$

The standard state is that state for which $\mu_i = \mu_i^\circ$. In the above case, it would be the state for which $a_i = 1$; since Raoult's law is a limiting law for all solutions, it follows that as $N_i \rightarrow 1$, $f_i \rightarrow 1$, and $a_i \rightarrow 1$. The standard state is then the pure liquid species.

Now it is perfectly possible to invoke Henry's law to say that P_i should be equal to $N_i k_i$. This substitution then gives

$$\mu_i(\ell) = \mu_i^\circ(g) + RT \ln N_i k_i = \mu_i^{\circ\prime}(\ell) + RT \ln N_i$$

The two μ_i°'s are not the same. Thus

$$\mu_i^\circ(\ell) = \mu_i^\circ(g) + RT \ln P_i^\circ \quad \text{and} \quad \mu_i^{\circ\prime}(\ell) = \mu_i^\circ(g) + RT \ln k_i$$

Again, solutions in general will not obey Henry's law exactly, so we adapt the procedure of convenience of writing $P_i = a_i k_i$, and, further, of defining an activity coefficient y_i such that $P_i = y_i N_i k_i$. We now have

$$\mu_i(\ell) \equiv \mu_i^{\circ\prime}(\ell) + RT \ln y_i N_i$$

Bear in mind that y_i is <u>not</u> equal to f_i; it is the corrective factor to make the vapor pressure of the ith species conform to Henry's law, f_i is the factor to make the vapor pressur conform to Raoult's law.

The Henry's law standard state is again that state for which $a_i = 1$, but our state of ideal behavior is that for which $y_i = 1$. Now, Henry's law is approached at infinite dilution, i.e., $y_i \to 1$ as $N_i \to 0$. The Henry's law standard state is then a hypothetical one in which the ith species has the chemical environment of its infinitely dilute solution, but a concentration such that its activity is unity. This state is therefore sometimes called the hypothetical mole-fraction-unity standard state. Were the molality concentration unit used rather than mole fraction, we would obtain a third equation

$$\mu_i(\ell) \equiv \mu_i^{\circ\prime\prime}(\ell) + RT \ln \gamma_i m_i$$

where the standard state would now be called the hypothetical unit-molality standard state.

These "hypothetical" standard states may seen rather odd to you. Bear in mind that they are rigorously defined so that $\mu_i^{\circ\prime}(\ell)$ and $\mu_i^{\circ\prime\prime}(\ell)$ have definite values, even though the states are not physically obtainable.

Equations and concepts

Vapor-Pressure Lowering: $P_1 = N_1 P_1^{\circ}$; $N_2 = 1 - N_1 = \Delta P/P_1^{\circ}$

Boiling-Point Elevation: $\ln N_1 = \dfrac{\Delta H_v}{R}(1/T - 1/T_b)$, where T_b is the boiling point of the solvent.

Dilute solution form: $\Delta T_b = K_b M$ where $K_b = \dfrac{RT_b^2}{\Delta H_v}\dfrac{M_1}{1000}$

Freezing-Point Depression: $-\ln N_1 = \dfrac{\Delta H_f}{R}(1/T - 1/T_f)$, where T_f is the freezing point of the solvent.

Dilute solution form: $\Delta T_f = K_f m$ where $K_f = \dfrac{RT_f^2}{\Delta H_f}\dfrac{M_1}{1000}$

Osmotic Pressure: $RT \ln P_1^{\circ} = RT \ln P_1 + \int \overline{V}_1 \, d\pi$

Ideal solution form: $-RT \ln N_1 = \int \overline{V}_1 \, d\pi \cong \overline{V}_1 \pi$

Dilute solution form: $\pi V = n_2 RT$

Van't Hoff i factor: $\pi V = in_2RT$. In the case of electrolytes, i, is interpreted as giving the number of ions into which one formula weight dissociates.

Activity Coefficients: Mole-fraction-unity standard state: $P_i = f_i N_i P_i^\circ$

Hypothetical mole-fraction-unity standard state: $P_i = y_i N_i k_i$, where k_i is the Henry's law constant for the ith species.

Problems

1. (15 min) Given the following data: solubility of sucrose in water at 25°C is 6.2 molal, molecular weight of sucrose is 342, melting point is 200° C, heat of fusion of water is 1400 cal/mole, molecular weight and melting point of water, calculate the heat of fusion of sucrose assuming ideal solutions.

2. (15 min) The vapor pressure of water under 10 atm pressure is increased from 30 to 31 mm Hg at 25°C. How much NaCl would have to be added to 55.5 moles (1 liter) of water at 25°C so that the vapor pressure of the solution under 10 atm pressure would be 30 mm Hg? Calculate the osmotic pressure of this solution. (Assume that NaCl, although fully dissociated, gives otherwise ideal solutions.)

3. (24 min) (final examination question) Using the vapor pressure data shown in Fig. 10-1, (a) calculate the Henry's law constant for A, i.e., k_A in the equation $P_A = k_A N_A$, where this equation is valid, (b) calculate f_A for $N_A = 0.6$, i.e., the activity coefficient of A for this composition, assuming that the standard state of A is the pure liquid, and (c) calculate y_A for $N_A = 0.6$, where y_A is the activity coefficient taking the standard state to be hypothetical mole fraction unity.

4. (12 min) A 1.25 weight % solution of a substance of unknown molecular weight, in benzene as solvent, has a vapor pressure of 752.4 mm Hg at 80°C and a boiling point of 80.25°C. The normal boiling point of benzene is 80.00°C. Assuming the solute to be nonvolatile, calculate its molecular weight and the heat of vaporization (per gram) for benzene. The molecular weight of benzene is 78.

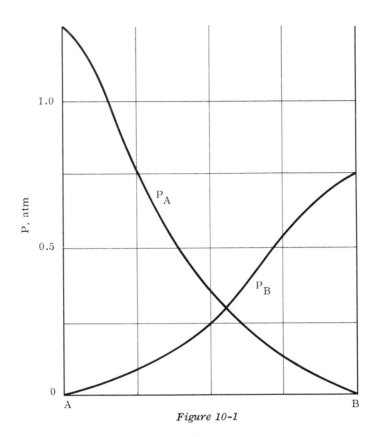

Figure 10-1

5. (15 min) Figure 10-2 shows a schematic representation of an apparatus for determining the osmotic pressure of a solution. At equilibrium enough solvent has passed through the membrane to cause the solution to rise to a height h. At this point, the hydro-static pressure on the solution equals its osmotic pressure. The vapor pressure of pure solvent is $P°$, and that of the solvent above the solution is P. Considering the solution to be dilute, derive the equation:

$$RT \ln P/P° = -Mgh \qquad \text{(M is the molecular weight of the solvent)}$$

It is no coincidence that the above equation is just the baromet-ric formula for the decrease in the pressure of a gas over a height h. Discuss why this is so.

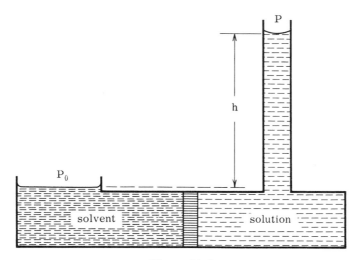

Figure 10-2

6. (18 min) Calculate the solubility of benzoic acid in ethanol at 80°C, and the vapor pressure of this saturated solution. You may assume the solution to be ideal, with benzoic acid nonvolatile and not associated or dissociated to any extent.

Compound	Mol. wt.	M.p.,°C	Normal b.p.	ΔH, cal/mole Fusion	Vaporiz.
Benzoic acid	122	122	249°C	4,000	12,000
Ethanol	46	−114	80	2,000	9,500

7. (12 min) A solution of NaCl of concentration m has an osmotic pressure of 2.0 atm at 25°C. Calculate ΔF_{298} for the process

$$H_2O(\text{solution, } 25°C) = H_2O(\text{pure, } 25°C)$$

8. (13.5 min) A solution of sucrose in water freezes at −0.200°C. Calculate the vapor pressure of this solution at 25°C (accurate to 0.001 mm Hg). The vapor pressure of pure water at 25°C is 23.506 mm Hg and the molal freezing-point constant for water is 1.86°C/m.

9. (3 min) Calculate ΔF per mole of NaCl for the process:

NaCl(0.01 m, 25°C) = NaCl(0.001 m, 25°C)

(neglect activity coefficients)

10. (24 min) (final examination question) The vapor pressures of solid and of liquid benzene are plotted on the P vs. T diagram of Fig. 10-3. A 10% by weight solution of substance A in benzene is cooled until solid benzene just begins to freeze out. The vapor pressure of benzene above the mixture is then measured and found to be 20 mm Hg; A is nonvolatile. Assuming the liquid solution to be ideal, estimate the freezing point of the solution and molecular weight of A. The molecular weight of benzene is 78.

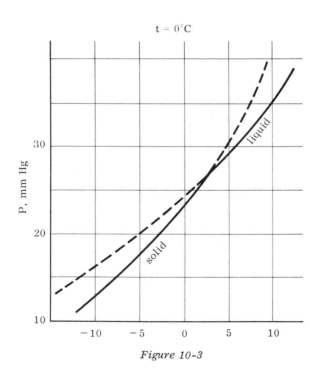

Figure 10-3

11. (24 min) (final examination question) The total vapor pressure of a 4 mole % solution of NH_3 in water at 20°C is 50.00 mm Hg; the vapor pressure of pure water is 17.00 mm Hg at this temperature. Apply Henry's and Raoult's laws to calculate the two partial pressures and the total vapor pressure for a 5 mole % solution.

12. (12 min) A 2% solution (by weight) of a substance of unknown molecular weight in toluene as solvent has a vapor pressure of 752.4 mm Hg at 110°C, and a normal boiling point of 100.25°C. The normal boiling point of toluene is 110.00°C; the solute is non-volatile. Calculate the molecular weight of the solute and the heat of vaporization (per gram) of toluene ($C_6H_5CH_3$).

13. (12 min) A solution of a sugar (molecular weight unknown) and one of sodium chloride (both aqueous) are placed side by side in a closed container and left until equilibrium is reached. During the equilibration, water distills from one solution to the other until the two have the same vapor pressure. The two solutions are then analyzed and are found to contain 5% sugar and 1% sodium chloride, by weight. Calculate the molecular weight of the sugar, assuming ideal solutions. The atomic weight of sodium is 23, and that of chlorine is 35.5.

14. (24 min) (final examination question) As shown in Fig. 10-4, pure solvent is separated from an ideal solution by a semipermeable membrane and, owing to the osmotic effect, the solution has

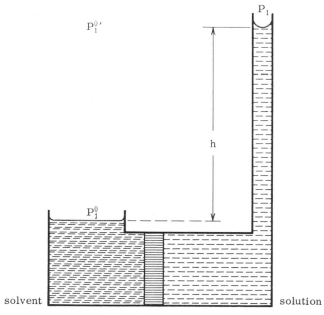

Figure 10-4

risen to an equilibrium height h. The vapor pressure of the solution is P_1, and that of the pure solvent is P_1^o (the solute being nonvolatile). Because of the barometric effect, P_1^o decreases to $P_1^{o\prime}$
at height h. Derive the barometric formula by making use of the
osmotic-pressure equation and the assumption that $P_1^{o\prime} = P_1$. Reasonable simplifying assumptions can be made to expedite the derivation.

15. (19.5 min) The normal boiling point of a saturated solution of
benzanilide in ethanol is 82.00°C. The melting point of benzanilide
is 161°C, the melting and normal boiling points of ethanol are
−117°C and 80.00°C. K_b for ethanol is 1.22. Molecular weights
are 46 for ethanol and 197 for benzanilide.

(a) Calculate the composition of this saturated solution of benzanilide.

(b) Calculate the molar heat of fusion of benzanilide. You may
select the appropriate colligative-property equations so that your
answers will be accurate only to about 1%, and you may assume
ideal solution behavior.

16. (10.5 min) The osmotic pressure of blood is 7 atm at 30°C.
What is the molarity of the isotonic saline solution if the i factor
for sodium chloride is taken to be 1.9?

17. (12 min) On cooling a 50 mole % solution of ethyl bromide and
benzene, which substance should freeze out first? Show how you
reach your conclusions. Assume the solution to be ideal.

	Mol. wt.	K_f	T_f, °C
Ethyl bromide	109	12.12	7
Benzene	78	5.0	7

(The melting points have been given as the same in order to facilitate your work.)

18. (24 min) (final examination question) The freezing point of
a 0.02-mole-fraction solution of acetic acid in benzene is 4.4°C.
Acetic acid exists partly as a dimer:

$$2CH_3COOH = H_3C \overset{\displaystyle O-H-O}{\underset{\displaystyle O-H-O}{<}} > CH_3$$

Calculate the equilibrium constant for the dimerization. The melting point of pure benzene is 5.4°C, its heat of fusion is 2400 cal/mole, and its molecular weight is 78. Assume the monomer and the dimer form ideal solutions.

19. (21 min) Some anthracene (molecular weight = 178) known to be contaminated with naphthalene (molecular weight = 128) is to be used in a research problem. In order to estimate the naphthalene content, the student takes 1.6 g, heats it until it is molten, then allows it to cool, and observes that the temperature of first appearance of solid is 175°C, 40°C below the melting point of pure anthracene. He now looks for a value of ΔH_f for anthracene (which he should have done first), and can't find any.

Persisting with the freezing-point approach, the student then dissolves the 1.6 g in 100 g benzene (molecular weight = 78) and observes a freezing-point depression of 0.50°C. The freezing point of pure benzene is 5.4°C; its heat of fusion is known to be 2240 cal/mole.

(a) Calculate the mole fraction of the napthalene in the anthracene.

(b) Calculates the heat of fusion of anthracene.

20. (30 min) A fairly concentrated solution of naphthalene in p-xylene freezes at 7.4°C (first appearance of solid) and boils at 147°C. Pure p-xylene melts at 16°C and boils at 138°C (1 atm pressure) and its heat of sublimation is 12.80 kcal/mole. Calculate (a) the heat of fusion and the heat of evaporation of p-xylene, (b) the mole fraction of naphthalene in the solution, and (c) list all the assumptions and approximations emboiled in the equations you use. These should not be such as to lead to more than 1% error if the solution is ideal.

21. (24 min) (final examination question) A solution comprising 0.1 mole of naphthalene and 0.9 mole of benzene is cooled until some solid benzene freezes out. The solution is then decanted off from the solid, and warmed to 80°C, at which temperature its vapor pressure is found to be 670 mm Hg. The freezing and normal boiling points of benzene are 5.5°C and 80°C, respectively, and its heat of fusion is 2550 cal.

Calculate the temperature to which the solution was cooled originally and the number of moles of benzene that must have frozen out. Assume ideal solutions.

22. (21 min) The molecular weight of a solid nonvolatile organic substance is to be determined by means of the following experiment:

Two open beakers are placed in a closed container. Beaker A initially contains 0.1 mole of naphthalene in 100 g of benzene, and beaker B initially contains 10 g of the unknown dissolved in 100 g of benzene. The beakers are allowed to stand side by side in the container until equilibrium is reached. Beaker A is then removed and weighed; it is found to have lost 8 g.

(a) Calculate the molecular weight of the unknown substance, assuming ideal solution behavior and (b) state all the assumptions and approximations necessary to obtain the numerical answer in (a) with 1% accuracy.

23. (30 min) A solution of ethyl alcohol and water contains 90% by weight of alcohol. Demonstrate by means of a calculation which substance freezes out first on cooling this solution and determine the approximate temperature of this freezing point. List separately all the assumptions and approximations necessary to obtain a numerical value for the freezing point from the data given. Draw a qualitative freezing-point diagram for this system and label the phase regions.

Heats of fusion are 1440 cal/mole and 1150 cal/mole for water and alcohol, respectively, and the freezing point of alcohol is $-114°C$.

24. (24 min) A philosophy student, who by some accident is taking a physical chemistry laboratory course, is assigned a molecular-weight determination by means of a colligative-property measurement. He dissolves his entire sample of unknown (2 g) in 120 g of mesitylene (a bottle of the stuff has been lying around) and finds the normal boiling point to be 169°C. He then tries to find data on mesitylene but can only locate its normal boiling point (164°C), its heat of sublimation (9,500 cal/mole), and its melting point ($-52°C$). Its molecular weight is 120.

To take his mind off the mess he is in, he runs a freezing-point depression on his solution, and finds that its freezing point is $-55.6°C$.

In desperation he finally takes his problem to "The Chemistry Club," and after a brief conclave a committee informs him that he does have enough data after all. Assuming the unknown to be non-volatile, that mesitylene froze out in his second experiment, and that the solution was dilute and ideal, he can calculate not only the

molecular weight of his unknown but also the heats of fusion and
of vaporization of mesitylene.

As Chairman of the committee, you are assigned the job of
writing out the details of the above calculations. Proceed!

Answers

1. This problem is easy if you recognize that the situation can be
treated as a freezing-point depression with sucrose as the solvent.
The equation is then

$$-\ln N_s = \frac{\Delta H_f}{R} (1/T - 1/T_f)$$

where ΔH_f and T_f are the heat of fusion and melting point of sucrose. N_s, for a 6.2-molal solution, is $6.2/(6.2 + 55.5) = 0.10$,
and $-\ln N_s$ is therefore 2.3. Then $\Delta H_f = 2.3 \times 1.98 \times 298 \times 473/175 = \underline{3650\text{ cal.}}$

2. The osmotic pressure of the required solution is, of course,
precisely 10 atm. The effective mole fraction of the NaCl must
be 1/31 or 0.032 and the actual mole fraction, allowing for two
ions per formula weight, will then be 0.016. The moles to be added
to 55.5 of water are then given by $0.016 = x/(55.5 + x)$ or $x \cong
0.016 \times 55.5$ or $\underline{0.88\text{ mole.}}$

3. (a) k_A is most easily determined as the intercept at $N_A = 1$ of
the straight line to which the P_A curve approaches as $N_A \rightarrow 0$. As
indicated in Fig. 10-5, this intercept is $\underline{0.5\text{ atm.}}$ (b) f_A is given by
the equation $P_A = f_A N_A P_A^{\circ}$ or $f_A = P_A/P_{A,\text{ ideal}}$. At $N_A = 0.6$,
we find $f_A \cong 0.45/0.74 = \underline{0.61.}$ (c) Similarly y_A is given by

$$P_A = y_A N_A k_A \quad \text{or} \quad y_A = P_A/P_{A,\text{ideal}}$$

where $P_{A,\text{ ideal}}$ is now read off the Henry's law line. Thus $y_A \cong
0.45/0.30 = \underline{0.15.}$

4. The vapor-pressure lowering at 80°C is $760 - 752.4$ mm Hg
or 7.6 mm Hg. The mole fraction of solute is then $N_2 = 7.6/760 =
0.01$. Taking as a basis a solution containing 100 g of benzene,
$0.01 = n_2/(n_2 + 1.29)$, since 100 g corresponds to 1.29 moles. Then
$n \cong 0.0129$, and this must correspond to the 1.27 g of solute present,

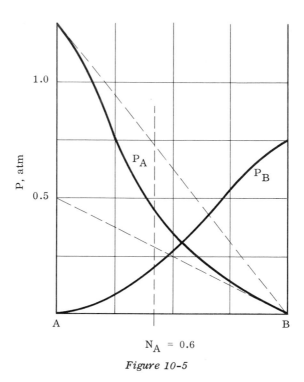

$$N_A = 0.6$$

Figure 10-5

so its molecular weight is <u>ca. 100.</u> The solution is dilute enough
that the simple boiling-point-elevation equation can now be used:
$\Delta T = (RT_b^2/1000h_f)m$ where m is the molality, here equal to
0.01×12.9 or 0.129, and ΔT is 0.25. Then

$$h_f = 1.98 \times 353^2 \times 0.129/1000 \times 0.25 = \underline{129 \text{ cal/g}}$$

5. The basic osmotic-pressure equation is $RT \ln P^\circ = RT \ln P + \int V \, d\pi$ or $RT \ln P^\circ/P = \overline{V}\pi$, assuming the liquid to be incompressible. Here, π can be equated to the hydrostatic head ρgh or, alter-
natively, $\pi = Mgh/\overline{V}$. Thus substitution for π leads to the desired
equation, $RT \ln P^\circ/P = Mgh$. If the system were placed in a closed
box, one might expect a circulation of vapor, with solvent evaporating at P° and condensing on the solution whose vapor pressure
is only P. This, if it did occur, would constitute a perpetual motion machine and thus a violation of the first law of thermodynamics. For it <u>not</u> to occur, the vapor pressure P° over the pure
solvent must diminish to exactly the value P at a height h, which
is just what the barometric formula would predict.

This analysis, incidentally, provides a way of proving that the molar volume V in the osmotic-pressure equation is that of a single molecule of solvent, and not of dimers, trimers, etc., even though in the liquid state one may have largely such forms.

6. The solubility can be obtained easily if the situation is viewed as the freezing-point depression of benzoic acid by ethanol. Thus, in the equation

$$-\ln N_1 = \frac{\Delta H_f}{R} (1/T - 1/T_f), \text{ we use } \Delta H_f = 4{,}000 \text{ and } T_f = 395$$

Then

$$-\ln N_1 = \frac{4000}{1.98}(1/353 - 1/395) = 0.61 \quad \text{and} \quad N_1 = 0.55$$

The saturated solution is then 0.55 mole fraction in benzoic acid.

The vapor pressure of the ethanol will then be $0.45 \times P°$ or 0.45×1 atm, since at 80° we are at the boiling point of pure ethanol.

7. ΔF for the process can be formulated as follows:

	H_2O(solution	H_2O(pure)
F:	$F° + RT \ln P$	$F° + RT \ln P°$

so $\Delta F = RT \ln P°/P$. The osmotic pressure equation is $RT \ln P° = RT \ln P + \int \overline{V} \, d\pi$ or $RT \ln P°/P \cong \overline{V}\pi = 18 \times 2 = 36$ cc-atm.

8. The molality of the solution must be $m = 0.2/1.86 = 0.108$. The mole fraction of the sucrose is then $0.108/(0.108 + 55.5) = 0.00192$, and this in turn is equal to $\Delta P/P°$, so $\Delta P = 0.00192 \times 23.5 = 0.0452$ mm Hg. P is then $23.506 - 0.045 = 23.461$ mm Hg.

9. Since NaCl is fully dissociated, the process is better written:

$$Na^+ (0.01 \text{ m}) + Cl^-(0.01 \text{ m}) = Na^+ (0.001 \text{ m}) + Cl^- (0.001 \text{ m})$$

F:	$F°_{Na^+} + RT \ln 0.01$	$F°_{Na^+} + RT \ln 0.001$
	$F°_{Cl^-} + RT \ln 0.01$	$F°_{Cl^-} + RT \ln 0.001$

or $\Delta F = 2RT \ln 0.001/0.01 = 2 \times 1.98 \times 298 \times (-1) \times 2.3 = -2710$ cal.

10. Since solid is in equilibrium with the solution, the solid vapor pressure must also be 20 mm Hg. From Fig. 10-6, the temperature is then $-3°C$. At this temperature, the pure (supercooled) liquid would have a vapor pressure of about 22 mm Hg. The mole fraction of A is then $N_A = \Delta P/P° = 2/22 = 0.091$.

100 g of solution contain 10 g of A and 90 g or 1.15 moles of benzene. The moles of A present are then:

$$0.091 = n_A/(n_A + 1.15)$$

from which $n_A = 0.105$. The molecular weight of A is then $10/0.105$ or 95 g/mole.

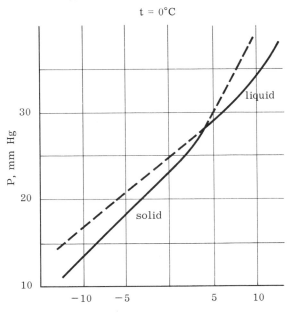

Figure 10-6

11. By Raoult's law, the partial pressure of the water must be 0.96×17 or 16.3 mm Hg. The partial pressure of the NH_3 must then be 33.7 mm Hg, from which the Henry's law constant for ammonia is $k = P/N = 33.7/4 = 8.42$.

For the 5 mole % solution, the partial pressure of the water will be $0.95 \times 17 = 16.1$, and that for the ammonia, $8.42 \times 5 = 42.1$; so the total pressure will then be 58.2 mm Hg.

12. The vapor-pressure lowering at 110°C is $760 - 752.4$ or 7.6 mm Hg, so that $N_2 = 7.6/760 = 0.01$. Taking 100 g of solution as a basis, there are 2 g of solute and 98 g or $98/92 = 1.065$ moles of toluene. Then $0.01 = n_2/(n_2 + 1.065)$ or $n_2 = 0.0106$ and the molecular weight is $2/0.0106 = \underline{189}$.

The molality of the solution is $m = 0.01 \times 10.9 = 0.109$, and the boiling-point elevation is given as 0.25°C; so from the dilute solution form of the boiling-point-elevation equation,

$$\Delta T = RT_b^2 m/1000\ell_v \qquad \ell_v = 1.98 \times 383^2 \times 0.109/1000 \times 0.25$$

$$= 127 \text{ cal/g}$$

13. To have the same vapor pressure, the two solutions must have the same mole fraction of water and of solute. Taking 100 g as a basis, the sodium chloride solution has $1/58.5$ or 0.0171 mole of solute and $99/18$ or 5.50 moles of water. Since sodium chloride is fully dissociated, the effective mole fraction in solute is:

$$N_2 = 0.0342/(0.0342 + 5.50) - 0.00619$$

This must then be equal to the mole fraction of the sugar, i.e.,

$0.00619 = \dfrac{n_S}{n_S + 95/18}$, from which $n_S = 0.0324$. The molecular weight is then $5/0.0324 = \underline{154}$.

14. The general form of the osmotic-pressure equation is

$$RT \ln P_1^{\circ} = RT \ln P_1 + \int \overline{V}_1 \, d\pi \quad \text{or} \quad RT \ln P_1^{\circ}/P_1 = V_1 \pi$$

if the simplifying assumption is made that the molar rather than the partial molar volume of the solvent may be used, and that the solvent is incompressible. Since π is equal to ρgh, where ρ is the density of the solution, and since the solution is dilute ρ is essentially the density of the solvent, we can write for $V_1\pi$, $\rho_1 ghV_1$. But $\rho_1 V_1 = M_1$, so we have $RT \ln P_1^{\circ}/P_1 = M_1 gh$. If $P_1 = P_1^{\circ\prime}$, the barometric formula has been derived.

Note that P_1 really should be equal to $P_1^{\circ\prime}$; if there were any difference in the two vapor pressures, it should be possible to devise a perpetual motion machine that would constitute a violation of the first law of thermodynamics.

15. (a) The boiling-point elevation is $82.00 - 80.00$ or $2.00°C$, hence $m = 2.00/1.22 = 1.64$, where m is the molality of the benzanilide.

(b) Since the solution is saturated with respect to benzanilide, the situation may now be viewed as a freezing-point-depression one, in which benzanilide is the solvent. The appropriate equation is then

$$-\ln N_b = \frac{\Delta H_f}{R} (1/T - 1/T_f)$$

where T and T_f are $355°K$ and $434°K$. N_b is given by $1.64/(1.64 + 1000/46) = 0.0705$. The heat of fusion is then $\Delta H_f = -2.3(\log 0.0705) \times 1.98 \times 355 \times 434/79 = \underline{10.2\ kcal.}$

16. The van't Hoff i factor is defined as $\pi = icRT$, where c is the molarity in formula weights per liter. Here, $c = 7/1.9 \times 0.082 \times 303 = \underline{0.148\ M.}$

17. One cannot draw a conclusion just by comparing the K_f values, since the actual solution is not dilute. Treating each component as potential solvent (i.e., species that will freeze out first), we have

$$-\ln 0.5 = \frac{\Delta H_{f,eb}}{R} (1/T_{eb} - 1/300)$$

$$= \frac{\Delta H_{f,b}}{R} (1/T_b - 1/300)$$

Then

$$\frac{(1/T_{eb} - 1/300)}{(1/T_b - 1/300)} = \frac{\Delta H_{f,b}}{\Delta H_{f,eb}}$$

Since

$$K_f = \frac{RT_f^2 M}{1000\Delta H_f}$$

the ratio of ΔH_f values becomes

$$\frac{\Delta H_{f,b}}{\Delta H_{f,eb}} = \frac{M_b}{M_{eb}} \frac{K_{f,eb}}{K_{f,b}} = \frac{78 \times 12.12}{109 \times 5} = 1.74$$

Therefore $(1/T_b - 1/300)$ is less than $(1/T_{eb} - 1/300)$, and T_b is then closer to 300 than is T_{eb}, i.e., benzene will freeze out first. (For the purposes of answering the quiz question, it was not necessary to do more than set up the above equations and, by inspection, determine whether the ratio of temperature terms was greater or less than unity.)

18. The freezing-point-depression constant for benzene is:

$$K_f = RT_f^2 M/1000\Delta H = 1.98 \times 278^2 \times 78/1000 \times 2400 = 4.98$$

The molality of the solution was then $(5.4 - 4.4)/4.98 = 0.2$ m, whereas if no dimerization were occurring, it should have been $m° = 0.02 \times 1000/78 = 0.257$. If m_d is the molality of the dimer present, and m_m that of the monomer, then

$$m_m + m_d = 0.2 \quad \text{and} \quad m_m + 2m_d = 0.257$$

or $m_m = 0.143$ and $m_d = 0.057$, and the equilibrium constant for dimerization is $K = (0.057)^2/0.143 = \underline{0.0227.}$

19. (a) The freezing-point-depression constant for benzene is:

$$K_f = RT_f^2 M/1000\Delta H = 1.98 \times 278^2 \times 78/1000 \times 2240 = 5.33$$

The benzene solution was then $0.5/5.33$ or 0.0937 molar, and the solution contained $0.0937 \times 100/1000$ or 0.00937 mole. The apparent molecular weight was then $1.6/0.00937$ or 170. We can now write

$$170 = N_a \times 178 + N_n \times 128 = 178 - 50\,N_n \quad \text{or} \quad N_n = \underline{0.16}$$

(b) The dilute-solution equation cannot be used to treat the freezing-point depression of the anthracene, and we must write:

$$-\ln N_a = \frac{\Delta H_f}{R} (1/T - 1/T_f)$$

or ΔH_f = 2.3 (log 0.84) × 1.98 × 448 × 488/40 or ΔH_f = 1870 cal/mole.

20. (a) The solution, being concentrated, must be treated in terms of the nondilute forms of the freezing-point-depression and boiling-point-elevation equations. Thus

$$-\ln N_x = \frac{\Delta H_f}{R} (1/280.5 - 1/289)$$

$$= \frac{\Delta H_v}{R} (1/411 - 1/420)$$

On elimination of the log term,

$$\Delta H_f (8.6/280.5 \times 289) = \Delta H_v (9/411 \times 420)$$

or ΔH_v = 2.03ΔH_f. Since ΔH_s = 12.80 = ΔH_v + ΔH_f, we can now solve simultaneously to get ΔH_v = 8.6 kcal/mole and ΔH_f = 4.2 kcal/mole.

(b) $-\ln N_x = \dfrac{4200}{1.98} (8.6/280.5 \times 289) = 0.226$ or N_x = 0.80 and N_{naphth} = 0.20.

(c) The various assumptions and approximations are:
1. Those involved in the Clausius-Clapeyron equation, i.e., first and second laws of thermodynamics, ideal gas behavior for the vapor, volume of vapor much larger than volume (per mole) of liquid, heat of vaporization independent of temperature, heat of sublimation independent of temperature, molar volume of solid much smaller than molar volume of vapor (see Problem 23).
2. For the boiling-point-elevation equation: ideal solution, solute nonvolatile.
3. For the freezing-point-depression equation: ideal solution, solute insoluble in the solid solvent.

21. Since 80°C is its normal boiling point, the vapor pressure of pure benzene is 760 mm Hg as compared to 670 mm Hg for the solution. The vapor-pressure lowering is thus 90 mm Hg, and the mole fraction of benzene is N_b = 670/760 = 0.882. Then, according to the freezing-point-depression equation:

$$-\ln N_b = \frac{\Delta H_f}{R}(1/T - 1/278.6)$$

or $1/T = -2.3(\log 0.882) \times 1.98/2550 + 1/278.6 = 9.62 \times 10^{-5} + 1/278.6$.

Since T is evidently close to 278.6, a way to retain precision in the calculation is to write $\Delta T/278.6^2 \cong 9.62 \times 10^{-5}$ or $\Delta T = 7.48$; a second round of approximation is then: $\Delta T/271.1 \times 278.6 = 9.62 \times 10^{-5}$ or $\Delta T = 7.25$ and $t = 5.5 - 7.25 = -1.75°C$.

The mole fraction of the napthalene in the freezing solution is 0.118. Then $0.118 = 0.1/(0.1 + n_b)$ or $n_b = 0.748$. Thus $0.9 - 0.748$ or about 0.15 mole of benzene must have frozen out.

22. (a) At equilibrium the mole fraction of benzene must be the same in the two solutions and hence so must the mole fraction of solute. In the case of beaker A this last is: $N_2 = 0.1/(0.1 + 92/78) = 0.0782$. Then for beaker B: $0.0782 = n_x/(n_x + 108/78)$ (since the 8 g lost from beaker A must have condensed into the solution in beaker B), or $n_x = 0.117$. The molecular weight of the unknown is then $10/0.117$ or 85.

(b) We assume ideal solution, nonvolatile solutes, and, more trivially, that the vapor space is small enough that the entire 8 g lost from one beaker must have condensed in the other. Of course, the two beakers are assumed to be at the same temperature.

23. On the basis of 100 g of solution, there would be 90/46 or 1.96 moles of alcohol and 10/18 or 0.556 g of water. The two mole fractions are then $N_a = 0.778$ and $N_w = 0.222$. In order to decide which will freeze out first, it is necessary to calculate the freezing point, assuming first the one and then the other possibility.

Alcohol as solvent:

$$-\ln N_a = \frac{1150}{1.98}(1/T - 1/159)$$

$$1/T = -2.3(\log 0.778) \times 1.98/1150 + 1/159 = 67.3 \times 10^{-4}$$

$$T = 148°K$$

Water as solvent:

$$-\ln N_W = \frac{1440}{1.98}(1/T - 1/273) \qquad \text{from which } T = 174°K$$

We conclude that water freezes out first, and at 174°K.

The assumptions and approximations are:

1. Those embodied in the Clausius-Clapeyron equation: (a) first and second laws of thermodynamics; (b) molar volume of vapor large compared to that of the solid and of the liquid solvent; (c) ideal gas law behavior for the vapor; and (d) heats of sublimation and vaporization independent of temperature. Actually, of course, the derivation does not need to involve arguments about equal vapor pressures for the solid and the solvent in the solution, and may be made purely in terms of the free energy of the solid vs. that for the solvent in the solution. We still assume that the heat of fusion is independent of temperature, and the first and second laws.

2. That the solution is ideal and that the solute is not soluble in solid solvent.

The qualitative diagram called for is sketched in Fig. 10-7. From the above calculation, it is evident that the eutectic must lie at greater than 90% alcohol content.

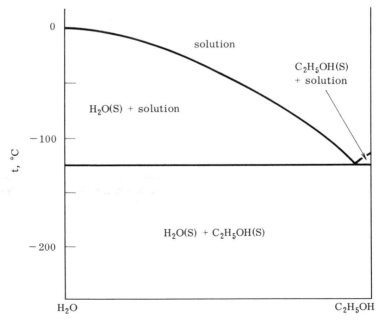

Figure 10-7

24. Using the dilute solution forms, we have the two equations:

$$\Delta T_b = (169 - 164) = 5 = \frac{R \times 437^2}{\Delta H_v} \frac{120}{1000} m$$

$$\Delta T_f = (55.6 - 52) = 3.6 = \frac{R \times 217^2}{\Delta H_f} \frac{120}{1000} m$$

or, on eliminating m,

$$437^2/5\Delta H_v = 217^2/3.6\Delta H_f \quad \text{or} \quad \Delta H_v = 2.9\Delta H_f$$

We also know that $\Delta H_f + \Delta H_v = 9500$, so $\Delta H_f = 9500/3.9 =$ 2.43 kcal/mole and $\Delta H_v = 7.07$ kcal/mole.

We can now calculate either K_b or K_f. Choosing the former,

$$K_b = \frac{1.98 \times 437^2 \times 0.12}{7070} = 6.42$$

Then m = 5/6.42 = 0.78. The grams of unknown per 1000 g of mesitylene would be 2 × 1000/120 or 16.7 g. The molecular weight is then 16.7/0.78 = 21.4.

11 *Heterogeneous and homogeneous gas equilibrium*

Comments

There are three general types of problems in this chapter. First, you will find a number that involve equilibria between gaseous substances and require that you calculate K_p from the data, or, given K_p, determine the extent of reaction at equilibrium. In most cases stoichiometry is very important — that is, you must utilize the equation for the over-all process to determine the mole ratios in which reactants disappear and products form. Often it will be convenient to set up stoichiometric relationships between the various mole numbers, and insert the results in the expression for K_n. K_p then follows, if the total pressure is known (and N, the total moles, can be obtained from the sum of the various mole numbers). If the amount of initial substance is not specified, it is often less confusing to assume some convenient amount as a basis; your choice should cancel out in the course of the calculation.

The second group of problems consists of those dealing with

equilibria between solids and gases. Here, it is important to remember that, although the solids do not appear in the K_p expression, they must be present in the physical system for K_p to hold. Remember, too, that in a reaction of the type $A(s) + B(g) =$ products, the amount of B needed to convert all of A to products is the sum of the equilibrium amount required by K_p, plus the amount needed by stoichiometry to convert A to products. Finally, if a solid dissociates into gaseous products, these will be formed in stoichiometric ratio; hence they, and K_p, can be expressed in terms of the total pressure if no other gases were present initially.

Last, you will find a number of simple thermodynamic calculations involving conversion of K_p to $\Delta F°$, the relation between $\Delta F°$, $\Delta H°$ and $\Delta S°$, and the variation of $\Delta F°$ and of K_p with temperature. Look for occasional short-cuts.

Equations and concepts

Equilibrium Constant Expressions: Given the general reaction involving only ideal gases at a given temperature,

$$aA + bB + \cdots = mM + nN + \cdots$$

$$K_p = \frac{P_M^m \, P_N^n \cdots}{P_A^a \, P_B^b \cdots} - \frac{n_M^m \, n_N^n \cdots}{n_A^a \, n_B^b \cdots} (P/N)^{\Delta n} - K_n (P/N)^{\Delta n}$$

Here, N denotes the total moles present, P the total pressure, n the moles of a particular species, and Δn the moles of products minus the moles of reactants.

If solids are involved in the reaction, K_p will contain only the terms that refer to gaseous species, and Δn will be the difference between moles of gaseous products and moles of gaseous reactants. The solid species must, of course, be present in the actual system if K_p is to hold.

Thermodynamic Relationships:

$$\Delta F° = \Delta H° - T\Delta S°$$

$$\Delta F° = -RT \ln K_p$$

van't Hoff equation: $d \ln K_p/dT = \Delta H°/RT^2$

$$\ln K_2/K_1 = - \frac{\Delta H°}{R} (1/T_2 - 1/T_1)$$

Problems

1. (19.5 min) SO_3 is formed according to the reaction:

$$O_2 + 2SO_2 = 2SO_3$$

by passing a mixture of air and SO_2 over a catalyst at 600°C. The total pressure is maintained at 10 atm. Air is 20% oxygen, and the initial mixture contained SO_2 and O_2 in the ratio of two to one (mole basis).

(a) Calculate $\Delta F°$ for the reaction at 600°C, if K_p is 100 atm^{-1}.

(b) Calculate $\Delta F°$ for the reaction at 25°C if $\Delta S°$ is 0.5 cal/deg and $\Delta C_p°$ is negligible, again assuming K_p to be 100 atm^{-1} at 600°C.

(c) Calculate the actual value of K_p if in the above process two-thirds the SO_2 was converted to SO_3.

2. (10.5 min) K_p is 9 atm^2 for the reaction:

$$LiCl \cdot 3NH_3(s) = LiCl \cdot NH_3(s) + 2NH_3(g)$$

at 40°C. How many moles of ammonia must be added at this temperature to a 5-liter flask containing 0.1 mole of $LiCl \cdot NH_3$ in order to completely convert the solid to $LiCl \cdot 3NH_3$? Show your calculations.

3. (30 min) K_p is 10^5 atm^{-1} at 700°K for the reaction

$$2NO + O_2 = 2NO_2$$

and $\Delta S°$ is -40.7 cal/deg and $\Delta C_p°$ is zero.

(a) Some pure NO_2 is introduced into a 30-liter flask at 700°K until the equilibrium pressure is 0.2 atm. Calculate α, the degree of dissociation of the NO_2.

(b) If α were 0.3 under the above conditions, what would be the average molecular weight of the gas mixture? Show your calculation.

(c) Calculate $\Delta F°$ for the reaction at 25°C.

(d) Calculate the temperature coefficient of K at 700°K, i.e., the per cent change in K per degree temperature change. (You may neglect the $NO_2-N_2O_4$ equilibrium, i.e., assume no N_2O_4 is present.)

4. (24 min) K_p is 8×10^{-9} atm at 100°C for the equilibrium:

$$COCl_2(g) = CO(g) + Cl_2(g)$$

$\Delta S^\circ_{373°K}$ is 30 cal/deg.
  (a) Calculate the degree of dissociation of phosgene at 100°C and 2 atm total pressure.
  (b) Calculate $\Delta H^\circ_{373°K}$ for the reaction.
  (c) Assuming ΔC°_p to be zero, at what temperature would the degree of dissociation of phosgene be 0.1%, again at 2 atm total pressure? Show your calculations.

5. (12 min) Ferrous sulfate undergoes a thermal decomposition as follows:

$$2FeSO_4(s) = Fe_2O_3(s) + SO_2(g) + SO_3(g)$$

At 929°K the total gas pressure is 0.9 atm with both solids present.
  (a) Calculate K_p for this temperature.
  (b) Calculate the equilibrium total pressure that will be obtained if excess ferrous sulfate is placed in a flask at 929°K, which contains an initial SO_2 pressure of 0.6 atm.

6. (24 min) (final examination question) Gaseous COF_2 is passed over a catalyst at 1000°C and comes to equilibrium according to the equation:

$$2COF_2 = CO_2 + CF_4$$

The pressure is maintained at 10 atm. A sample of the equilibrium mixture is quickly cooled (which stops any shift in concentrations) and analysis shows that, out of 500 cc (STP) of the mixture, there are 300 cc (STP) of combined COF_2 and CO_2. (This is done by passing the mixture through barium hydroxide solution, which absorbs COF_2 and CO_2 but not CF_4).
  (a) Calculate K_p for the equilibrium.
  (b) If K_p increases by 1% per degree around 1000°C, calculate $\Delta H°$, $\Delta S°$, and $\Delta F°$ at this temperature.

7. (24 min) (final examination question) One-tenth mole of H_2 and

0.2 mole of CO_2 are introduced into an evacuated flask at 450°C, and the reaction

(a) $H_2 + CO_2 = H_2O + CO$

occurs to give an equilibrium pressure of 0.5 atm. Analysis of the mixture shows that it contains 10 mole % water.
    A mixture of CoO(s) and Co(s) is then introduced so that the additional equilibria (b) and (c) are established:

(b) $CoO(s) + H_2 = Co(s) + H_2O$

(c) $CoO(s) + CO = Co(s) + CO_2$

Analysis of the new equilibrium mixture shows it to contain 30 mole % water.
    Calculate the three equilibrium constants. If K_a increases by 1% per degree for temperatures around 450°C, calculate ΔH_a°.

8. (15 min) K_p is 10^{-3} atm$^{1/2}$ at 2000°K and ΔS° is 21 cal/deg ($\Delta C_p = 0$) for the reaction:

$CO_2 = CO + \frac{1}{2} O_2$

(a) Calculate ΔF° at 2000°K.
(b) Calculate ΔF° at 298°K.
(c) Calculate the degree of dissociation of CO_2 if the equilibrium mixture is brought to 2000°K and 2 atm total pressure.

9. (15 min) K_p is 0.05 atm^2 at 20°C for the reaction:

$NH_4HS(s) = NH_3(g) + H_2O(g)$

0.06 mole of solid NH_4HS are introduced into a 2.4 liter flask at 20°C.
    (a) Calculate the per cent of the solid that will have decomposed into NH_3 and H_2S at equilibrium.
    (b) Calculate the number of moles of ammonia that would have to be added to the flask to reduce the decomposition of the solid to 1%.
    (c) Having reached the state of equilibrium described in (b), explain whether the addition of more $NH_4HS(s)$ would increase, decrease, or leave unchanged the ammonia pressure.

10. (30 min) CO_2 reacts rapidly with H_2S at elevated temperatures to give carbon oxysulfide (COS) and water. In an experiment to determine K_p for this reaction, 4.4 g of CO_2 was placed in a 2.5-liter flask at 337°C, and enough H_2S was introduced to bring the total pressure to 10 atm. (<u>Note</u>: to save calculation time, PV/RT is then 0.5.)

A sample of the equilibrium mixture was then withdrawn and cooled rapidly to a point such that the water froze out, but not the other gases present. The sample was thus found to have contained 2 mole % of water.

In a second experiment, the above procedure was repeated, but for an equilibrium mixture at 347°C, and the sample withdrawn was now found to contain 3 mole % water.

(a) Calculate K_p at 337°C for the reaction

$$CO_2(g) + H_2S(g) = COS(g) + H_2O(g)$$

(b) Find $\Delta F°$ at 337°C.

(c) Calculate $\Delta H°$ (it is sufficient to set up an equation in which $\Delta H°$ is the only non-numerical quantity).

(d) If inert gas were added to the equilibrium mixture at 337°C until the pressure was doubled (keeping V constant), would the amount of COS formed have been greater, less, or unchanged? If inert gas were added at constant pressure until the volume doubled, would the amount of COS formed have been greater, less, or unchanged? Explain.

11. (20 min) (final examination question) One and one-tenth grams of NOBr is placed in an evacuated 1-liter flask at $-55°C$. The flask is then warmed to 0°C, at which temperature the contents are gaseous and exert a pressure of 0.3 atm. On further warming to 25°C, the equilibrium total pressure rises to 0.35 atm. At both 0°C and 25°C the equilibrium

$$2NOBr = 2NO + Br_2$$

is present. Calculate K_p for the reaction at 0°C, and $\Delta H°$. The atomic weight of Br is 80.

12. (20 min) (final examination question) In a study of the equilibrium, $H_2 + I_2 = 2HI$, a certain number of moles x of HI are formed when 1 mole of H_2 and 3 moles of I_2 are introduced into a flask of volume V at temperature T. On introducing 2 additional

moles of H_2, the amount of HI formed is found to be 2x. Calculate K_p.

13. (30 min) Four and four-tenths grams of CO_2 are introduced
into a 1-liter flask containing excess solid carbon, at 1000°C, so
that the equilibrium

$$CO_2 + C(s) = 2CO$$

is reached. The gas density at equilibrium corresponds to an average molecular weight of 36.
  (a) Calculate the equilibrium pressure and the value of K_p.
  (b) If, now, an additional amount of He (inert) is introduced
until the total pressure is doubled, the equilibrium amount of CO
will be (increased, decreased, unchanged, insufficient information
to tell). If, instead, the volume of the flask were doubled, with He
introduced to maintain the same total pressure, the equilibrium
amount of CO would (increase, decrease, be unchanged, insufficient
data to tell).
  (c) If in (a) there were actually 1.2 g of C(s) present, how
many moles of CO_2 would have to be introduced so that at equilibrium only a trace of carbon remained?
  (d) If the K_p for the equilibrium doubles with a 10°C increase
in temperature, what is $\Delta H°$ for the reaction?

14. (20 min) (final examination question) For the reaction below
K_p is 0.05 and $\Delta F°$ is 5.35 kcal at 900°K:

$$C_2H_6(g) = C_2H_4(g) + H_2(g)$$

If an initial mixture comprising 20 moles of C_2H_6 and 80 moles of
N_2 (inert) is passed over a dehydrogenation catalyst at 900°K, what
is the equilibrium per cent composition of the effluent gas mixture? The total pressure is kept at 0.5 atm. Given that $\Delta S°$ is
32.3 cal/deg at 900°K, calculate $\Delta F°$ at 300°K (assume $\Delta C_p° = 0$).

15. (18 min) (final examination question) A 2-liter flask maintained at 700°K contains 0.1 mole of CO and a catalyst for the reaction

$$CO(g) + 2H_2(g) = CH_3OH(g)$$

Hydrogen is introduced until the equilibrium total pressure is
7 atm, at which point 0.06 mole of methanol are formed.

(a) Calculate K_p.

(b) What would the final pressure be were the same amounts of CO and H_2 used but with no catalyst present so that no reaction occurs?

16. (18 min) K_p has the value 10^{-5} for the equilibrium

$$CO_2 + H_2 = CO + H_2O(g)$$

at 25°C, and $\Delta S°$ is -10 cal/deg. ($\Delta H°$ and $\Delta S°$ do not change much with temperature.) One mole of CO, 2 moles of H_2, and 3 moles of CO_2 are introduced into a 5-liter flask at 25°C. Calculate (a) $\Delta F°$ at 25°C, (b) the equilibrium pressure, (c) the moles of each species present at equilibrium, and (d) K_p at 100°C.

17. (12 min) Calculate K_p for the reaction

$$S(s) + 2CO(g) = SO_2(g) + 2C(s)$$

At the temperature in question, two atmospheres of CO are introduced into a vessel containing excess solid sulfur, and a final equilibrium pressure of 1.03 atm is observed.

18. (24 min) (final examination question) K_p has the value 10^{-6} atm^3 and 10^{-4} atm^3 at 25°C and 50°C, respectively, for the reaction:

$$CuSO_4 \cdot 3H_2O = CuSO_4 + 3H_2O(g)$$

(a) What is the minimum number of moles of water vapor that must be introduced into a 2-liter flask at 25°C in order to completely convert 0.01 mole of $CuSO_4$ to the trihydrate. Show your calculations.

(b) Calculate $\Delta H°$ for the reaction.

19. (30 min) $\Delta F°$ is 300 cal at 40°C for the reaction:

$$2NO_2 = N_2O_4$$

(a) Calculate K_p for this reaction at 40°C.

(b) The density of an equilibrium mixture of NO_2 and N_2O_4 gases is found to be 5.85 g/liter at 40°C and a certain pressure. Using the value in (a) for K_p, calculate the degree of dissociation of the N_2O_4, the average molecular weight of the mixture, and the total pressure of the mixture.

20. (15 min) The absolute entropies (in cal/deg-mole) of H_2, O_2, and HCl are 31.2, 49.0, and 44.7, respectively, when these substances are in the gaseous state at 1 atm pressure and 25°C. The heat of formation of HCl(g) is -22.1 kcal/mole at 25°C. Calculate K_p for $H_2 + Cl_2 = 2HCl$ at 125°C. State any important assumption(s) and explain whether much error is involved.

21. (15 min) Ammonium chloride vaporizes according to the process:

$$NH_4Cl(s) = NH_3 + HCl$$

The vapor pressure of $NH_4Cl(g)$ is negligible. It is found that at 520°K the equilibrium dissociation pressure (P_{total}) is 0.050 atm. In a second experiment, 0.02 mole of $NH_4Cl(s)$ and 0.02 mole of NH_3 are introduced into a 42.7-liter flask maintained at 520°K. Calculate the amount of each substance present at equilibrium and the partial pressures of the two that are gaseous.

22. (17 min) (final examination question) A container whose volume is V liters contains an equilibrium mixture that consists of 2 moles of PCl_5, 2 moles of PCl_3, and 2 moles of Cl_2 (all as gases). The pressure is 3 atm, and the temperature is T°K.

A certain amount of Cl_2 is now introduced, keeping the pressure and temperature constant, until the equilibrium volume is 2V liters. Calculate the moles of Cl_2 that were added, and the value of K_p for the equilibrium.

23. (18 min) An equilibrium mixture for the reaction

$$CO + 2H_2 = CH_3OH$$

at 700°K consists of 2 atm of CH_3OH, 1 atm of CO, and 0.1 atm of H_2. The above mixture is allowed to expand to twice its original volume, still at 700°K. Calculate the new equilibrium pressures.

Answers

1. (a) $\Delta F° = -RT \ln K_p = -1.98 \times 873 \times 2 = -7.95$ kcal.

(b) Since $\Delta F° = \Delta H° - T \Delta S°$, then at 600°C, we find $\Delta H° = -7.95 + 873 \times 0.5/1000 = -7.51$ kcal. Then at 25°C, since $\Delta C_p°$ is zero, $\Delta F° = -7.51 - 298 \times 0.5/1000 = \underline{-7.66 \text{ kcal.}}$

(c) The equilibrium constant is

$$K_p = \frac{P^2_{SO_3}}{P_{O_2} \times P^2_{SO_2}} = \frac{n^2_{SO_3}}{n_{O_2} \times n^2_{SO_2}} \frac{N}{P}$$

If we take as a basis 2 moles of SO_2 and 1 of O_2 initially, then

$$n_{SO_2} = \tfrac{2}{3}, \text{ i.e., } \tfrac{1}{3} \text{ remains}$$

$$n_{O_2} = \tfrac{1}{3}, \text{ i.e., the } \tfrac{4}{3} \text{ moles of } SO_2 \text{ reacting use up } \tfrac{2}{3} \text{ mole of } O_2.$$

$$n_{N_2} = 4$$

$$n_{SO_3} = \tfrac{4}{3}$$

$$N = \tfrac{19}{3} \text{ and } P = 10$$

Then $K_p = \dfrac{(4/3)^2 (19/3)}{(1/3)(2/3)^2} 10 = \underline{7.6 \text{ atm}^{-1}}.$

2. Since $K_p = P^2_{NH_3}$, the equilibrium ammonia pressure must be 3 atm, and the amount of ammonia gas in the flask would then be: $3 \times 5/0.082 \times 313 = 0.58$. In addition, 0.2 mole of ammonia is needed to effect the conversion to $LiCl \cdot 3NH_3$, so the total ammonia required is $\underline{0.78 \text{ mole.}}$

3. (a) It is convenient to write K_p in the form:

$$K_p = \frac{n^2_{NO_2}}{n^2_{NO} \times n_{O_2}} \frac{N}{P}$$

Let $n^\circ_{NO_2}$ be the number of moles of NO_2 before dissociation, then

$$n_{NO_2} = (1 - \alpha)n^\circ_{NO_2}$$

$$n_{NO_2} = \alpha n^\circ_{NO_2}$$

$$n_{O_2} = \frac{\alpha}{2} n^\circ_{NO_2}$$

$$N = (1 + \alpha/2)n^\circ_{NO_2}$$

$$10^5 = \frac{(1 - \alpha)^2 n^{\circ 2}_{NO_2}}{\alpha^2 n^{\circ 2}_{NO_2} \times (\alpha/2)n^\circ_{NO_2}} \frac{(1 + \alpha/2)n^\circ_{NO_2}}{0.2}$$

Since K_p is so large, it should be safe to neglect α in comparison with unity, and we can then write

$$10^5 = \frac{1}{\alpha^2(\alpha/2) \times 0.2}$$

or $\alpha^3 = 10^{-4}$ and $\alpha = 0.046$.

As a second approximation we write $(1 - \alpha)$ as 0.954 and $(1 + \alpha/2)$ as 1.02. This leads to $\alpha^3 = 0.93 \times 10^{-4}$ and $\alpha = \underline{0.045}$.

(b) On substituting $\alpha = 0.3$ into the above equations, $n_{NO_2} = 0.7n^\circ_{NO_2}$, etc., and the mole fractions become $N_{NO_2} = 0.7/1.15 = 0.61$, $N_{NO} = 0.3/1.15 = 0.26$ and $N_{O_2} = 0.13$. The average molecular weight of the mixture is then $M_{av} = 0.61 \times 46 + 0.26 \times 30 + 0.13 \times 32 = \underline{40}$.

(c) ΔF° at 700°K is $-1.98 \times 700 \times 2.3 \log 10^5 = -15.9$ kcal, hence $\Delta H^\circ = -15.9 + 700 \times (-40.7)/1000 = -44.4$ kcal. Then at 25°C: $\Delta F^\circ = -44.4 - 298 \times (-40.7)/1000 = \underline{-32.4}$ kcal.

(d) It is convenient here to use the van't Hoff equation in differential form:

$$d \ln K_p/dT = \Delta H^\circ/RT^2 = -44,400/1.98 \times 700^2 = -0.046$$

Since $d \ln K_p$ is the same as dK_p/K_p, the above is the desired temperature coefficient, or, in % per degree: $\underline{-4.6\%}$.

4. (a) $K_p = \dfrac{n_{CO} \times n_{Cl_2}}{n_{COCl_2}} \dfrac{P}{N}$. Assuming 1 mole of phosgene initially, $n_{COCl_2} = 1 - \alpha$, $n_{CO} = n_{Cl_2} = \alpha$, and $N = 1 + \alpha$. Then $8 \times 10^{-9} = [\alpha^2/(1 - \alpha)] \times [2/(1 + \alpha)]$ and, since α will be small, $8 \times 10^{-9} \cong 2\alpha^2$ or $\alpha = \underline{6.3 \times 10^{-5}}$.

(b) $\Delta F^{\circ}_{373^{\circ}K} = -1.98 \times 373 \times 2.3 \log 8 \times 10^{-9} = 13.7$ kcal, $\Delta H^{\circ} = 13.7 + 373 \times 30/1000 = \underline{24.8 \text{ kcal.}}$

(c) If α is to be 0.001, then $K_p = 2 \times 10^{-6}$ and, from the van't Hoff equation, $\log 8 \times 10^{-9}/2 \times 10^{-6} = -(24,800/2.3 \times 1.98)(1/373 - 1/T)$ or $(1/373 - 1/T) = 4.43 \times 10^{-4}$ or $\underline{T = 448^{\circ}K.}$

5. (a) $K_p = P_{SO_2} P_{SO_3}$. Since each gas is formed in equal amounts, their partial pressures are each 0.45 atm. K_p is then 0.45^2 or $\underline{0.203 \text{ atm}^2.}$

(b) Let P_{SO_3} be the equilibrium SO_3 pressure; then $P_{SO_2} = P_{SO_3} + 0.6$, so $0.203 = P_{SO_3}(P_{SO_3} + 0.6)$ or $P_{SO_3} = 0.24$, $P_{SO_2} = 0.84$, and $P_{total} = \underline{1.08 \text{ atm.}}$

6. (a) There must have been $500 - 300$ or 200 cc (STP) of CF_4, and hence also 200 cc (STP) of CO_2 since this is formed in equimolar amounts. There were then 100 cc (STP) of COF_2. The mole fractions are then 0.4, 0.4, and 0.2 for these substances, respectively, and the partial pressures are then 4, 4, and 2 atm. K_p is thus $(4)(4)/(2)^2 = \underline{4 \text{ atm.}}$

(b) We use the equation: $d \ln K_p/dT = \Delta H^{\circ}/RT^2$, where $d \ln K_p/dT$ is simply the fractional change in K_p per degree and is equal to 0.01. Then $\Delta H^{\circ} = 0.01 \times 1.98 \times 1273^2 = \underline{32.1 \text{ kcal.}}$ Also, $\Delta F^{\circ} = -RT \ln K_p = -1.98 \times 1273 \times 2.3 \log 4 = \underline{-3.47 \text{ kcal.}}$ Therefore $\Delta S^{\circ} = (\Delta H^{\circ} - \Delta F^{\circ})/T = \underline{27.9 \text{ cal/deg.}}$

7. Since the number of moles of gaseous species are the same on both sides of equation (a), $K_p = K_n = n_{H_2O} n_{CO}/n_{H_2} n_{CO_2}$, where n denotes number of moles. Then if $x = n_{H_2O}$:

$$n_{H_2O} = x, \quad n_{CO} = x, \quad n_{H_2O} = 0.1 - x, \quad n_{CO_2} = 0.2 - x$$

The mole fraction of water is thus $x/0.3 = 0.1$, whence $x = 0.03$. K_a is then $(0.03)^2/(0.07)(0.17) = \underline{0.0757.}$

Neither reaction (b) nor (c) changes the total moles of gas present, which therefore remains at 0.3. According to the new equilibrium composition, 0.09 mole of water are present, or an increase of 0.06. This must have come about through reaction (b), so that 0.06 mole of H_2 were used up, and $0.07 - 0.06$ or 0.01 are left. K_b is then $0.09/0.01 = \underline{9.}$ Since reaction (b) minus reaction (a) gives reaction (c), $K_c = K_b/K_a = \underline{119.}$

From the van't Hoff equation, $d \ln K_p/dT = \Delta H°/RT^2$, where $d \ln K_p/dT$ is the fractional change in K_p per degree and is given as 0.01. Then $\Delta H_a° = 0.01 \times 1.98 \times 723 = \underline{10.3 \text{ kcal.}}$

8. (a) $\Delta F° = -RT \ln K_p = -1.98 \times 2000 \times 2.3 \times \log 10^{-3} = \underline{27.3 \text{ kcal.}}$

(b) $\Delta H° = \Delta F° + T \Delta S° = 27.3 + 2000 \times 21/1000 = 69.3 \text{ kcal}$, so at $298°K$, $\Delta F° = 69.3 - 298 \times 21/1000 = \underline{63.0 \text{ kcal.}}$

(c) $K_p = \dfrac{n_{CO} \, n_{O_2}^{1/2}}{n_{CO_2}} (P/N)^{1/2}$

then

$$n_{CO_2} = (1 - \alpha)n°_{CO_2}$$

$$n_{CO} = \alpha n°_{CO_2}$$

$$n_{O_2} = \tfrac{1}{2} \alpha n°_{CO_2}$$

$$N = (1 + \tfrac{1}{2} \alpha)n°_{CO_2}$$

and therefore $0.001 = (\tfrac{1}{2}\alpha)^{1/2}(\alpha)(2)^{1/2}/(1 - \alpha)(1 + \tfrac{1}{2}\alpha)^{1/2}$. Since K_p is small, a first approximation is $0.001 = \alpha^{3/2}$, or $\underline{\alpha = 0.01.}$

9. (a) $K_p = P_{NH_3} P_{H_2S} = \tfrac{1}{4} P^2$, since $P_{NH_3} = P_{H_2S} = P/2$. Therefore $P^2 = 0.2$ and $P = 0.447$ atm. The moles of gas present are then $n = 0.447 \times 2.4/0.082 \times 293 = 0.0447$ mole. The moles of NH_3 or of H_2S are then 0.0223, and the moles of solid remaining are $0.06 - 0.0223 = 0.0377$ mole, or $\underline{37.2\%}$ decomposed.

(b) If the decomposition is to be kept to 1%, the moles of H_2S present must be 0.0006, and $P_{H_2S} = 0.006$. From K_p, the pressure of NH_3 is then $0.05/0.006$ or 8.33 atm. The moles of ammonia will then be $\underline{0.833.}$ (Notice that 2.4 liters is just 0.1 molar volume if P is 1 atm, so moles of gas $= 0.1 \times P$).

(c) No change. Addition of more solid does not affect its thermodynamic activity.

10. (a) Since the number of moles of gas are unchanged by the reaction, $K_p = K_n = n_{COS} \, n_{H_2O}/n_{CO_2} \, n_{H_2S}$. The 4.4 g of CO_2 amounts to 0.1 mole, and there were evidently 0.5 mole total of gas present. Let $x = n_{H_2O}$, then $n_{H_2O} = x$, $n_{COS} = x$, $n_{CO_2} = 0.1 - x$;

total: $0.1 + x$. The moles of H_2S were then $0.5 - (0.1 + x)$. Also, $x/0.5 = 0.02$, or $x = 0.01$. Then

$$K_p = (0.01)(0.01)/(0.09)(0.39) = \underline{0.00285}$$

(b) $\Delta F° = -RT \ln K_p = -1.98 \times 610 \times 2.3 \log (0.00285) = \underline{7.15}$ kcal.

(c) At $347°K$, $n_{H_2O} = 0.468 \times 0.03 = 0.0145$, etc., so $K_p = (0.0145)(0.0145)/(0.085)(0.371)$. Then $K_p = 0.00672$ and, from the van't Hoff equation, $\log 0.00672/0.00285 = -(\Delta H°/2.3 \times 1.98) \times (1/620 - 1/610)$.

(d) Addition of inert gas at constant volume will not change any of the partial pressures and therefore will not shift the equilibrium (if the gases are ideal), but addition at constant pressure dilutes the system and reduces the partial pressures. In this case, however, there is no change in the number of moles of gas when reaction occurs, so the position of equilibrium will not be affected.

11. The 1.1 g of NOBr corresponds to 0.01 mole, and if α denotes the degree of dissociation, then at equilibrium

$$n_{NOBr} = (1 - \alpha)0.01$$

$$n_{NO} = 0.01\alpha$$

$$n_{Br_2} = 0.005\alpha$$

$$N = 0.01(1 + \alpha/2)$$

But

$$N = PV/RT = 0.3 \times 1/0.082 \times 273 = 0.0134$$

hence

$$1.34 = 1 + \alpha/2 \quad \text{or} \quad \alpha = 0.68$$

$$K_p = \frac{n_{NO}^2 n_{Br_2}}{n_{NOBr}^2} \frac{P}{N} = (0.68)^2(0.34)(0.3)/(0.32)^2(1.34) = \underline{0.345 \text{ atm.}}$$

Repeating the calculation for $25°C$, $N = 0.0143$, $\alpha = 0.86$ and $K_p = 3.97$. Then

$$\log 3.97/0.345 = -\frac{\Delta H^\circ}{1.98 \times 2.3} (1/298 - 1/273)$$

and $\Delta H^\circ = 1.061 \times 1.98 \times 2.3 \times 298 \times 273/25 = \underline{15.7 \text{ kcal.}}$

12. By material balance:

$$n_{HI} = x \qquad\qquad\qquad n_{HI} = 2x$$

$$n_{H_2} = 1 - x/2 \quad \text{and} \quad n_{H_2} = 3 - x$$

$$n_{I_2} = 3 - x/2 \qquad\qquad n_{I_2} = 3 - x$$

Since there are an equal number of moles of gaseous species on both sides of the equation, $K_p = K_n$, hence

$$\frac{x^2}{(1 - x/2)(3 - x/2)} = \frac{(2x)^2}{(3 - x)^2}$$

On solving, $x = 3/2$ and $K_p = 3^2/(3/2)^2 = \underline{4.}$

13. (a) From the definition of average molecular weight,

$$36 = 44N_{CO_2} + 28N_{CO} \quad \text{or} \quad N_{CO_2} = N_{CO} = \tfrac{1}{2}.$$

The initial 4.4 g correspond to 0.1 mole of CO_2, and if x denotes the moles of CO formed, $0.1 - x/2 =$ moles CO_2 remaining and $0.1 + x/2$ the total moles. Hence $\tfrac{1}{2} = x/(0.1 + x/2)$ or $x = 0.0667$ and the total moles are 0.133. The total pressure is then $P = 0.133 \times 0.082 \times 1273/1$ or $\underline{P = 13.9 \text{ atm,}}$ and $P_{CO_2} = P_{CO} = 6.95$ atm and $K_p = (6.95)^2/6.95 = \underline{6.95 \text{ atm.}}$

(b) Introducing inert gas at constant volume will not change the equilibrium partial pressures and hence will not change the position of equilibrium. Doing so at constant total pressure, however, dilutes the mixture, and the equilibrium will shift in the direction of forming more CO.

(c) The moles of CO formed must be 0.2 since the 0.1 mole of carbon is to be essentially used up. P_{CO} is then $0.2 \times 0.082 \times 1273/1 = 20.9$, and, from the equilibrium constant, P_{CO_2} must be $(20.9)^2/6.95 = 62.9$ atm, so there must be $62.9 \times 1/0.082 \times 1273$ or 0.602 moles of CO_2 present. The total moles of CO_2 required will then be 0.1 + 0.602 or $\underline{0.702.}$

(d) From the van't Hoff equation,

$$\log 2 = \frac{\Delta H^\circ}{1.98 \times 2.3} (1/1283 - 1/1273)$$

or

$$\Delta H^\circ = 0.3 \times 1.98 \times 2.3 \times 1283 \times 1273/10 = \underline{22.3 \text{ kcal}}$$

14. Let x denote the moles of C_2H_4 present at equilibrium, then

$$n_{C_2H_4} = x \qquad n_{C_2H_6} = 20 - x \qquad N = 100 + x$$

$$n_{H_2} = x \qquad n_{N_2} = 80 \qquad P = 0.5 \text{ atm}$$

Then

$$K_p = \frac{(x)(x)}{20 - x} \frac{0.5}{100 + x} = 0.05$$

and on solving the quadratic, $x = 10.3$ moles. The various mole fractions are then $N_{H_2} = N_{C_2H_4} = 10.3/110.3 = 0.093$ (9.3%), $N_{C_2H_6} = 9.7/110.3 = 0.088$ (8.8%), and $N_{N_2} = 0.72$ (72%).

$\Delta H^\circ = \Delta F^\circ + T \Delta S^\circ = 5.35 + 900 \times 32.3/1000 = 34.4$ kcal, hence at 300°K, $\Delta F^\circ = 34.4 - 300 \times 32.3/1000 = \underline{24.7 \text{ kcal}}$.

15. (a) The final total moles is $7 \times 2/0.082 \times 700 = 0.244$, of which 0.06 is of methanol, so 0.184 is the moles of CO and H_2. The moles of CO, however, must be $0.1 - 0.06 = 0.04$, so the moles of H_2 present is 0.144. Then $K_p = (0.06)(0.244)^2/(0.04) \times (0.144)^2(7)^2 = \underline{0.088 \text{ atm}^{-2}}$.

(b) Had no reaction occurred, the moles of CO would remain 0.1, and the moles of H_2 would be 0.144 plus twice the moles of methanol in (a), or $0.144 + 0.12 = 0.264$. The total moles are then 0.364 and P = $\underline{10.4 \text{ atm}}$.

16. (a) $\Delta F^\circ = -RT \ln K_p = -1.98 \times 298 \times 2.3 \log 10^{-5} = \underline{6.78 \text{ kcal}}$.

(b) Since no change in the number of moles occurs on reaction, there will still be 6 moles of gas, and P = $0.082 \times 298 \times 6/5 = \underline{29.3 \text{ atm}}$.

(c) Let x = moles of H_2O, then since $K_p = K_n$ in this case, $10^{-5} = (1 + x)x/(3 - x)(2 - x)$. As a first approximation, then, $x = 6 \times 10^{-5}$ (no further approximations are needed). Then the moles of CO_2, H_2, CO, and H_2O are 3, 2, 1, and 6×10^{-5}, respectively.

(d) $\Delta H° = \Delta F° + T \, \Delta S° = 6.78 + 298 \times (-10)/1000 = 3.80$ kcal, so, at 100°C, $\Delta F° = 3.80 - 373 \times (-10)/1000 = 7.53$ kcal. From this $K_p = 3.8 \times 10^{-5}$.

17. Let α be the fraction of CO reacted, then $P_{SO_2} = 2(\alpha/2)$ and $P_{CO} = 2(1 - \alpha)$. The total pressure is $2(1 - \alpha/2) = 1.03$, whence $\alpha = 0.97$. Then $K_p = 0.97/(0.06)^2 = \underline{270 \text{ atm}^{-1}}$.

18. (a) Since $K_p = P_{H_2O}^3$, the equilibrium H_2O pressure at 25°C is 10^{-2}atm. The flask must then contain $0.01 \times 2/0.082 \times 298 = 8.2 \times 10^{-4}$ mole. The total amount of water needed is then $3 \times 0.01 + 8.2 \times 10^{-4} = \underline{3.08 \times 10^{-2}}$ mole.

(b) From the van't Hoff equation,

$$\log 10^{-4}/10^{-6} = - \frac{\Delta H°}{1.98 \times 2.3} (1/323 - 1/298)$$

or

$$\Delta H° = 2 \times 1.98 \times 2.3 \times 323 \times 298/25 = \underline{35.1 \text{ kcal}}$$

19. (a) $\Delta F° = -RT \ln K_p$ or $\log K_p = -300/1.98 \times 313 \times 2.3 = -0.21$ or $K_p = \underline{0.62}$.

(b) From the ideal gas law, $PM = \rho RT = 5.85 \times 0.082 \times 313 = 150$. Let $n°$ denote the number of moles if the H_2O_4 were completely undissociated and α, the degree of dissociation. Then $n_{N_2O_4} = (1 - \alpha)n°$, $n_{NO_2} = 2\alpha n°$ and $N = (1 + \alpha)n°$. The average molecular weight M is:

$$M = 46 N_{NO_2} + 92 N_{N_2O_4}$$

or

$$M = 46 \frac{2\alpha}{1 + \alpha} + 92 \frac{1 - \alpha}{1 + \alpha} = 92/(1 + \alpha)$$

Since $P = 150/M$, we find $P = (1 + \alpha)(150/92)$. Finally, the equilibrium constant is

$$K_p = \frac{n_{N_2O_4}}{n_{NO_2}^2} \frac{N}{P} = (1 - \alpha)(1 + \alpha)/4\alpha^2 P$$

or

$$0.62 = 92(1 - \alpha)/150 \times 4\alpha^2$$

Then $(1 - \alpha)/\alpha^2 = 4.04$ or $\alpha = \underline{0.39}$. M is then $92/1.39 = \underline{66}$, and $P = 150/66 = \underline{2.28 \text{ atm}}$.

20. $\Delta S°$ for the reaction is $2 \times 44.7 - 31.2 = 9.2$. $\Delta F°$ is then $-22.1 \times 2 - 398 \times 9.2/1000 = -47.9$ kcal, and $\log K_p = 47,900/1.98 \times 2.3 \times 398 = 26.4$; and $K_p = \underline{2.5 \times 10^{26}}$.

The principal assumption is that $\Delta H°$ and $\Delta S°$ do not change with temperature or that $\Delta C_p°$ is small. This is a fairly good assumption, as the reaction involves 2 moles of diatomic molecules on each side, and all should have rather similar molar heat capacities.

21. Since $K_p = P_{NH_3} \cdot P_{HCl}$ and, in the first case, $P_{NH_3} = P_{HCl}$, then $K_p = (P/2)^2 = 0.025^2 = 6.25 \times 10^{-4}$ atm^2. The 0.02 mole of NH_3 corresponds to a pressure of $0.02 \times 0.082 \times 520/42.7$ or 0.02 atm. Then $K_p = P_{HCl}(P_{HCl} + 0.02) = 6.25 \times 10^{-4}$ or $P_{HCl} = \underline{0.0169}$, and $P_{NH_3} = \underline{0.0369}$. The moles of HCl are then

$$0.0169 \times 42.7/0.082 \times 520 = \underline{0.0169}$$

and similarily the moles of NH_3 are $\underline{0.0369}$. (Notice that the volume was chosen so that pressure and mole number are equal.) The moles of NH_4Cl remaining are then $0.020 - 0.0169 = \underline{0.0031}$.

22. Since

$$K_p = \frac{P_{PCl_3}P_{Cl_2}}{P_{PCl_5}}$$

for the reaction

$$PCl_5 = PCl_3 + Cl_2$$

we can write immediately that

$$K_p = \left(\frac{2 \times 2}{2}\right)\left(\frac{3}{6}\right) = 1 \text{ atm}$$

On introduction of more Cl_2, the qualitative effect will be to shift the equilibrium to the left, so let x denote the moles of PCl_5 formed as a result of the shift. Then:

$$n_{PCl_5} = 2 + x \qquad n_{Cl_2} = 2 + n'_{Cl_2} - x$$

$$n_{PCl_3} = 2 - x \qquad N = 6 + n'_{Cl_2} - x$$

where n'_{Cl_2} denotes the moles of Cl_2 added. Since the new equilibrium volume is 2V liters, with P and T constant, it follows that the addition of Cl_2 doubled the number of moles present, so N = 12 and therefore $n'_{Cl_2} - x = 6$. We can now write:

$$K_p = 1 = \frac{(2 - x)(8)}{(2 + x)} \frac{3}{12}$$

from which $x = \frac{2}{3}$. The moles of Cl_2 added were then $n'_{Cl_2} = 6 + 2/3 = \underline{20/3.}$

23.

$$K_p = \frac{P_{CH_3OH}}{P_{CO} P^2_{H_2}} = \frac{2}{1 \times 0.01} = 200 \text{ atm}^{-2}$$

A little reflection at this point shortens the problem considerably. The qualitative effect of expanding the mixture will be to shift the equilibrium to the left, but the shift cannot affect the CO and CH_3OH pressures very much since there isn't much H_2 present. As a first approximation, then, consider that the expansion halves the CO and CH_3OH pressures, and find the H_2 pressure required by K_p:

$$200 = \frac{1}{0.5P^2_{H_2}} \quad \text{or} \quad P_{H_2} = 0.1$$

as before. Had no shift in equilibrium occurred, P_{H_2} would have been 0.05, so evidently as a second approximation we should take the CO pressure as 0.525 and the CH_3OH pressure as 0.975. On doing this, and recalculating P_{H_2}, we get $\underline{0.096 \text{ atm.}}$

12 *Heterogeneous equilibrium; phase diagrams*

Comments

The problems that follow are restricted to one-, two-, and three-component systems. In the first case, data are provided that allow the construction of a P vs. T diagram. Such diagrams will consist of single-phase regions, line of two-phase equilibria, and points of crossing of three such lines, or triple points at which three phases are in equilibrium. Note that the three lines that cross at the triple point for phases A, B, and C must comprise the lines for the three two-phase equilibria A-B, A-C, and B-C. Remember, too, that the vapor-pressure curve for a solid will always be steeper than that for the liquid phase of the same substance, and use the Clapeyron equation to determine the slope of solid-solid and solid-liquid two-phase lines.

The two-component systems involved here are mostly freezing-point ones, and you will be dealing with T vs. composition diagrams for the most part. There will now be one-phase regions and two-phase regions (alternating in any horizontal traverse of the diagram, if immiscible pure solids are taken to be narrow one-phase regions) and lines of three-phase equilibrium. In the case of cooling curves, there is a change of slope on passing from a one- into a two-phase region, and a halt at a line of three-phase equilibrium. Such lines are boundaries between one two-phase region below (above) and two two-phase regions above (below) and are then eutectic (peritectic) in type.

There are a few diagrams dealing with salt hydrate systems, and you are occasionally asked to consider the vapor region in your labeling.

The three-component systems are mostly of the solubility type, i.e., two salts plus water. Use triangular graph paper for these isobaric isothermal diagrams. There will now be one-, two-, and three-phase regions, the latter always triangular in shape. Tie lines in the two-phase regions need not be parallel, of course.

By way of reassurance, the answers are not really as long as they may appear to be. Much of the reasoning has been given in considerably more detail than would be required on the actual examination.

Equations and concepts

Phase Rule: $F + P = C + 2$, where F = degrees of freedom, P = phases present, and C = components.

Material Balance Calculations: If a system of composition P_1° is partitioned into two phases of composition P_1 and P_2, the relative amounts of phase 1 and phase 2 will be in the proportion $(P_2 - P_1^\circ)/(P_1 - P_1^\circ)$ or the fraction of the system present as phase 1 will be $(P_2 - P_1^\circ)/(P_1 - P_2)$. P denotes any additive property, usually mole or weight fraction, in the case of phase diagrams. If P denotes mole (weight) fraction, then the ratio of amounts of phases will be in terms of moles (weights). It is often convenient to estimate this ratio by measuring on the graph the two portions of a tie line to which the above composition differences correspond. Because of analogy that can be made, the above procedure is sometimes known as the "lever principle."

A similar procedure can be used in the case of triangular plots of three-component systems. As illustrated in Fig. 12-1, a

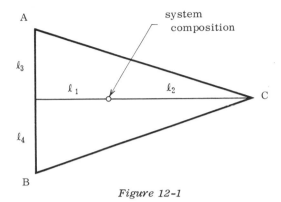

Figure 12-1

system whose composition lies within a three-phase region will consist of the three phases A, B, and C in proportions that can be expressed in terms of certain ratios of lengths. Thus:

$$\frac{C}{A + B} = \frac{\ell_1}{\ell_2} \qquad \frac{A}{B} = \frac{\ell_4}{\ell_3}$$

Problems

1. (15 min) Table 12-1 gives the break and halt temperatures for the cooling curves of melts of metals A and B. Construct a phase diagram (use Fig. 12-2) consistent with these curves and label the phase regions. Give the probable formula of any compounds.

Table 12-1

Mole %A	First break, °C	First halt, °C	Second halt, °C
100		1100	
90	1060	700	
80	1000	700	
70	940	700	400
60	850	700	400
50	750	700	400
40	670	400	
30	550	400	
20		400	
10	450	400	
0		500	

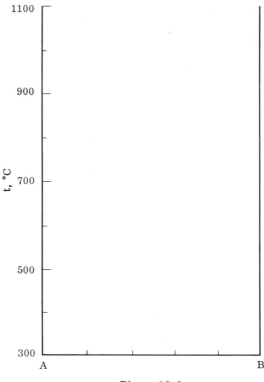

Figure 12-2

2. (15 min) Given the solubility diagram of Fig. 12-3 for the salt MX and its hydrates, label each phase region and describe the sequence of phase changes that would occur on isothermal evaporation at 30°C of a solution of composition A (indicated on the diagram) to dryness.

3. (15 min) Thermal analysis of the two–component system A, B (metals melting at 1200°C and 600°C, respectively) shows that two solid phases of composition 40% B and 60% B, respectively, are in equilibrium at 800°C with liquid of composition 80% B. Construct the simplest melting-point diagram consistent with this information and label all phase regions. Sketch the cooling curves for compositions 20% B, 50% B, and 70% B and fully label what happens at each break and halt.

4. (15 min) The isobaric solubility diagram for the system $CHCl_3$—CH_3COOH—H_2O is shown in Fig. 12-4, with some

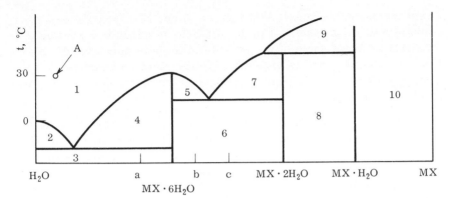

Figure 12-3

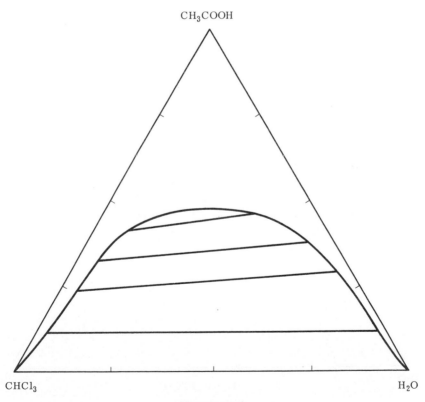

Figure 12-4

representative tie lines. What phase(s) and of what composi-
tion(s) will be present if 1 mole of $CHCl_3$ is added to a system
consisting of 0.6 mole of water and 0.4 mole of acetic acid? If
more than one phase is present, give the relative amounts of
each. Explain clearly your procedure. (The composition scale is
in mole fraction.)

5. (24 min) (final examination question) In the triangular diagram
of Fig. 12-5 shown for the system H_2O—Na_2SO_4—$NaCl$ at 25°C,
the line ab gives the compositions of solutions saturated with
respect to NaCl, the line bc, those saturated with respect to
Na_2SO_4, and the line cd, those saturated with respect to
$Na_2SO_4 \cdot 10H_2O$. (The diagram is on a weight % basis.)
  (a) Complete the diagram and label all phase regions.
  (b) Describe carefully the sequence of events on complete

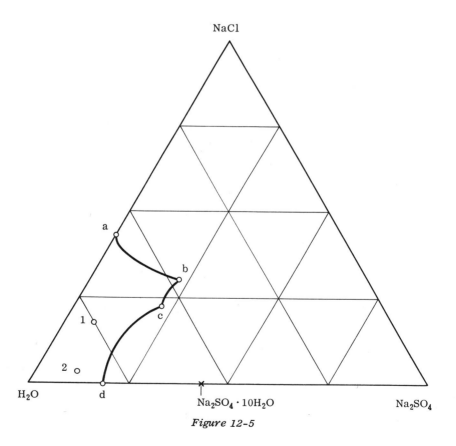

Figure 12-5

dehydration at 25°C of solutions of compositions 1 and 2 shown on the diagram.

6. (24 min) (final examination question) Thermal analysis of the well-known system A-B gives the following information:

    10 mole %B: break at 900°C, second break at 650°C
    30 mole %B: break at 650, halt at 450
    50 mole %B: break at 550, halt at 450
    60 mole %B: break at 650, halt at 600, second halt at 450
    80 mole %B: break at 750, halt at 600
    90 mole %B: break at 780, halt at 600

A and B melt at 1000° and 850°, respectively. Sketch the simplest phase diagram consistent with these data. Label all phase regions and give the formulas of any compounds.

7. (12 min) The cooling curve data of Table 12-2 are for the system silver-platinum; the second column gives the temperature at which a break or change in rate of cooling occurs, and the last column, the temperature of a halt.

Table 12-2

Pt mole %	Break, °C	Halt, °C
0		960
10	1025	
20	1075	1050
30	1100	1050
40	1200	1050
50	1250	1050
60	1300	1050
70	1350	1050
80	1400	1050
90	1600	
100		1770

Construct the simplest phase diagram (use Fig. 12-6) consistent with the above data, label each phase region, and give the phase reaction occuring during the 1050°C halt.

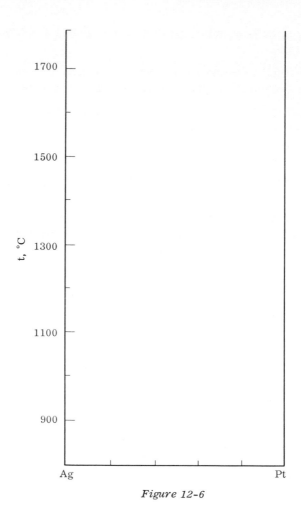

Figure 12-6

8. (24 min) (final examination question) Na and K melt at 98°C and 65°C, respectively; they form one solid compound, NaK, which decomposes at 10°C to give a solid and a melt containing 60% K (mole %). There is a eutectic at −5°C. Sketch the simplest phase diagram consistent with the above data, label the phase regions, and draw cooling curves for melts containing 40% K, 55% K and 90% K. Indicate the phases appearing or disappearing at each break or halt.

9. (24 min) (final examination question) The diagram of Fig. 12-7 is for the system H_2O—$CuSO_4$. Fill in the additional lines needed

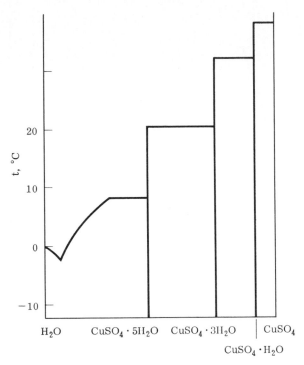

Figure 12-7

to define the various phase areas, and label each area as to the phase present.

Describe the sequence of phase changes if a dilute solution of copper sulfate is dehydrated at 5°C, ending up with anydrous copper sulfate.

10. (24 min) (final examination question) Iron, m.p. 1500°C, and antimony, m.p. 630°C, form one compound, $FeSb_2$, which decomposes at 800°C into a liquid and Fe. There is a eutectic at 600°C. Sketch the simplest phase diagram consistent with this information and label all phase regions. Sketch and label the cooling curve for a melt containing 50 mole % iron, i.e., state what happens at each break and halt. (Liquid Fe and Sb are completely miscible.)

11. (20 min) (final examination question) Given the solubility data for $CaCl_2$, where the curve ab of Fig. 12-8 gives the solubility of $CaCl_2 \cdot 6H_2O$, and the curve bc, that for $CaCl_2 \cdot H_2O$.

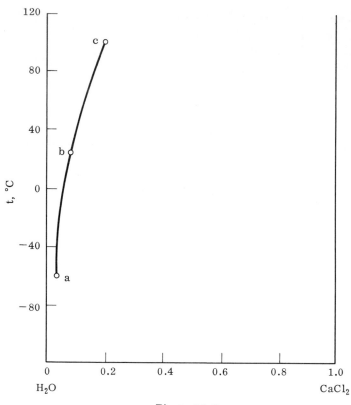

Figure 12-8

(a) Sketch the completed phase diagram between $-75°C$ and $100°C$ and label all phase regions.

(b) One mole of $CaCl_2 \cdot H_2O$ and 9 moles of water are mixed and heated to $100°C$. The resulting solution is allowed to cool to $-75°C$. Describe the sequence of phases that would appear and/or disappear during this cooling.

12. (18 min) Thermal analysis of the system A–B showed the presence of a line of three-phase equilibrium at $1000°C$, and one at $600°C$. In no case, however, was there more than one halt for any one cooling curve. A and B melt at $800°C$ and $1300°C$, respectively, and the compound A_2B is known, with a melting point of $700°C$. Sketch the simplest phase diagram that conforms with the above data, and label all the phase regions.

13. (12 min) White phosphorus melts at 44°C and 0.2 mm pressure, red phorphorus melts at 490°C and 43 atm pressure. White phosphorus is more dense than the liquid, and the red form is less dense than the liquid. The vapor pressure of the white form is everywhere greater than that of the red. Sketch the P vs. T diagram in Fig. 12-9, label the areas, and explain which triple point(s) are stable and which metastable.

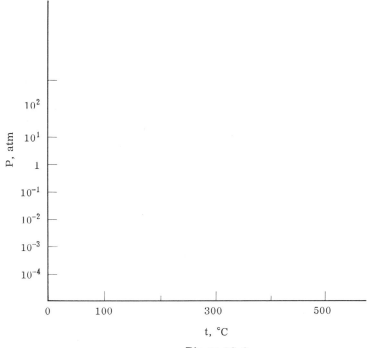

Figure 12-9

14. (24 min) (final examination question) Au and Sb melt at 1060°C and 630°C, respectively, and form one compound, $AuSb_2$, which melts incongruently at 800°C. Sketch the simplest phase diagram consistent with this information and label all phase regions. Give the cooling curve for a melt containing 50% Au, and label each break and halt.

15. (30 min) Metals A and B form the compounds AB_3 and A_2B_3. Solids A, B, AB_3, and A_2B_3 essentially are immiscible in each

other, but are completely miscible as liquids. A and B melt at
600°C and 1100°C, respectively. Compound A_2B_3 melts congruently
at 900°C and gives a simple eutectic with A at 450°C. Compound
AB_3 decomposes at 800°C to give the other compound and a melt.
There is a eutectic at 650°C.

(a) Draw the simplest phase diagram consistent with this information, and label all phase regions.

(b) Sketch cooling curves for melts of composition 90% A and
30% A, and label as to phases appearing or disappearing at each
break and halt.

16. (24 min) (final examination question) Metals A and B melt at
1200°C and 1600°C, respectively. A thermal analysis shows the
presence of the following three-phase equilibria:

at 1400°C: melt containing 10% B and two solid solutions containing 20% B and 30% B, respectively.

at 1250°C: solid solution containing 65% B, melt containing
75% B, and solution containing 95% B.

There is one compound, A_2B_3, which melts at 1700°C (congruently).
Construct the simplest phase diagram that will correspond to
the above data and label the phase regions. Draw semiquantitative
cooling curves for melts of composition 25% B and 90% B, and give
the phases appearing or disappearing at each break or halt.

17. (18 min) Table 12-3 gives the break and halt temperatures
for the cooling curves of melts of metals A and B. Construct a
phase diagram (use Fig. 12-10) consistent with these curves and

Table 12-3

mole % A	Break, °C	Halt, °C	Halt, °C
100		1000	
90	950	800	
80	900	800	
70	900	800	
60	1000	800	
50		1100	
40	1000	700	
30	750	700	500
20	550	500	
10	575	500	
0		600	

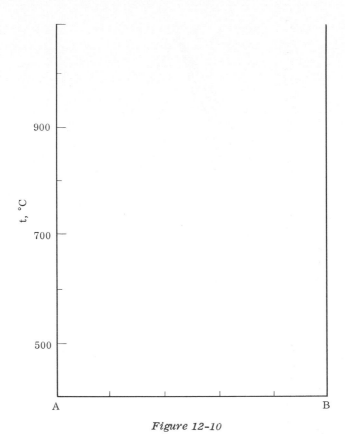

Figure 12-10

label each phase region. Give the probable formulas of any compounds.

18. (12 min) The isothermal, isobaric solubility diagram for the system $H_2O-KI-I_2$ is shown in Fig. 12-11. Compositions are in mole %; one compound, $KI \cdot I_2 \cdot H_2O$, is formed. Complete the diagram (if necessary) and label the various phase regions.

A solution containing 75 mole % H_2O, 20% KI and 5% I_2 is evaporated at constant T and P. What phase or phases would be present and in what approximate amounts when the evaporation has proceeded until only 50 mole % of H_2O is present? Make your calculations clear.

19. (24 min) The following data are given for the system $Na_2SO_4-MgSO_4-H_2O$ at 40°C and 1 atm.

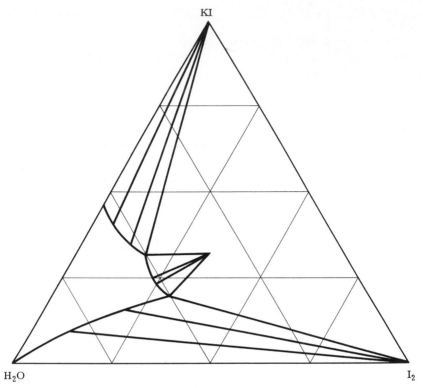

Figure 12-11

Solution phase	In equil. with solid phase
1. 35% NaS_2O_4 0% $MgSO_4$	Na_2SO_4
2. 0% Na_2SO_4 30% $MgSO_4$	$MgSO_4$
3. 25% Na_2SO_4 15% $MgSO_4$	Na_2SO_4 + $Na_2SO_4 \cdot MgSO_4 \cdot 4H_2O$
4. 5% Na_2SO_4 28% $MgSO_4$	$MgSO_4$ + $Na_2SO_4 \cdot MgSO_4 \cdot 4H_2O$

The above are compositions of solutions saturated with respect to the solid phases given. Compositions are in weight per cent ($Na_2SO_4 \cdot MgSO_4 \cdot 4H_2O$ is 42.4% Na_2SO_4 and 36% $MgSO_4$).

(a) Sketch the phase diagram in Fig. 12-12 and label all phase regions.

(b) If a solution containing 10% Na_2SO_4 and 10% $MgSO_4$ is evaporated, what solid will appear first, and what is the composition of the last solution to exist before the system becomes entirely solid?

(c) If equal weights of Na_2SO_4 and of solution (2) above are mixed, how many phases will be present at equilibrium and what will be their compositions? Make your procedures in obtaining the above answers clear.

20. (30 min) The isobaric isothermal diagram for the system $H_2O-Li_2SO_4-(NH_4)_2SO_4$ is given in Fig. 12-13.

(a) Label all phase regions.

(b) Describe in detail the sequence of events on evaporation of a solution of composition A.

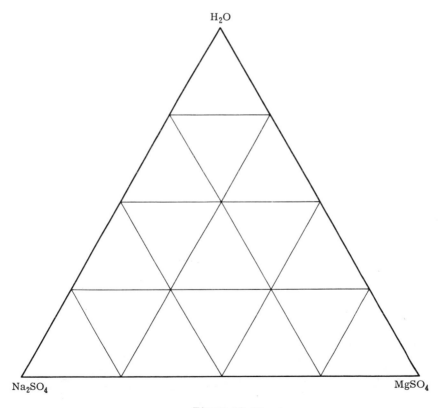

H_2O

Na_2SO_4

$MgSO_4$

Figure 12-12

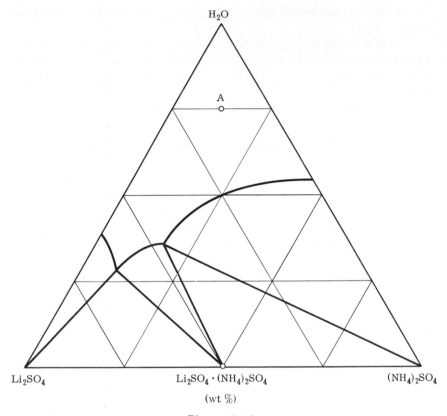

Figure 12-13

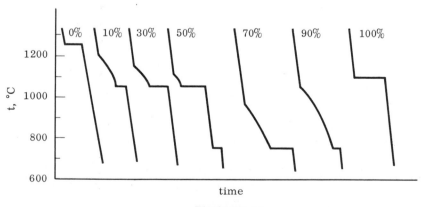

Figure 12-14

(c) Calculate the maximum number of grams of Li_2SO_4 that can be added to 100 g of solution A, if ammonium sulfate is still to be the first solid to separate out on evaporation.

(d) Show that, on evaporation of a dilute solution of the double salt $Li_2SO_4 \cdot (NH_4)_2SO_4$, one can never obtain a system consisting of the solid double salt in equilibrium with saturated solution.

21. (15 min) The cooling curves of Fig. 12-14 are obtained for the system CaF_2–$CaCl_2$ (compositions are in mole % of $CaCl_2$ in the melt). Construct the most reasonable semiquantitative freezing-point diagram, label all phase regions, and give the probable formulas of any compounds that are formed.

22. (15 min) Given the solubility diagram of Fig. 12-15 for the salt X and its hydrates, label each phase region and describe what sequence of phase changes would occur upon isothermal evaporation of solution A.

23. (24 min) (final examination question) The data of Table 12-4 is for the isobaric isothermal system H_2O–Na_2SO_4–$NaCl$ (at 25°C and 1 atm). Sketch a reasonable phase diagram consistent with the above data and label all phase regions (use Fig. 12-16). Describe the sequence of events on evaporating a solution containing 5% NaCl, 5% Na_2SO_4, and 90% H_2O.

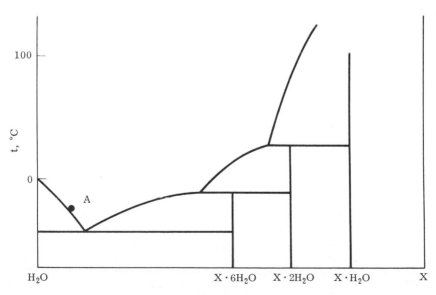

Figure 12-15

Table 12-4

Saturated solution	In equilibrium with solid phases

(weight % compositions)

1. 80% H_2O,   0% Na_2SO_4 NaCl
2. 85% H_2O,   0% NaCl $Na_2SO_4 \cdot 10H_2O$
3. 75% H_2O, 10% Na_2SO_4 NaCl + Na_2SO_4
4. 75% H_2O, 15% Na_2SO_4 Na_2SO_4 + $Na_2SO_4 \cdot 10H_2O$

(formula weights)

Na_2SO_4 = 142; $Na_2SO_4 \cdot 10H_2O$ = 322; NaCl = 58

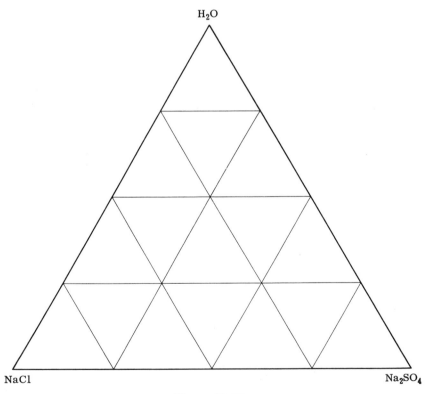

Figure 12-16

24. (18 min) Metals A and B melt at 600°C and 950°C, respectively. They form no compounds. At 750°C, two solid solutions, containing 20 and 40 mole % of B, respectively, are in equilibrium with melt. Sketch the simplest phase diagram consistent with the above data and label the phase regions. Give cooling curves for melts containing 90% B and 30% B, and state the phases appearing or disappearing at each break or halt.

25. (12 min) A saturated solution of KCl in water contains 35% by weight KCl, whereas one of NaCl contains 20% NaCl. Solution S, saturated with respect to both NaCl and KCl, contains 20% KCl and 10% NaCl. On Fig. 12-17, sketch the simplest triangular diagram that fits the above data. Label each phase region. If equal weights of water saturated with KCl and solution S are mixed, should a precipitate form? If so, how much, roughly, per 100 g of the mixture?

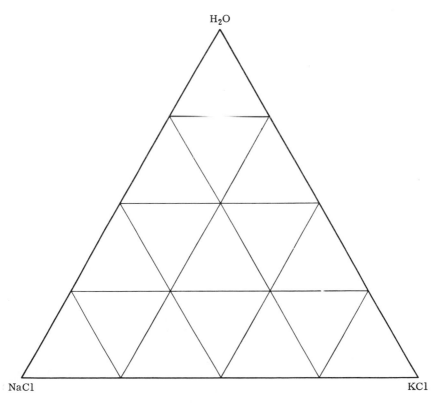

Figure 12-17

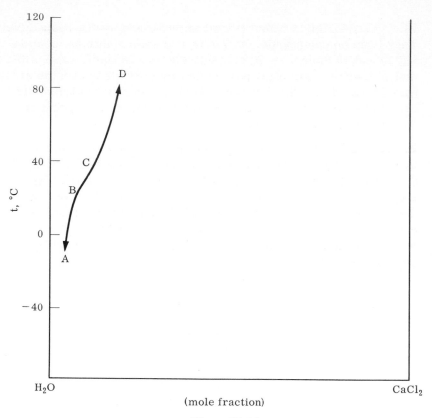

Figure 12-18

26. (15 min) A section of the solubility vs. temperature curve for the system $CaCl_2$-water is shown in Fig. 12-18. Along AB, BC, and CD, the solutions are saturated with respect to $CaCl_2 \cdot 6H_2O$, $CaCl_2 \cdot 4H_2O$, and $CaCl_2 \cdot 2H_2O$, respectively.

(a) Sketch the complete temperature-composition diagram for 1 atm., including vapor-phase regions, filling in missing details in a plausible fashion.

(b) Describe in detail what would happen on heating at 1 atm a system initially consisting of 1 mole of ice and 1 mole of $CaCl_2 \cdot 6H_2O$ at $-50°C$. A closed container, such as a piston and cylinder arrangement, is used.

27. (15 min) Substance X exists in two crystalline modifications, here called A and B. At temperatures below 90°C, the vapor pressure of the A form is less than that of the B form; above

90°C, the reverse is true. The A form is 5% denser than liquid X, and the B form is 10% less dense than the A form. There is an A-L-V triple point at 110°C. Sketch the P-T diagram for X, filling in missing details in a plausible fashion. Label the phase regions, lines of two-phase equilibrium, and triple points. Discuss briefly whether the triple points you show represent stable, metastable, or entirely unstable equilibria.

28. (15 min) Figure 12-19 shows a melting-point diagram for a hypothetical system A—B. Label each phase region. Designate pure A and B as such, and any compounds by C_1, C_2, etc. Also, designate liquid solutions or melts by L or by L_1, L_2, etc., and solid solutions by α, β, or γ, according to whether they are rich in A, B, or a compound.

Construct and fully label cooling curves for the two compositions indicated by the dotted lines.

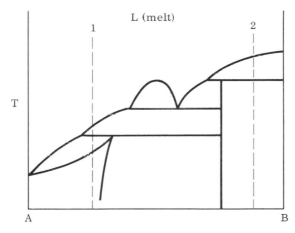

Figure 12-19

Answers

1. Each halt corresponds to a line of three-phase equilibrium and each break to a boundary between a one- and a two- phase region. With this guide, the simplest diagram is that shown in Fig. 12-20.

An unstable compound is indicated that must contain less than 80% and more than 70% A, since it is between these limits that the lower three-phase line appears. A good guess is 75% A, corresponding to the formula A_3B.

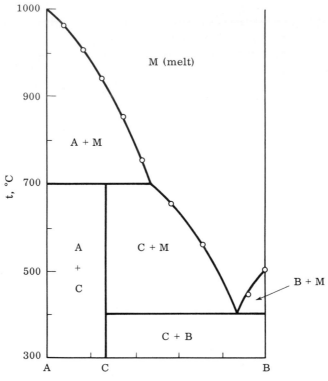

Figure 12-20

2. The phase regions are:

(1) solution

(2) solution + ice

(3) ice + $MX \cdot 6H_2O$

(4) solution + $MX \cdot 6H_2O$

(5) solution + $MX \cdot 6H_2O$

(6) $MX \cdot 6H_2O$ + $MX \cdot 2H_2O$

(7) solution + $MX \cdot 2H_2O$

(8) $MX \cdot 2H_2O$ + $MX \cdot H_2O$

(9) solution + $MX \cdot H_2O$

(10) $MX \cdot H_2O$ + MX

To follow the evaporation, draw a horizontal line through point A.

(1) The solution increases in concentration to the value indicated by point a on the bottom of the graph. (2) At a, $MX \cdot 6H_2O$ begins to precipitate out and eventually the system consists of pure $MX \cdot 6H_2O$. (3) Further removal of water produces solution of composition b and eventually all the $MX \cdot 6H_2O$ disappears. (4) The solution concentrates to composition c, at which point solid $MX \cdot 2H_2O$ begins to come out, and eventually only pure solid $MX \cdot 2H_2O$ is present. (5) Further removal of water produces some

$MX \cdot H_2O$; the proportion of this increases until the system consists entirely of $MX \cdot H_2O$. (6) Still further drying produces some MX and eventually all water is removed and the system consists of pure MX.

3. The diagrams of Fig. 12-21 are largely self-explanatory. The coexistence of three phases, two solid, at a temperature between the two melting points is a clear indication of a peritectic-type diagram.

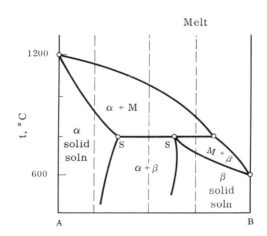

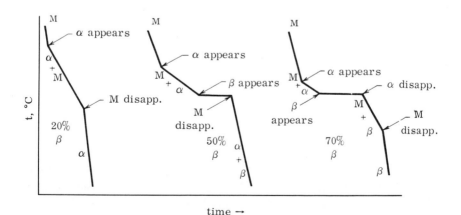

time →

Figure 12-21

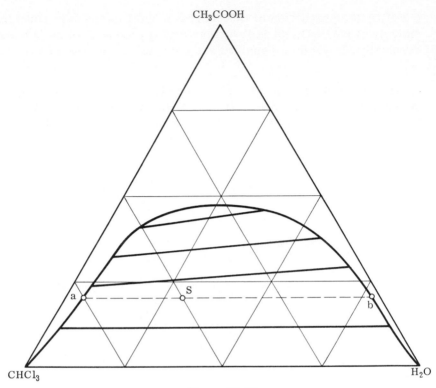

Figure 12-22

4. The system composition is evidently 50% $CHCl_3$, 30% H_2O, and 20% acetic acid; this point is shown in Fig. 12-22, along with an intermediate tie line. The ends of the tie line are at: (a) 75% $CHCl_3$, 5% H_2O, and 20% CH_3COOH; and (b) 4% $CHCl_3$, 76% H_2O, and 20% CH_3COOH. The relative amounts of the two phases are most easily obtained by the lever principle, i.e., the ratio of moles of phase (a) to (b) is that of the distance sb to the distance sa, or about 1.75.

5. The phase regions are, A: solution; B: solution of composition along ab plus solid NaCl; C: solution of composition along cd plus solid $Na_2SO_4 \cdot 10H_2O$; D: solution of composition c plus solid $Na_2SO_4 \cdot 10H_2O$ plus solid Na_2SO_4; E: solution of composition along bc plus solid Na_2SO_4; F: solution of composition b plus solid NaCl plus solid Na_2SO_4.

On dehydration of solution (1), the system moves along the

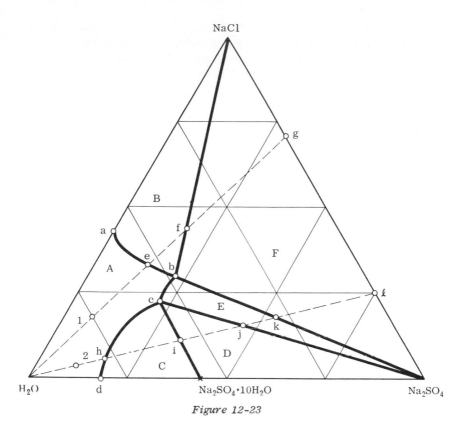

Figure 12-23

dotted line of Fig. 12-23 away from the water corner. At e solid
NaCl appears, and the solution composition moves toward b.
When the system composition reaches f, solution is at b and
solid Na_2SO_4 also begins to precipitate out. With further dehydration, the solution drys up leaving mixture g of solid NaCl and
Na_2SO_4.

In the case of solution (2), $Na_2SO_4 \cdot 10H_2O$ begins to precipitate
out when composition h is reached. The solution moves toward c
and, when the system reaches i, solution of composition c is in
equilibrium with $Na_2SO_4 \cdot 10H_2O$ and Na_2SO_4. Further dehydration
reduces the amount of $Na_2SO_4 \cdot 10H_2O$ until at j only solution c
and Na_2SO_4 are present. The solution composition then moves
toward b, and, on reaching it, the further sequence is the same
as for solution (1).

6. The required diagram (Fig. 12-24) largely draws itself once the break and halt data are located. The simplest explanation for the two halts at 60% B is that an unstable compound forms. Its composition must lie between 60% and 80% B, and if it is 75% B, the formula would be AB_3. Alternatively, it might be AB_2 (67% B).

7. A halt temperature lying between the two melting points suggests a peritectic-type diagram (see Fig. 12-25). The limits of the α and β solid solutions are merely suggestive, as the data do not allow a precise locating of them.

The phase reaction is:

$$\text{phase} + \text{melt} \rightarrow \alpha \text{ phase}$$

For compositions to the left of point (a), β phase disappears before melt does, on cooling, whereas to the right of point (a), melt disappears before β phase.

8. Since the compound decomposes into a melt richer in K than

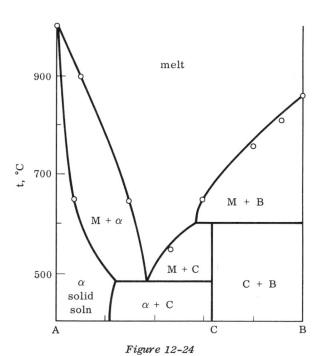

Figure 12-24

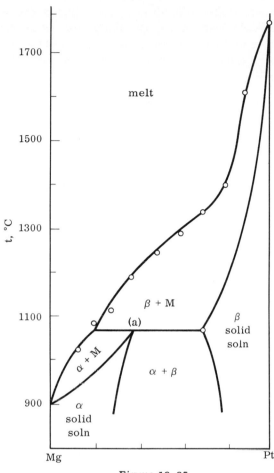

Figure 12-25

it is, the residual solid must be richer in Na. The simplest assumption is that the solid is pure Na. (See Fig. 12-26.)

9. The added lines are shown in Fig. 12-27 as dotted, and the various phase regions are:

1. ice + $CuSO_4 \cdot 5H_2O$
2. $CuSO_4 \cdot 5H_2O$ + $CuSO_4 \cdot 3H_2O$
3. $CuSO_4 \cdot 3H_2O$ + $CuSO_4 \cdot H_2O$
4. $CuSO_4 \cdot H_2O$ + $CuSO_4$
5. ice + solution
6. solution + $CuSO_4 \cdot 5H_2O$
7. solution
8. H_2O vapor + $CuSO_4 \cdot 5H_2O$
9. H_2O vapor + $CuSO_4 \cdot 3H_2O$
10. H_2O vapor + $CuSO_4 \cdot H_2O$
11. H_2O vapor + $CuSO_4$

   The horizontal dotted line shows the motion of the system
composition on dehydration. At a, $CuSO_4 \cdot 5H_2O$ precipitates out,
and when system of composition b is reached, pure solid
$CuSO_4 \cdot 5H_2O$ is present. further dehydration produces increasing
amounts of $CuSO_4 \cdot 3H_2O$ and at c only this is present. Next,

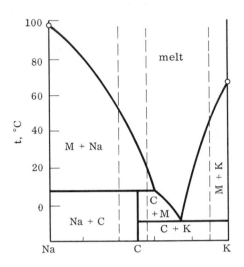

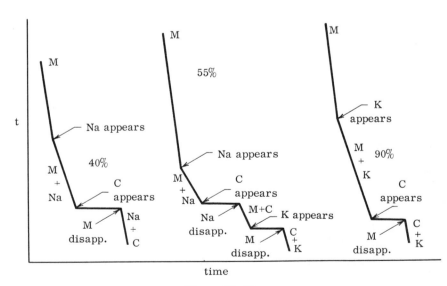

Figure 12-26

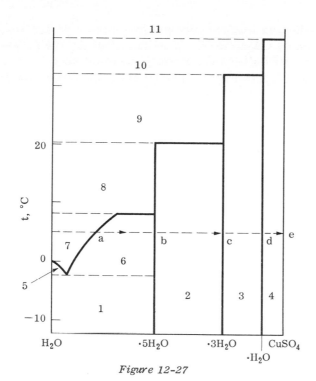

Figure 12-27

$CuSO_4 \cdot H_2O$ begins to form and at d pure monohydrate is present. Finally anhydrous $CuSO_4$ is formed, and when e is reached pure $CuSO_4$ is present.

10. The unstable compound, since it decomposes to give iron as one product, must produce melt richer than 50% in antimony as the other. This establishes how the liquid lines are to be drawn (see Fig. 12-28).

11. The phase regions (see Fig. 12-29) are:

1. solution
2. solution + ice
3. ice + $CaCl_2 \cdot 6H_2O$ (14.3% $CaCl_2$)
4. solution + $CaCl_2 \cdot 6H_2O$
5. $CaCl_2 \cdot 6H_2O$ + $CaCl_2 \cdot H_2O$ (50% $CaCl_2$)
6. $CaCl_2 \cdot H_2O$ + $CaCl_2$
7. solution + $CaCl_2 \cdot H_2O$

The indicated solution consists of 1 mole of $CaCl_2$ and 10 moles of water and so is 9% $CaCl_2$, as shown by the dotted line. On cooling, $CaCl \cdot 6H_2O$ will crystallize out (at about 20°C), and at about −60°C, ice will also freeze out. The temperature will

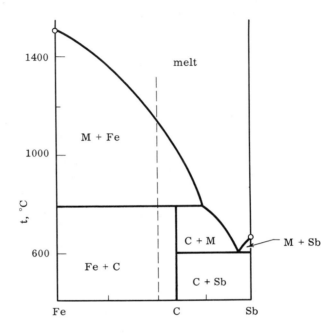

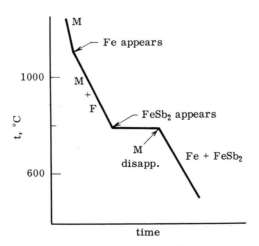

Figure 12-28

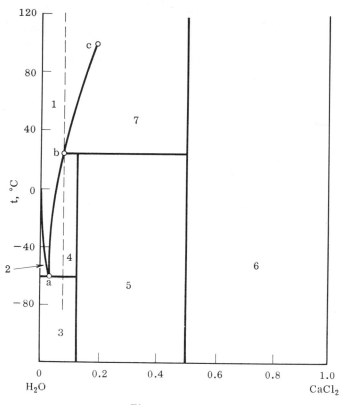

Figure 12-29

then remain at −60°C until all the solution is converted to ice and CaCl$_2$·6H$_2$O.

12. The 600°C three-phase line is probably a simple eutectic line, as it lies below the melting point both of A and of A$_2$B. (See Fig. 12–30.)

The other three-phase line, however, lies between the melting points of A$_2$B and of B. An unstable compound is ruled out, since this would require that there be a cooling curve with halts at both 600°C and 1000°C. The next simplest solution is that shown, i.e., a peritectic, and limited solid solutions formed between A$_2$B and B.

13. (a) locates in Fig. 12–31 a metastable triple point, W (white phosphorus), L, and V; it is metastable since the vapor pressure of W is greater than that of R (red phosphorus).

(b) locates a stable triple point, R–L–V.

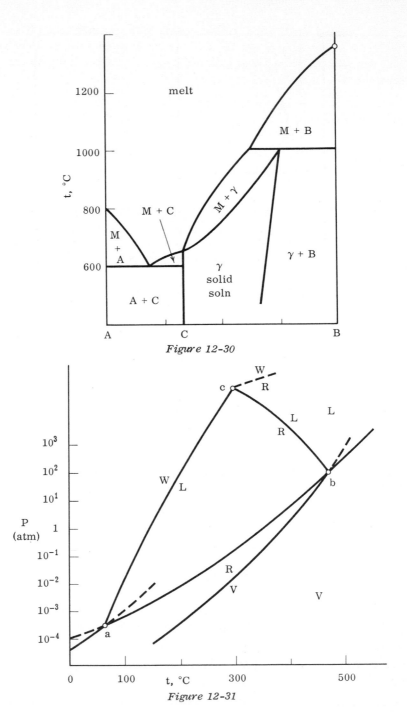

Figure 12-30

Figure 12-31

(c) locates the W–R–L triple point, which should be stable, but the fourth triple point, W–R–V, is totally unstable, as it probably lies above the melting point of the liquid and one assumes that solids cannot be superheated.

14. Since the incongruently melting compound decomposes above the m.p. of Sb but below that of Au, the simplest supposition is that solid Au is one of the decomposition products, and a melt, of > 67% Sb, the other. The additional eutectic provides a simple way to connect up the rest of Fig. 12-32.

15. Figure 12-33 largely draws itself once the information is located on it. The composition of the first eutectic melt could lie either to the right or to the left of the 90% composition point. If it lay to the left, the order of appearance of A and C_1 would be the reverse of that shown in the cooling curve.

16. Note that a congruently melting compound essentially divides the phase diagram (Fig. 12-34) into two parts whose behavior can be quite disparate. The A–A_2B_3 system is most simply taken to be a peritectic type, since the three-phase line lies between the two melting points, whereas the A_2B_3–B system is obviously a simple eutectic.

17. (See Fig. 12-35.) There is evidently a congruently melting compound at 50% A, shown as a halt, but no break is observed; this corresponds to the formula AB. The double halt for the 30% melt suggests an unstable compound. Its composition must lie between 40% A and 30% A; it is, say, 33% A; then the formula would be AB_2.

18. The labelling is given in Fig. 12-36. Note the additional lines drawn in to define the various three-phase triangular regions.

On evaporation, the system composition follows the dotted line drawn from the starting composition through the water corner. At 50% H_2O, the system will be at point X shown on the diagram, and the tie line through X goes from the KI corner to point (1) on the solution line. This point corresponds to about 55% H_2O, 35% KI and 15% I_2, and the relative amounts of solution and of KI can be judged from the relative lengths of the two sections of the tie line, i.e., the distance KI–X vs. the distance X–solution, to be about 10 moles of solution to 1 of KI.

19. (a) The phase regions are as shown in Fig. 12-37. Note that

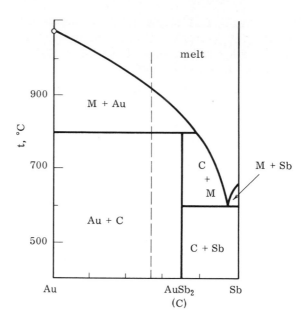

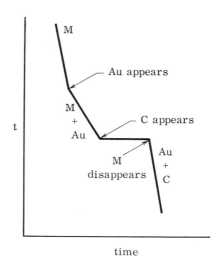

Figure 12-32

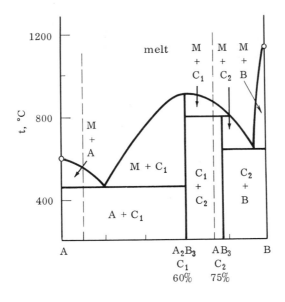

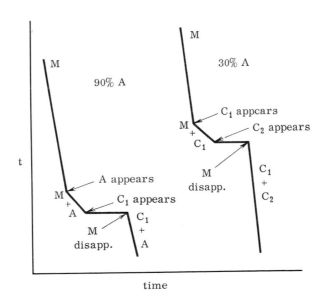

Figure 12-33

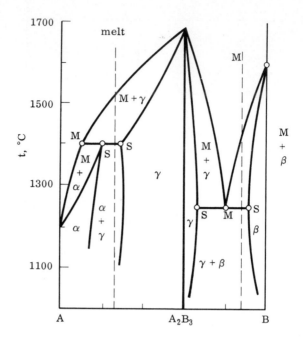

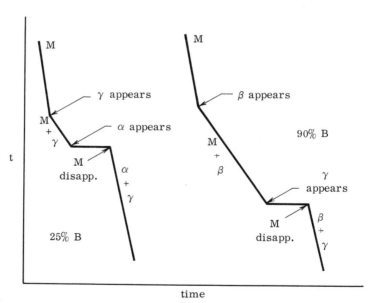

Figure 12-34

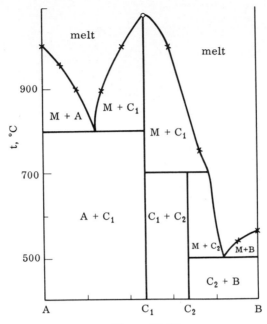

Figure 12-35

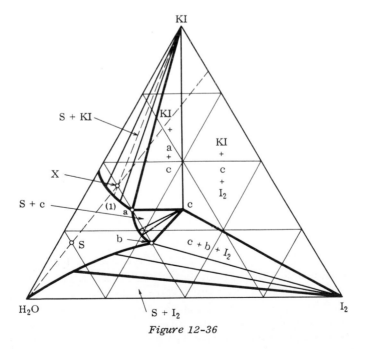

Figure 12-36

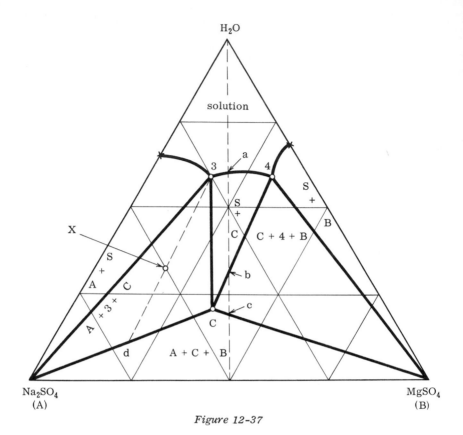

Figure 12-37

solutions 3 and 4 mark the limits of the solutions compositions in equilibrium with the compound.

(b) The system follows the dotted line drawn from the water corner through the solution composition, when evaporation occurs. At point a, the system enters the S + C two-phase region, so compound begins to crystallize out. When the system composition reaches b the solution has moved over to point 4, and both $MgSO_4$ and compound crystallize out; when the system reaches c, the last trace of solution (4) disappears.

(c) The point marked X locates the system composition (50% Na_2SO_4 and 15% $MgSO_4$); it lies in the A + 3 + C three-phase region, so these are the phases present. To estimate the relative amounts, the dotted line is drawn from 3 through X, intersecting the AC line at d. Point X lies about midway, so there are about equal weights of solution 3 and the mixed solids.

Point d lies about midway between A and C, so there is about equal weight of the two solids. The system thus consists of about 50% solution 3, and 25% each of Na_2SO_4 and compound.

20. (a) The phase regions are labeled on Fig. 12-38.

(b) On evaporation of A, the system composition follows the dotted line drawn from the water corner through A. When its composition reaches 1, ammonium sulfate begins to crystallize out, and the solution composition moves toward c. When the system composition has reached 2, the solution is at c and the compound begins to crystallize out. Both solution c and $(NH_4)_2SO_4$ diminish in amount until finally the system dries up as pure $Li_2SO_4 \cdot (NH_4)_2SO_4$. (This is a special case, because solution A contains equal weights of the two salts.)

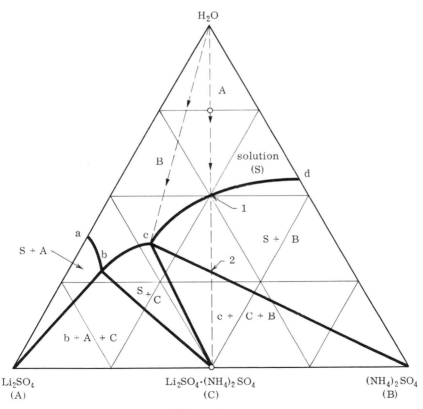

Figure 12-38

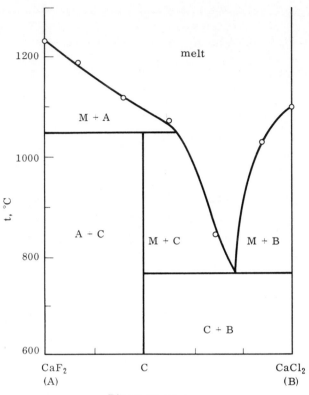

Figure 12-39

(c) For $(NH_4)_2SO_4$ to be the first salt to crystallize out, the evaporation line must intersect the c-d solubility curve. The maximum possible Li_2SO_4 content that will still allow this to happen is that for a solution whose evaporation line just hits point c, as shown. The composition at c corresponds approximately to 15 g $(NH_4)_2SO_4$ to 47 g Li_2SO_4 or 12.5 g to 39. Solution A would have 12.5 g Li_2SO_4, 12.5 g $(NH_4)_2SO_4$ (and 75 g H_2O), so to shift its proportion of salts to that of line B about 26 g of Li_2SO_4 should be added to the 100 g of A.

(d) It is evident from part (b) that solution A in fact corresponds to a solution of the compound, and it has already been found that the first solid to crystallize out is $(NH_4)_2SO_4$ and that the compound cannot exist with solution unless some ammonium sulfate is also present.

21. The curves of Fig. 12-14 at 0% and 100% obviously give the two melting points of the pure components. The two halts shown in the 50% curve fit the case of unstable compound formation, if the compound has a composition between 30% and 50% $CaCl_2$. The figure 40% is chosen in Fig. 12–39, corresponding to $(CaF_2)_3(CaCl_2)_2$.

22. The phase regions are labelled in Fig. 12–40. Evaporation of solution A proceeds as follows. When composition 1 is reached, $X \cdot 6H_2O$ begins to crystallize out, and when the system reaches 2, pure hexahydrate is present. Further dehydration produces increasing amounts of $X \cdot 2H_2O$ and, when the system reaches 3, pure dihydrate is present. Further dehydration produces $X \cdot H_2O$, then, at 4, pure monohydrate, then X, and finally pure X.

23. The diagram, with the phase regions labelled, is shown as Fig. 12–41. On evaporation of solution of the given composition (marked X on the diagram), the system composition moves along the dotted line drawn from the water corner through X. Na_2SO_4 starts crystallizing out when the system is at the point where the dotted line crosses the 2–3 solubility curve. The solution then moves in composition toward 2 and reaches point 2 when the system composition reaches point 4. NaCl now begins to crystallize out, and both salts continue to deposit until the system is dry.

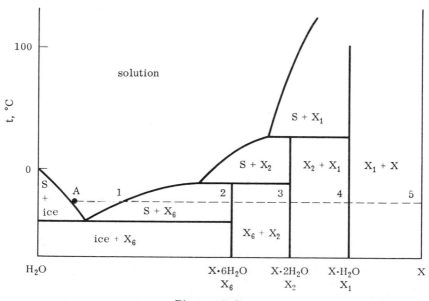

Figure 12-40

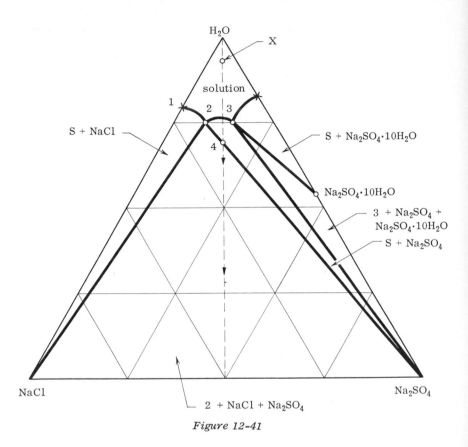

Figure 12-41

24. (See Fig. 12-42.) The system is evidently a peritectic type since the three-phase equilibrium lies between the two melting points.

25. Figure 12-43 with phase regions labeled is shown. The dotted line drawn from S to point 1 is the locus of all mixtures of S, is water saturated with KCl, and probably lies within the region of solution + KCl phase. A 50% mixture would lie at point 3, and the diagram indicates that about 95% of the system will be solution of composition 2. That is, the 2-3 distance is about 1/20 of the 3-KCl distance. About 5 g of solid KCl should be present in 100 g of the mixture.

26. In the completed diagram (Fig. 12-44), the dashed lines are plausibly located expected features, and the solid lines are those phase boundaries definitely required.

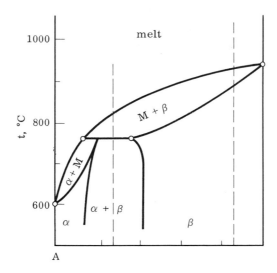

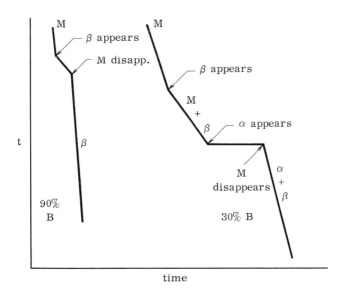

Figure 12-42

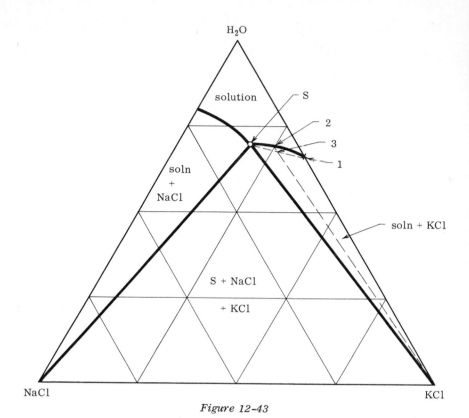

Figure 12-43

1. ice + $CaCl_2 \cdot 6H_2O$	7. solution
2. ice + solution	8. solution + $CaCl_2 \cdot 4H_2O$
3. solution + $CaCl_2 \cdot 6H_2O$	9. solution + $CaCl_2 \cdot 2H_2O$
4. $CaCl_2 \cdot 6H_2O$ + $CaCl_2 \cdot 4H_2O$	10. water vapor + solution
5. $CaCl_2 \cdot 4H_2O$ + $CaCl_2 \cdot 2H_2O$	11. solution + $CaCl_2$
6. $CaCl_2 \cdot 2H_2O$ + $CaCl_2$	12. water vapor + $CaCl_2$

The system to be heated is 12.5% $CaCl_2$, as indicated by point X. On heating, the system then moves along the dotted vertical line. At about −45°C, the ice melts and one has solution plus $CaCl_2 \cdot 6H_2O$ at about 30°C, $CaCl_2 \cdot 4H_2O$ begins to form, and above 30°C there is solution + $CaCl_2 \cdot 4H_2O$. At about 35°C, the $CaCl_2 \cdot 4H_2O$ is completely dissolved. There is no further change until about 105°C, when water vapor begins to form, and at 120°C, the solution precipitates $CaCl_2$. Above 120°C there exists only water vapor and $CaCl_2$.

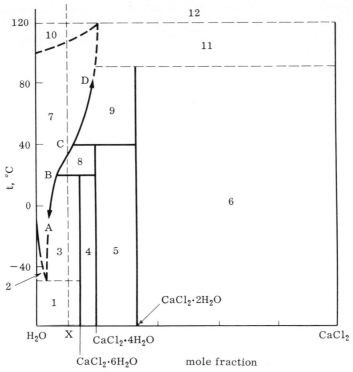

Figure 12-44

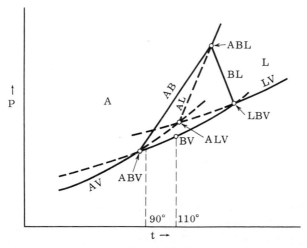

Figure 12-45

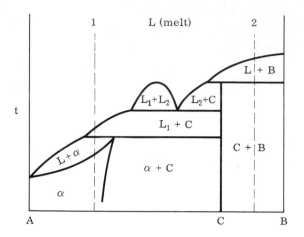

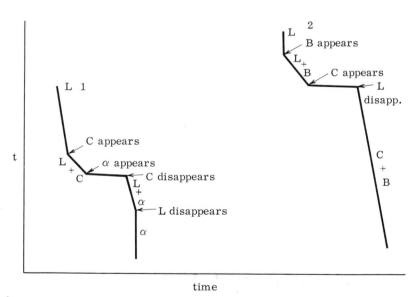

Figure 12-46

27. Evidently, the vapor pressure curve for A rises in Fig. 12-45 more steeply with temperature than does that for B, and this in turn, is steeper than the vapor-pressure curve for the liquid. The AV and LV curves cross at the ALV triple point; the AV and

BV curves at the ABV triple point at 90°C; and the BV and LV curves at the LBV triple point, which must lie above 110°C. A is then the low-temperature stable form.

From the relative densities, the AB line must slope to the right, as must the AL line, but less so, and the BL line must slope to the left. These lines must then meet at the ABL triple point. The triangular region enclosed by solid lines is then the region of stability of B.

The stable triple points are those formed by the intersection of three solid (i.e., stable equilibrium) lines, i.e., ABV, LBV, and ABL. The ALV triple point is metastable as phase A is unstable toward eventual transformation to B.

28. The labeled diagram is shown in Fig. 12-46. Since we know that the upper region must consist of a single phase (melt), it is fairly straightforward to determine which are single and which are two-phase regions by applying the rule that such regions must alternate in any horizontal traverse. The cooling curves follow easily once the diagram is labeled.

Appendix to Part One

Partial derivatives

Comments

This short collection of problems on partial differentiation is added as an afterthought but, I hope, as a useful one. Quite commonly, students entering physical chemistry find that the calculus course they took or are taking leaves them unprepared to handle the type of partial differential relationships that occur in, say, chemical thermodynamics.

The mathematics department is apt to regard the subject of partial differentiation as part of a more advanced course in partial differential equations and may therefore minimize the subject in the standard introductory calculus course. What is involved in beginning physical chemistry, however, is not the formidable matter of partial differential equations, but rather the fairly straightforward notion of a partial derivative, plus the relationships stemming from the concept of a total (or perfect, or exact) differential.

On first encounter with these relationships, it is easy to be a

253.1

little suspicious of whether they really work; it is certainly easy
to feel insecure about using them! The problems that follow are
designed to help relieve this feeling. A simple system of related
variables is set up, consisting of the length, width, perimeter, diagonal, and area of a rectangle. The problems then consist of
finding a desired partial derivative in terms of known other ones.
The desired partial can always be found directly, so you have the
opportunity to check the correctness of your manipulations. These
problems, incidentally, are not original; their source is lost in the
antiquity of my student days!

Equations and concepts

Partial Derivatives: If a quantity y depends on the variables u, v,
and w,

$$y = f(u,v,w)$$

then the following partial derivatives exist:

$$(\partial y/\partial u)_{v,w} \quad (\partial y/\partial v)_{u,w} \quad \text{and} \quad (\partial y/\partial w)_{u,v}$$

The subscripts signify that these variables are held constant
while the function is differentiated with respect to the third variable. Thus $V = nRT/P$ for an ideal gas, and

$$(\partial V/\partial T)_{n,p} = nR/P \quad (\partial V/\partial n)_{T,P} = RT/P$$

and

$$(\partial V/\partial P)_{n,T} = -nRT/P^2$$

Total Differentials: If u, v, and w change simultaneously by small
increments, then in the limit, the resulting change in $y = f(u,v,w)$
is:

$$dy = (\partial y/\partial u)_{v,w} \, du + (\partial y/\partial v)_{u,w} \, dv$$
$$+ (\partial y/\partial w)_{u,v} \, dw \tag{1}$$

Thus for an ideal gas:

$$dV = (nR/P) \, dT + (RT/P) \, dn - (nRT/P^2) \, dP$$

Relationships between Partial Derivatives: For simplicity, we take y to be a function of two variables, u and v. We assume that the functions and their derivatives are continuous and single-valued, as is ordinarily true of physical-chemical relationships. Then

$$y = f(u,v) \quad \text{and} \quad dy = (\partial y/\partial u)_v \, du + (\partial y/\partial v)_u \, dv \qquad (2)$$

The condition may be imposed that y be held constant:

$$0 = (\partial y/\partial u)_v \, du + (\partial y/\partial v)_u \, dv \qquad (3)$$

Or, expressing the constancy of y in the equation itself:

$$(\partial y/\partial u)_v = -(\partial y/\partial v)_u (\partial v/\partial u)_y \qquad (4)$$

or

$$(\partial v/\partial u)_y = - \frac{(\partial y/\partial u)_v}{(\partial y/\partial v)_u} \qquad (5)$$

Thus for 1 mole of an ideal gas (i.e., n = 1),

$$(\partial P/\partial T)_V = -(\partial P/\partial V)_T (\partial V/\partial T)_P \qquad (6)$$

Equation (6) may be checked by computing each partial derivative scparately and substituting into the equation.

The condition may be imposed that some other dependent variable z is held constant:

$$(\partial y/\partial u)_z = (\partial y/\partial u)_v + (\partial y/\partial v)_u (\partial v/\partial u)_z \qquad (7)$$

Thus energy is also a function of T and P, so:

$$(\partial V/\partial T)_E = (\partial V/\partial T)_P + (\partial V/\partial P)_T (\partial P/\partial T)_E \qquad (8)$$

Finally, if y = f(u,v) as before, and u is some function of w, i.e., u = g(w), then:

$$(\partial y/\partial w)_v = (\partial y/\partial u)_v (\partial u/\partial w)_v \qquad (9)$$

Higher Derivatives: For functions of the type encountered in physical chemistry, the order of successive differentiation is immaterial. Thus

$$\frac{\partial}{\partial u}\left(\frac{\partial y}{\partial u}\right)_v = \left(\frac{\partial^2 y}{\partial u^2}\right)_v \tag{10}$$

and

$$\frac{\partial}{\partial v}\left(\frac{\partial y}{\partial u}\right)_v = \frac{\partial}{\partial u}\left(\frac{\partial y}{\partial v}\right)_u = \frac{\partial^2 y}{\partial u\,\partial v} = \frac{\partial^2 y}{\partial v\,\partial u} \tag{11}$$

Test for a Total Differential: Equation (2) may be written in the form:

$$dy = A\,du + B\,dv \tag{12}$$

where $A = (\partial y/\partial u)_v$ and $B = (\partial y/\partial v)_u$. It is not necessarily true, however, that any equation of the form of (12) is the total differential of some function. Thus the expression

$$M\,du + N\,dv \tag{13}$$

will be a total of perfect differential of a function y only if

$$M = (\partial y/\partial u)_v \quad \text{and} \quad N = (\partial y/\partial v)_u \tag{14}$$

If relationships (14) hold, the derivative of M with respect to v must be equal to the derivative of N with respect to u:

$$(\partial M/\partial v)_u = \frac{\partial^2 y}{\partial v\,\partial u} = (\partial N/\partial u)_v \tag{15}$$

The test, then, of whether an expression such as (13) is a total differential is that the cross-differentiation (15) give the same result. Conversely, where we have a known total differential, the cross-differentiation equation provides a useful additional equation. Such equations are known as Euler relationships.
Thus

$$dE = T\,dS - P\,dV$$

is a known total differential from the combined first and second laws of thermodynamics. It then must be true that

$$(\partial T/\partial V)_S = -(\partial P/\partial S)_V$$

Problems

Let a represent the area, p the perimeter, d the diagonal, b the breadth, and ℓ the length of a rectangle. One can easily write down from analytical geometry all the various relationships between the above variables, and from these obtain directly a variety of partial differential quantities.

Thus,

$$a = b\ell$$

hence $(\partial a/\partial b)_\ell = \ell$, $(\partial a/\partial \ell)_b = b$, etc. In this way a complete family of partial differentials could be evaluated. Alternatively, however, one partial differential can be obtained from another through the use of the various rules given above.

The following table of partial differentials is given:

$(\partial a/\partial \ell)_b = b$ $\quad (\partial \ell/\partial b)_d = -b/\ell$ $\quad (\partial p/\partial b)_\ell = 2$

$(\partial a/\partial b)_\ell = \ell$ $\quad (\partial d/\partial b)_\ell = b/d$ $\quad (\partial \ell/\partial b)_p = -1$

In the following problems you are asked to find the stated partial derivative first by the direct method, and then by using only the partial derivatives given in the table above, plus the various rules for interconverting derivatives.

1. Find $(\partial a/\partial \ell)_d$.
2. Find $(\partial a/\partial b)_p$.
3. Find $(\partial a/\partial p)_\ell$.
4. Find $(\partial a/\partial b)_d$.
5. Find $(\partial a/\partial d)_\ell$.
6. Find $(\partial b/\partial a)_\ell$.
7. Find $(\partial \ell/\partial b)_a$.

Find, using appropriate derivatives from any of those given above, including Problems 1 through 7:

8. $(\partial d/\partial \ell)_p$,
9. $(\partial d/\partial b)_p$.
10. $(\partial a/\partial d)_p$.

11. Find $(\partial b/\partial p)_d$, and by appropriate change of variables derive $(\partial a/\partial p)_d$ from it.

12. Show that $(\partial P/\partial V)_T = -P/V$ for 1 mole of an ideal gas. By interchange of T and V find $(\partial P/\partial T)_V$. Confirm your result by a direct method.

Answers

1. <u>Direct method:</u> $a = b\ell = (d^2 - \ell^2)^{1/2}\ell$

then

$$(\partial a/\partial \ell)_d = \frac{1}{2}\frac{1}{(d^2 - \ell^2)^{1/2}}(-2\ell)(\ell) + (d^2 - \ell^2)^{1/2}$$

$$= \underline{-\ell^2/b + b}$$

<u>Indirect method:</u> We want to express $(\partial a/\partial \ell)_d$ in terms of the differentials in the table. One writes

$$da = (\partial a/\partial b)_\ell db + (\partial a/\partial \ell)_b d\ell$$

By Equation (7),

$$(\partial a/\partial \ell)_d = (\partial a/\partial b)_\ell (\partial b/\partial \ell)_d + (\partial a/\partial \ell)_b$$

and, using the table of differentials,

$$(\partial a/\partial \ell)_d = (\ell)(-\ell/b) + b = \underline{-\ell^2/b + b}$$

2. <u>Direct method:</u> $a = \ell b$ and $p = 2b + 2\ell$ so $\ell = (p - 2b)/2$ and $a = (p - 2b)/2b$. Then

$$(\partial a/\partial b)_p = \tfrac{1}{2}(-2)b + \frac{p - 2b}{2} = -b + \frac{p - 2b}{2} = \underline{\ell - b}$$

<u>Indirect method:</u> Consider a as a function of b and ℓ, then

$$da = (\partial a/\partial b)_\ell db + (\partial a/\partial \ell)_b d\ell$$

Divide by db, holding p constant:

$$(\partial a/\partial b)_p = (\partial a/\partial b)_\ell + (\partial a/\partial \ell)_b(\partial \ell/\partial b)_p$$

From the table of differentials,

$$(\partial a/\partial b)_p = \ell + b(-1) = \underline{\ell - b}$$

3. <u>Direct method:</u> $a = \ell b$ and $b = \dfrac{p - 2\ell}{2}$ so $a = \ell \dfrac{p - 2\ell}{2}$

Then $(\partial a/\partial p)_\ell = \underline{\ell/2}.$

<u>Indirect method:</u> By Equation (9): $(\partial a/\partial p)_\ell = (\partial a/\partial b)_\ell (\partial b/\partial p)_\ell$, and from the table of values, $(\partial a/\partial p)_\ell = (\ell)(1/2) = \underline{\ell/2}.$

4. <u>Direct method:</u> We want to get $a = f(b,d)$. First, $a = b\ell$, and second, $\ell = (d^2 - b^2)^{1/2}$, so $a = b(d^2 - b^2)^{1/2}$. Then

$$(\partial a/\partial b)_d = (d^2 - b^2)^{1/2} + \frac{b}{2}\frac{(-2b)}{(d^2 - b^2)^{1/2}} = \underline{\ell - b^2/\ell}$$

<u>Indirect method:</u> Try considering a as a function of b and ℓ. Then

$$da = (\partial a/\partial b)_\ell \, db + (\partial a/\partial \ell)_b \, d\ell$$

On dividing by db at constant d,

$$(\partial a/\partial b)_d - (\partial a/\partial b)_\ell + (\partial a/\partial \ell)_b(\partial \ell/\partial b)_d = \ell + b(-b/\ell)$$

$$= \ell - b^2/\ell$$

5. <u>Direct method:</u> We want $a = f(d, \ell)$, i.e., $a = \ell(d^2 - \ell^2)^{1/2}$. Then

$$(\partial a/\partial d)_\ell = \tfrac{1}{2}\ell \frac{2d}{(d^2 - \ell^2)^{1/2}} = \frac{\ell d}{(d^2 - \ell^2)^{1/2}} = \underline{\ell d/b}$$

<u>Indirect method:</u> By Equation (9), we can write

$$(\partial a/\partial d)_\ell = (\partial a/\partial b)_\ell(\partial b/\partial d)_\ell = (\ell)(d/b) = \underline{\ell d/b}$$

6. <u>Direct method:</u> We want $b = f(a, \ell)$, i.e., $b = a/\ell$. Then

$$(\partial b/\partial a)_\ell = \underline{1/\ell}$$

<u>Indirect method</u>: This is really trivial: $(\partial b/\partial a)_\ell = \dfrac{1}{(\partial a/\partial b)_\ell} =$ <u>$1/\ell$</u>.

7. <u>Direct method</u>: We write $\ell = a/b$, so $(\partial \ell/\partial b)_a = -a/b^2 = $ <u>$-\ell/b$</u>.

<u>Indirect method</u>: Consider $\ell = f(b,a)$, then

$$d\ell = (\partial \ell/\partial b)_a\, db + (\partial \ell/\partial a)_b\, da$$

By Equation (3)

$$0 = (\partial \ell/\partial b)_a(\partial b/\partial a)_\ell + (\partial \ell/\partial a)_b$$

from which $(\partial \ell/\partial b)_a = $ <u>$-\ell/b$</u>.

8. To find $(\partial d/\partial \ell)_p$:

<u>Direct method</u>: We want $d = f(\ell,p)$. Since $d = (\ell^2 + b^2)^{1/2}$ and $b = \dfrac{p - 2\ell}{2}$, we have

$$d = \left[\ell^2 + \frac{(p - 2\ell)^2}{4}\right]^{1/2} = (2\ell^2 - p\ell + p^2/4)^{1/2}$$

Then

$$(\partial d/\partial \ell)_p = \frac{1}{2}\frac{4\ell - p}{(2\ell^2 - p\ell + p^2/4)^{1/2}} = (4\ell - p)/2d = \underline{(\ell - b)/d}$$

<u>Indirect method</u>: This one is a little more difficult. We have the variables d, ℓ, and p, but none of the previous differentials involve these three. We must then use Equation (7) to permute in a fourth variable so as to give us combinations, taken three at a time, which we do have. A little reflection gives:

$$(\partial d/\partial \ell)_p = (\partial d/\partial \ell)_b + (\partial d/\partial b)_\ell(\partial b/\partial \ell)_p$$

But

$$(\partial d/\partial \ell)_b = -\frac{(\partial b/\partial \ell)_d}{(\partial b/\partial d)_\ell} = -(-\ell/b)/(d/b) = \ell/d$$

The other derivatives have already been obtained, so

$$(\partial d/\partial \ell)_p = \ell/d + (b/d)(-1) = \underline{(\ell - b)/d}$$

9. To find $(\partial d/\partial b)_p$:

<u>Direct method:</u> We want $d = f(b,p)$. We have $d = (\ell^2 + b^2)^{1/2}$ and $\ell = (p - 2b)/2$ so $d = \left[\dfrac{(p - 2b)^2}{4} + b^2\right]^{1/2}$. Then

$$(\partial d/\partial b)_p = \frac{1}{2}\,\frac{(-p + 4b)}{(p^2/4 - pb + 2b^2)^{1/2}} = \underline{(b - \ell)/d}$$

<u>Indirect method:</u> The procedure is much the same as for Problem 8. We write:

$$(\partial d/\partial b)_p = (\partial d/\partial b)_\ell + (\partial d/\partial \ell)_b (\partial \ell/\partial b)_p$$

But

$$(\partial d/\partial \ell)_b = -\frac{(\partial b/\partial \ell)_d}{(\partial b/\partial d)_\ell} = -(-\ell/b)/(d/b) = \ell/d$$

Then

$$(\partial d/\partial b)_p = b/d + (\ell/d)(-1) = \underline{(b - \ell)/d}$$

10. To find $(\partial a/\partial d)_p$:

<u>Direct method:</u> To get $a = f(d,p)$ we proceed as follows: $\ell = (d^2 - b^2)^{1/2}$ so $p = 2\ell + 2b = 2(d^2 - b^2)^{1/2} + 2b$ and, on solving for b,

$$b = \frac{4p \pm [16\,p^2 - 32(p^2 - 4d^2)]^{1/2}}{16} = \frac{4p \pm q}{16}$$

Then

$$a = b\ell$$
$$= \frac{4p \pm q}{16}\left[d^2 - \left(\frac{4p \pm q}{16}\right)^2\right]^{1/2}$$

From this we find (eventually) that $(\partial a/\partial d)_p = \underline{-d}$.

<u>Indirect method:</u> We first write

$$(\partial a/\partial d)_p = (\partial a/\partial d)_\ell + (\partial a/\partial \ell)_d (\partial \ell/\partial d)_p$$

From the results of Problems 5, 1, and 8, respectively, we can evaluate the three quantities on the right to get:

$$(\partial d/\partial d)_p = \ell d/b + (-\ell^2/b + b)\left(\frac{d}{\ell - b}\right) = \underline{-d}$$

11. To find $(\partial b/\partial p)_d$, and from it $(\partial a/\partial p)_d$ we first set,

$$(\partial b/\partial p)_d = (\partial b/\partial p)_\ell + (\partial b/\partial \ell)_p(\partial \ell/\partial p)_d = \tfrac{1}{2} + (-1)(\partial \ell/\partial p)_d$$

Then,

$$(\partial p/\partial \ell)_d = (\partial p/\partial \ell)_b + (\partial p/\partial b)_\ell(\partial b/\partial \ell)_d = (\partial p/\partial \ell)_b + 2\,(-\ell/b)$$

and

$$(\partial p/\partial \ell)_b = -(\partial p/\partial b)_\ell(\partial b/\partial \ell)_p = -(2)(-1) = 2$$

Then $(\partial p/\partial \ell)_d = 2 - 2\ell/b = (2b - 2\ell)/b$, and

$$(\partial b/\partial p)_d = \frac{1}{2} - \frac{b}{2b - 2\ell} = -\frac{\ell}{2b - 2\ell}$$

To get $(\partial a/\partial p)_d$, first write

$$(\partial a/\partial p)_d = (\partial b/\partial p)_d(\partial a/\partial b)_d = \left(-\frac{\ell}{2b - 2\ell}\right)(\partial a/\partial b)_d$$

Then

$$(\partial a/\partial b)_d = (\partial a/\partial b)_\ell + (\partial a/\partial \ell)_b(\partial \ell/\partial b)_d = \ell + b(-b/\ell)$$

$$= \ell - b^2/\ell$$

Finally,

$$(\partial a/\partial p)_d = -\frac{\ell}{2b - 2\ell}(\ell - b^2/\ell) = -\frac{\ell^2 - b^2}{2b - 2\ell} = \frac{b + \ell}{2} = \underline{p/4}$$

12. For an ideal gas, PV = RT or P = RT/V. Then $(\partial P/\partial V)_T = -RT/V^2 = -P/V$. For the second part, we write:

$$(\partial P/\partial T)_V = -(\partial P/\partial V)_T(\partial V/\partial T)_P = (P/V)(\partial V/\partial T)_P$$

To confirm by the direct method, we note that $(\partial P/\partial T)_V = R/V$ and that $(\partial V/\partial T)_P = R/P$. Then $R/V \overset{?}{=} (P/V)(R/P) = R/V$. Q.E.D.

Index

Absorbancy, 38
Acid:
    Brønsted, 280
    Lewis, 280
Activated complex, 346
Activation energy, 346
Activity:
    mean, 307
    specific, 408
Activity coefficient, 135, 167, 305
    mean, 307
Additive property, 343
Adiabat, reversible, 92
Adiabatic process, 56
Anode, definition of, 256
Apparent:
    activation energy, 347
    equivalent conductivity, 256
Arrhenius equation, 346
Atomic number, 407

Barn, as unit of cross section, 407
Barometric equation, 2
Beer-Lambert law, 38
Bohr theory, 427
Boiling point elevation, 168

Bonds, chemical, 450
Box, particle in, 428
Boyle temperature, 13
Bragg equation, 386
Broglie, de, equation, 428
Brønsted definition of acid, 280

Capillarity, 112
Capillary rise, 113
Carnot cycle, 92
Catalysis, 347
Cells — see Electrochemical cells
Character:
    of representations, 458
    tables of:
        C_{2v}, 470, 474
        C_{3v}, 458, 460
        D_3, 465
        D_{3h}, 466, 472
        D_{4h}, 470
        T_d, 455, 469, 473
Chemical:
    bonding, 450
    kinetics, 342
Clapeyron equation, 112
Clausius-Clapeyron equation, 112

Colligative properties, 165
Collision frequency, wall, 29
Colloid chemistry, 375
Combustion, heat of, 74
Compressibility factor, 13
Concentration, formality unit
    of, 277, 278
Condensation phenomena, 12
Conductance, 254
Conductivity:
    equivalent, 255
    specific, 255
Corresponding states, 13
Critical constants, 13
Cross section, 407
Crystal structure, 384
Crystals:
    cubic, 386
    density of, 386

Debye, as dipole moment unit,
    38
Debye–Hückel limiting law,
    278
Decay laws, 407
Density, of crystals, 386
Differential, total (or perfect
    or exact), 56, 253.1
Diffusion, 377
Dipole moment, 38
Disintegration rate, units of,
    407
Double repulsion, 387
Drop weight method, 113
Dulong and Petit, Law of, 83,
    84

Effusion of gases, 29
Einstein viscosity equation,
    377
Electrochemical cells, 304
    sign convention of, 305

thermodynamics of, 307
Electrochemistry, 254
Electrolytes, dissociation of
    weak, 278
Energy, 56
    units and conversion factors,
    407
Enthalpy, 56
Entropy, 91
Equation (*see also* under Law,
    Principle):
    barometric, 2
    Bohr, 427
    Bragg, 386
    Broglie, de, 428
    Clapeyron, 112
    Clausius–Clapeyron, 112
    Einstein viscosity, 377
    Euler, 493
    ideal gas, 2
    Gibbs, 375, 376
    Laplace, 112
    mass action, 346
    relativity, 409
    Schrödinger, 428
    van der Waals, 13
    virial, 13
Equilibrium:
    gas, 188
    ionic, 276
Equilibrium constant and free
    energy, 189
Equivalent conductivity, 255
Euler relationships, 92, 253.4
Explosion, maximum tempera-
    ture of, 74
Extinction coefficient, 38

Fick's law, 377
First order rate law, 345
Formality, 277
Formation, heat of, 74

Free energy, 92
  and equilibrium constant,
    189
Freezing point:
  depression, 168
  diagrams, 207
Frequency factor, 346
Friction coefficient, 29

Gas:
  constant, 2
  equilibrium, 188
  ideal, law, 2
Gases:
  effusion of, 29
  ideal, 1
  nonideal, 12
Gibbs' equation, 375, 376
Graham's law, 29
Group:
  symmetry, 454
  theory, 450

Half-life, 345, 346, 407
Heat:
  capacity, 55, 56, 73
  of combustion, 74
  engine, 92
  of formation, 74
  pump, 92
  of solution, 74
Henry's law, 133, 134
Hess' law, 74
Heterogeneous:
  catalysis, 347
  equilibrium, 207
Hittorf cell, 255
Hooke's law, 432
Hybrid orbitals, 458
Hydrogen–like atom, wave
    functions for, 429, 430
Hypothetical:
  unit molal standard state, 168

  unit mole fraction standard
    state, 167

Ideal gas law, 2
Intrinsic viscosity, 377
Ionic:
  equilibrium, 276
  velocities, 256
Irreversible processes, 91
Isobaric process, 56
Isochoric process, 56
Isothermal process, 56

Joule–Thompson coefficient,
    56
Junction:
  liquid, 307
  potential, 307

Kinetic molecular theory, 28
Kinetics, chemical, 342

Law (*see* Equation, Principle):
  Beer–Lambert, 38
  Dalton's, 2
  Dulong and Petit, 83, 84
  Fick's, 377
  gas, 2
  Graham's, 29
  Henry's, 133, 134
  Hess', 74
  Hooke's, 432
  of radioactive decay, 407
  Raoult's, 133, 134
  rectilinear diameters, 112
  Stokes', 29, 377
Laplace equation, 112
Lever principle, 134, 208
Lewis acid–base definition, 280
Liquids, 111
  tensile strength of, 13
  vapor pressure of, 112

vapor pressure of immis-
cible, 135
Logarithmic diagrams, 277,
279

Mass:
defect, 407
number, 407
Mass action rate law, 345
Maximum bubble pressure, 113
Melting point, effect of pressure on, 112
Miller indices, 386
Mobility, electrochemical, 256
Molality, mean, 307
Molar:
absorbancy index, 38
polarization, 38
refraction, 38
Molecular weight, average, 378
Multiplication table, group, 455
C_{2V}, 477
C_{3V}, 455
C_{4V}, 468
D_2, 485

Nernst equation, 305, 306
Nuclear chemistry, 405
Number average molecular
weight, 377

Optical density, 38
Orbitals:
hybrid, 458
hyhydrogen-like, 430, 450
Order of chemical rate law,
345
Osmotic pressure, 168

Parachor, 41
Parent-daughter decay equation, 408

Partial derivatives, 56, 253.1
Partial pressure, 2
Particle in a box, treatment of,
428
Pauli principle, 429
Phase diagrams, 207
Phase rule, 208
Pi bonds, 460
Point groups, 454
Polarization, molar, 38
Potential:
half-cell, 304, 306
junction, 307
Pressure, surface, 377
Principle (*see* Equation, Law):
lever, 134, 208
Pauli, 429
Property, additive, 343

Quantum theory, 425

Radioactive decay law, 407
Radiochemistry, 405
Raoult's Law, 133, 134
standard state, 167
Rate laws, 345
Rectilinear diameters, law of,
112
Refraction, molar, 38
Regular solutions, 135
Relativity equation, 409
Representations of groups, 456
Repulsion, double, 387
Resistance, specific, 255
Rule:
phase, 208
Trouton's, 112

Schrödinger equation, 428
Second order rate law, 346
Sedimentation, 377
Sigma bonds, 460

Solubility product, 278
Solution, heat of, 74
Solutions, 133
  nonideal, 135
  regular, 135
Specific:
  activity, 408
  conductivity, 255
  resistance, 256
  viscosity, 377
Standard states, 167
Steady state approximation,
  344
Stoichiometry in chemical
  kinetics, 343
Stokes' law, 29, 377
STP condition, 2
Sugden's parachor, 41
Surface:
  chemistry, 375
  pressure, 377
Symmetry element, 452

Tensile strength of liquids, 13
Tetrahedron, point group of,
  455
Thermochemistry, 73
Thermodynamic solubility
  product, 278

Thermodynamics:
  basic equations, 56
  of electrochemical cells, 307
  first law, 54, 56
  second law, 90
Total differential, 56, 253.1
Transference, 254
  number, 256
Transition state theory, 346
Trouton's rule, 112

van der Waals equation, 13
van't Hoff i factor, 169
Vapor pressure:
  effect of mechanical pressure
    on, 112
  lowering, 168
Velocity:
  distribution law, 29
  molecular, 29
Vibration, quantum theory of,
  432
Viscosity, 29, 377

Wave length, de Broglie, 428
Wave mechanics, 425
Weight, average molecular, 377
Work, reversible and irrevers-
  ible, 55, 56